JOHANSENS RECOMMENDED HOTELS IN GREAT BRITAIN & IRELAND 1991

The Johansens Standard of Excellence

A distinguished business associate told me that he recently sold his villa abroad and now instead relies entirely on Johansens to guide him and his wife in their holiday and weekend selections.

With such a wealth of quality hotels, inns and country houses offering excellence – at the right price – on our doorstep in this country, I never cease to wonder at our seeming preference to spend two days of our hard-earned holiday at airports and in transit to untested and distant destinations. Nor can I understand the logic of selecting yet another 'factory clone' hotel room for UK business trips when – usually for less money – far more interest, better service and better value for money, awaits the traveller in a Johansens establishment.

But you dear reader, are already converted! So please spread the word by introducing a friend to the Johansens secret: details of our new *Excellent Secrets* newsletter appear on page 23 of this guide.

Johansens' recommendations are in three books:
Book 1 – *Hotels in Great Britain and Ireland;* Book 2 – *Country Inns and Restaurants in Great Britain* and Book 3 – *Private Country Houses and Castles in Great Britain and Ireland.*

By far the majority of our hotels, inns and country houses are privately owned and managed, family run and independent.

They are visited regularly by our team of inspectors and are constantly monitored by the thousands of Guest Survey Reports sent to us by you, our Johansens readers.

Guest Survey Report forms are at the back of this book and are available from Johansens establishments. We welcome your opinions on all or any of our selections which you have visited within the past six months. We are also always interested to hear about omissions.

Comments are acted upon by our inspectors and both compliments and complaints are brought to the attention of the establishments concerned – without revealing your name. It is these comments and the statistical evidence of your Guest Survey Reports, together with our own inspectors' findings, which form the basis of the judging of the new Johansens Awards which are introduced this year.

Of nearly 2,500 establishments visited this year, only 750 were found to offer high enough standards of cuisine, service, bedrooms, surroundings, ambience and value for money to be offered Johansens membership.

I'm sure you will agree that our 1991 selection is the best ever. From impressive castles and private manor houses tucked away in the countryside, to country house hotels with their distinctive efficiency and Edwardian decorum, Johansens establishments offer unique choices for discerning travellers whether on business, family weekending or on a visit from abroad.

  This year we are particularly pleased to be launching The Johansens Awards for Excellence. A new special 'J' symbol indicates an establishment nominated for the Awards and the symbol 'R' denotes a restaurant of merit nominated for an Award.

In our idiosyncratic way I believe that with Johansens recommendations we have achieved a standard of excellence all of our own. I hope you will discover some memorable surprises as well as renewing old acquaintances with trusted friends in this year's selection. Perhaps you'll spend less of your holiday in an airport this year too!

Adrian Bridgewater, Chairman
Johansens Limited

Published by
Johansens Limited, Bateman Street, Cambridge CB2 1LZ
Chairman: Adrian Bridgewater
Managing Director: Martin Morgan
Publisher: Peter Law
Director, Hotel Services: Derek O'Connor
Senior Inspector: Peter Hancock
Regional Inspectors: Marie Iverson, Pauline Mason, Joan Henderson,
Mary O'Neill, Janice Watkins, Sarah Macpherson, Christopher Bond
Production Manager: Jannie Brightman
Managing Editor: Susan Walker
Production Editor: Lisa Dedman

Front Cover:
Chewton Glen Hotel at New Milton, Hampshire

Thanks are due to Britain on View for permission to
reproduce the photographs appearing on the
regional title pages (© BTA/ETB)

HOBSONS
DIRECTORY

Member of Association of British Directory Publishers

When it comes to mortgages, insurance and financial planning does your current advisor measure up?

If he doesn't it could be because he can't give you advice that is truly impartial. Or perhaps he doesn't specialise in your area of business.

Our team of experts understand the licensed business market and appreciate your individual needs, which is why RCC is the acknowledged specialist advising purchasers and owners of Country Houses, Hotels, Inns and Restaurants.

RCC can provide tailor made mortgage packages, that are designed to suit the exact needs of your business, whether buying, expanding or re-financing.

We can also put together individually designed insurance packages that are amongst the most cost effective available in the U.K. And also advise you on

a complete range of financial services including Investments, Tax planning and Pensions.

So if your present financial advisor doesn't measure up, try RCC for size:
Business Mortgages and Re-finance – Stuart Macdonald,
Insurance – David Hall, Financial Services – Matthew Wood.

RCC

4&6 York Street, London W1A 1BP. Tel: 071-487 3310

Offices also at Birmingham · Bristol · Canterbury · Carmarthen
Edinburgh · Exeter · Glasgow · Ipswich · Leeds · Manchester
Newcastle · Nottingham · Winchester · Boston · Paris · Dublin

Licensed under the Consumer Credit Act No 157023

A member of Christie Group plc.

Three years could pass before a sportsman sets his sights on owning a Purdey gun. That is how long it could take from order to delivery. But any expert on fine guns would reckon it time well spent.

As Chairman of James Purdey and Sons, the Honourable Richard Beaumont is supremely qualified to confirm this view. And in the Long Room of Purdey's headquarters the evidence is there, all around him.

A Georgian silhouette of the first James Purdey, a barrel-maker in the City of London, looks towards the portrait of 'James the First,' who founded the family firm in 1814. Since then, Purdeys have been gunmakers to the Royal Household from Queen Victoria to the present day.

But time has not stood still at Purdey. It has moved with measured precision. The latest example of the work that

Purdey guns have been taking their time since 1814.

THERE ARE FINE ENGRAVERS AMONG PURDEY'S CRAFTSMEN.

makes the name Purdey synonymous with perfection is, like every Purdey gun, built to the personal measurements and sporting requirements of one individual. It is an extension of the shooter's arm.

Purdey make only 60 or 70 guns a year and it takes several men many months to make just one gun. But each man is a specialist and each part of the gun is engraved with the craftsman's own initials.

Richard Beaumont also shares this sense of pride in work well done. "Hand-made things have a different quality.

They have been created by *someone*, not by a machine."

For this reason he has complete confidence in his Rolex watch, which he describes with quiet appreciation as "a lovely thing."

When handling one of his own guns or when consulting the watch on his wrist, Richard Beaumont knows that he is in touch with what he most admires: personal skills that can coax efficiency and beauty from basic materials.

DETONATING AN ACTION.

Purdey guns and Rolex watches take time, expertise and – above all – people who still care to do things well for people who can recognise that care has been taken.

ROLEX
of Geneva

THE ROLEX DATEJUST CHRONOMETER IN STEEL AND YELLOW METAL. ALSO AVAILABLE IN 18CT. GOLD OR IN STEEL WITH WHITE METAL BEZEL.

Only a select group of jewellers sell Rolex watches. For the address of your nearest Rolex jeweller, and for further information on the complete range of Rolex watches, write to: The Rolex Watch Company Limited, 1 Green Street, London W1Y 4JY or telephone 071-629 5071.

Introduction
by Martin and Brigitte Skan

Martin and Brigitte Skan are celebrating 25 glorious years of running their internationally famous hotel, Chewton Glen, on the edge of the New Forest at New Milton, Hampshire. This hotel is also a Relais & Chateaux member, a Leading Hotels of the World member, and it carries an 88% Egon Ronay rating with a star for cooking, as well as Michelin's five red turrets and a star. Chewton Glen has been an Egon Ronay Hotel of the Year, is the 1990 winner of The Times Hotel Restaurant of the Year and first appeared in Johansens in 1983.

As Chewton Glen enters its 25th anniversary year, we take great pride in looking back at what has been achieved during this time within the country house hotel industry in the British Isles. Twenty-five years ago there was just a handful of us rusty amateurs who had bought decayed old country houses. We were very slowly renovating them, and at the same time trying to improve the standard of cooking, service and hotelkeeping in general.

These pioneering days were exacting, hard work and it was sheer enthusiasm and dedication that brought success and, indeed, the foundations that were to inspire so many other people to enter the country house hotel scene.

Today we have many hundreds of fine and beautifully run country house hotels, as illustrated in this year's *Johensens Recommended Hotels Guide,* which are probably the best of their type in the world. In other Johansens guides in this three-book series, many of our finest inns and private country houses are also listed.

We know the high standard Britain offers, but overseas visitors, particularly our European neighbours, still believe that nothing happens outside London. This is now our challenge for the next 25 years. We have to promote our 'image' abroad, and we have to convince other people from other lands that one can eat very well in Britain today, that our country house hotels are as good as any in the world, that they have style and charm, and very often are set in areas of peace and beauty.

We have much to tell about our beautiful countryside, our pretty villages, our inns and country houses...and our wonderful way of life.

Martin and Brigitte Skan

the architects of

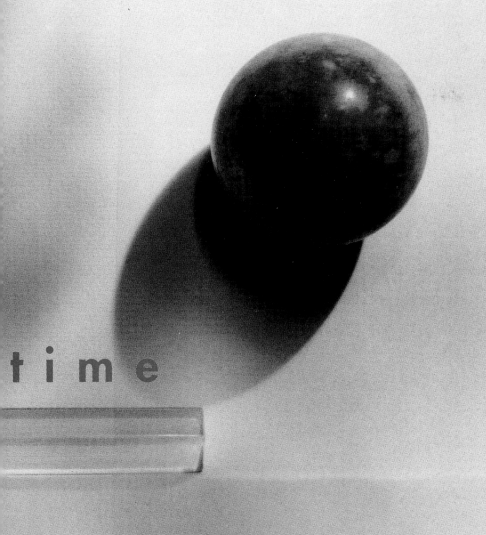

time

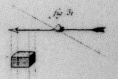

EBEL

1911. Designed to commemorate the founding of the Company by E. Blum in La Chaux-de-Fonds, Switzerland. A three-piece case with integrated back and over-sized gasket ensures water resistance. Curved sapphire glass. High-efficiency quartz or self-winding mechanical movement. Water-resistant to 30 metres. Entirely hand-crafted and hand-assembled bracelet, or water-resistant sharkskin strap. A broad range of options from stainless steel to 18 kt rose gold. Two sizes for men and one size for ladies. Five year international limited warranty. Sculpted by the architects of time.

DEFINITELY
THE BEST LAGER
IN THE WORLD:

CONTENTS

Africa, for those who don't want to be just one of the herd

Safari holidays are for those who seek adventure. For people who wish to explore life in the wild for themselves; who wish to relive the pioneering journeys of a bygone age.

But of course such a holiday must also be enjoyable. So, Safaris Cordon Bleu have arranged an exclusive selection of Kenyan safaris which are the perfect blend of comfort and excitement, haute cuisine and high adventure.

And how best to understand the challenge of the early settlers in East Africa, than by travelling through the stunning scenery of Kenya at the pace of yesterday.

This distinctively different form of safari is naturally only available to limited numbers of committed adventurers. You might like to be among the select few to experience this extraordinary new concept in safari holidays.

See Africa by Ox Wagon

Only with Safaris Cordon Bleu can you roam the African bush in a traditionally built ox wagon.

You'll leave the pressures of modern life behind as you forge a trail through big game country, crossing streams and seeing first hand the beautiful flowers and plants, exotic birds, magnificent vistas and majestic wildlife. Making progress at walking pace across the savannah you will see, hear and feel many things you can never experience in any other way.

. . . In safety and comfort

Today's wagons, whilst authentic in outward appearance, are fitted with comfortably

upholstered seats and offer refreshments and shade from the sun.

Expert guides are constantly on hand and at night you will stop over at a luxury tented camp with hot showers, welcoming fires and of course Cordon Blue cuisine.

Our unique ox wagon safari is just one of many superbly organised holidays ideally suited to photographers, naturalists or simply those with a desire to do something different on holiday. We also run a choice of using modern, 4 wheel drive vehicles.

. . . To your own specification

Whilst we recommend certain itineraries, at Safaris Cordon Bleu we believe in the freedom of holidaymakers to choose exactly where, when, how, and for how long they wish to travel.

Here are some of the areas covered by Safaris Cordon Bleu:

Maasai Mara Game Reserve
Meru National Park
Mount Marsabit National Park
The Abedare Mountains
Kisumu – Lake Victoria
Mount Elgon
Northern Coast – Lamu Island
Nakuru National Park
Kamnarok Game Reserve
Kakamega Forest

So if you don't want to be one of the herd, why not contact us right now and we'll show you the way.

Safaris ·CORDON BLEU·

34 Burton Lodge, Portinscale Road, Putney, London SW15 6TG. Tel: 081-874 8175. Fax: 081-877 9087

Great Britain and Ireland Counties Map

KEY

England listings pages 25–349

Wales listings pages 365–379

Scotland listings pages 403–470

Ireland listings pages 475–483

Channel Island listings pages 485–491

SHETLANDS

ORKNEYS

WESTERN ISLES

HIGHLAND

GRAMPIAN

SCOTLAND

TAYSIDE

CENTRAL

FIFE

STRATHCLYDE

LOTHIAN

BORDERS

DUMFRIES & GALLOWAY

NORTHUMBERLAND

TYNE & WEAR

CUMBRIA

DURHAM

CLEVELAND

NORTH YORKSHIRE

ISLE OF MAN

LANCASHIRE

WEST YORKS.

HUMBERSIDE

DONEGAL

DERRY

ANTRIM

TYRONE

NORTHERN IRELAND

FERMANAGH

ARMAGH

DOWN

SLIGO

LEITRIM

MONAGHAN

MAYO

CAVEN

LOUTH

ROSCOMMON

LONGFORD

MEATH

GALWAY

WEST MEATH

REPUBLIC OF IRELAND

OFFALY

DUBLIN

KILDARE

CLARE

LAOIS

WICKLOW

CARLOW

LIMERICK

TIPPERARY

KILKENNY

WEXFORD

KERRY

CORK

WATERFORD

MERSEYSIDE

GREATER MANCHESTER

S. YORKS.

CHESHIRE

DERBYSHIRE

NOTTS.

LINCOLNSHIRE

GWYNEDD

CLWYD

STAFFS

ENGLAND

LEICS.

NORFOLK

SHROPSHIRE

WEST MIDLANDS

WALES

POWYS

HEREFORD & WORC.

WARWICK.

NORTHANTS

CAMBS.

SUFFOLK

DYFED

BEDS.

HERTS

ESSEX

BUCKS.

GLOS.

OXON.

GREATER LONDON

WEST GLAM.

MID GLAM.

GWENT

SOUTH GLAM.

AVON

BERKS.

WILTS.

SURREY

KENT

HAMPSHIRE

SOMERSET

WEST SUSSEX

EAST SUSSEX

DEVON

DORSET

ISLE OF WIGHT

CORNWALL

CHANNEL ISLES

"If I didn't know you so well, I'd say you were trying to impress me."

HOW TO USE THIS GUIDE

KEY TO SYMBOLS

12 rms	Number of rooms
6 ens	Number of rooms en suite
BARCLAYCARD VISA	Visa accepted
Access	Access accepted
AMERICAN EXPRESS	American Express accepted
Diners Club	Diners Club accepted
♣	Quiet location
OPEN ALL YEAR	Open all year
♿	Wheelchair access to at least one bedroom and some or all public rooms
☎	Conference facilities
V	Vegetarian meals provided
👫	Children of all ages welcome
🐕	Dogs allowed
🛏	Four-poster beds available
📺	Television in bedroom
☎	Telephone in bedroom
↕	Lift available
≋	Indoor swimming pool
≋	Outdoor swimming pool
✆	Tennis court
↯	Fishing arranged
⌐	Golf facilities on site

JOHANSENS Helpline

Ring our toll-free numbers for details of all Johansens Recommended Hotels, Country Inns or Country Houses.

Your request for information or a room booking will be faxed to your selected establishment so that the Johansens hotelier can contact you direct.

Details can also be provided for ordering copies of the three Johansens Guides.

Ring 0 800 269 397
(from the UK)

Ring 1 800 548 056
(from the USA)

You can quickly find your Johansens Hotel:

By region: This guide is split into five sections: England (page 25), Wales (page 365), Scotland (page 403), Ireland (page 475) and the Channel Islands (page 485). The Alphabetical Index at the back of the guide lists hotels within each region.

By location: Turn to the maps on pages 14-20. The locations of the Johansens Recommended Hotels are highlighted in red and correspond to the PLACENAME in capital letters at the top of the page. Sometimes a hotel is listed under the name of a nearby town with its actual location given after, eg BARNSTAPLE (Bishops Tawton). In these instances, the actual location is also indicated by a red dot. Within each region, the hotels are arranged alphabetically by location.

This year we also include the locations of the Johansens Country Inns and Restaurants and Johansens Private Country Houses and Castles on the maps in all three Guides and in lists at the back of each regional section. The inns and restaurants' locations are indicated on the maps by a red triangle and the country houses and castles by a red square before the highlighted placename.

By facilities offered: Hotels with conference facilities, wheelchair access, golf, tennis, indoor or outdoor swimming pool, and welcoming children of any age, are listed in our indexes at the back of this Guide. Each entry also has symbols to indicate the many other facilities available.

By price: The prices quoted for each entry refer to the inclusive cost of one night's accommodation, with breakfast, for two people in a double or twin room. These rates are correct at the time of going to press but are subject to seasonal fluctuation, and we advise you to check them prior to booking.

Directions: To help you reach your chosen Johansens Hotel, brief directions are included in the text for each entry. However, for our more out of the way establishments, we advise you to check the route.

Note: Because there are many different levels of disability, where wheelchair access is indicated, we must emphasise strongly that you must check at the time of making your reservation to ensure that facilities are appropriate to your needs.

This year Johansens launches *The Johansens Awards for Excellence.* We are most grateful to our Judges: Sir David English (Editor of *The Daily Mail*), Chairman of Judges; Janet Simpson (Editor of *Catering*); Tony Levitt (Independent Johansens Hotel Guide User); Jenny Manley (Managing Director of Creative Food Designers) and Stanley Cox (formerly Director and General Manager of Konica Business Machines UK Limited).

Johansens Guest Survey is the starting point for judging and we very much welcome your completed forms which will be vital in selecting next year's Awards.

 Our new symbol of Awards for Excellence indicating Johansens' unique combination of value for money and merit is displayed on the page of each establishment nominated for the 1991 Awards.

 This symbol denotes restaurants nominated for the 1991 Most Excellent Restaurant Award.

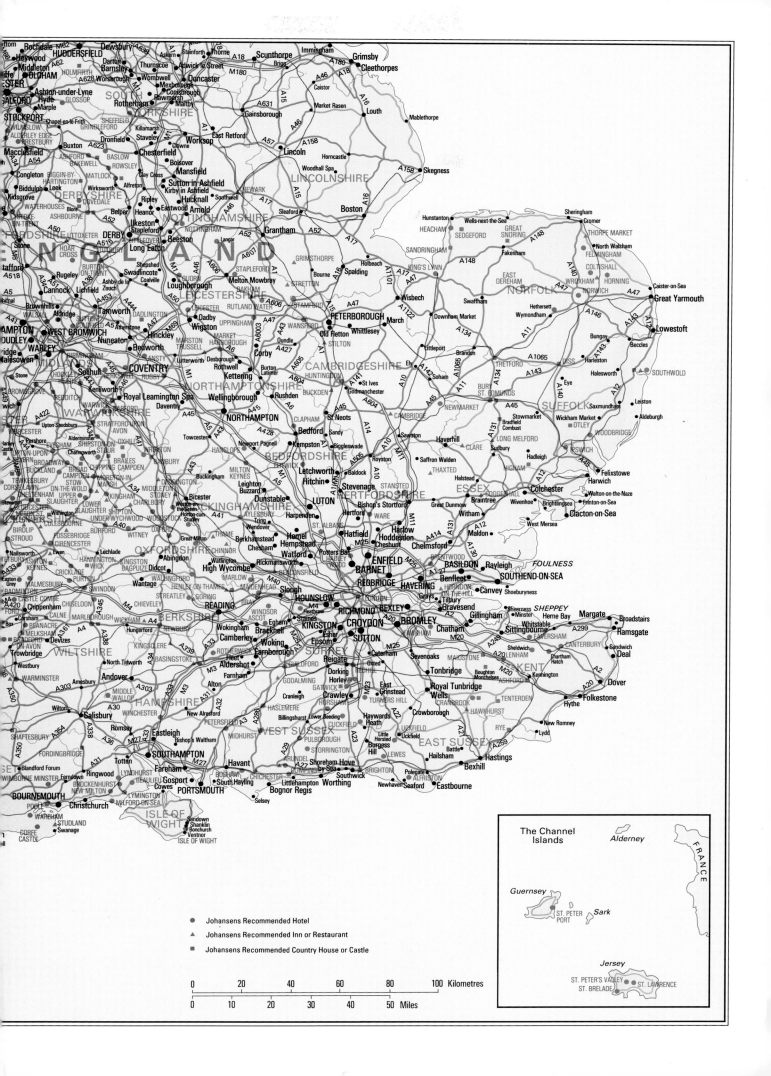

Johansens Recommended Hotel

Johansens Recommended Inn or Restaurant

Johansens Recommended Country House or Castle

The Channel Islands

Alderney

Guernsey
ST. PETER
PORT

Sark

Jersey
ST. PETER'S VALLEY
ST. BRELADE   ST. LAWRENCE

FRANCE

| 0 | 20 | 40 | 60 | 80 | 100 Kilometres |

| 0 | 10 | 20 | 30 | 40 | 50 Miles |

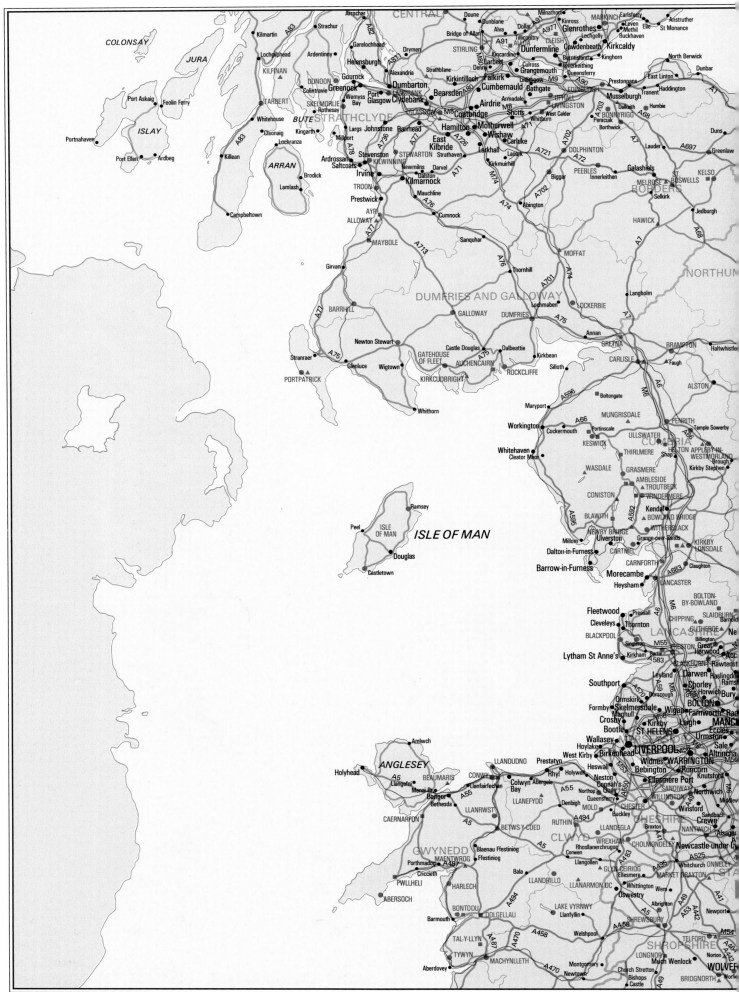

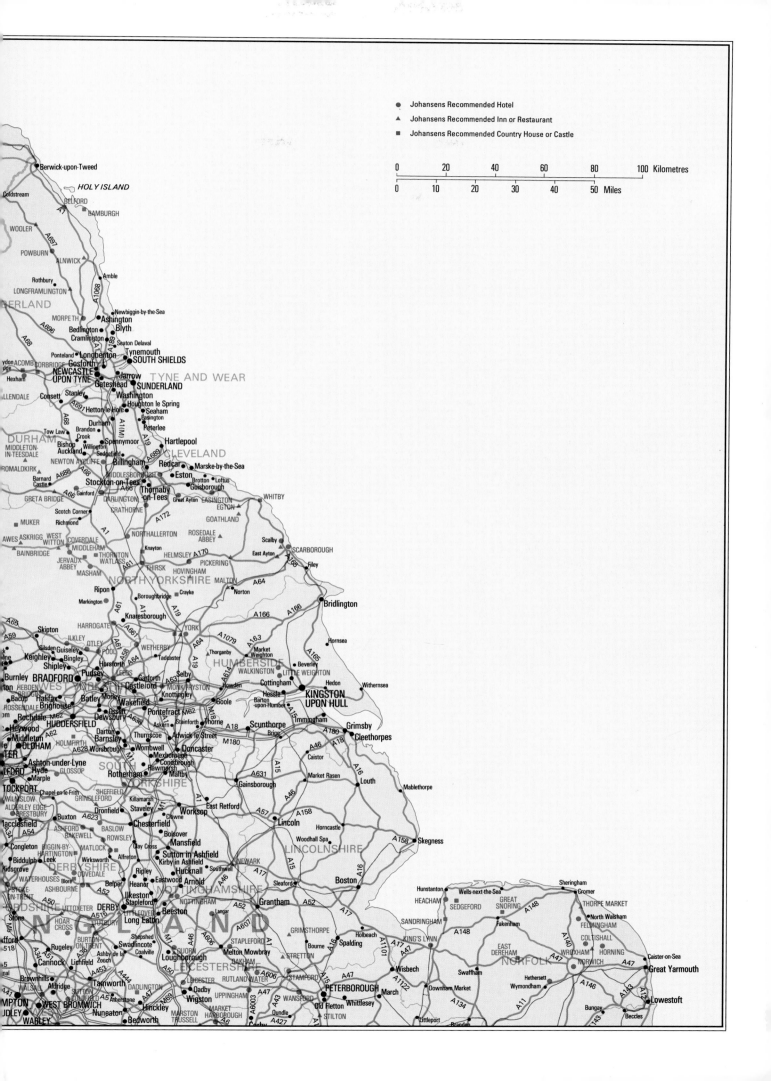

● Johansens Recommended Hotel

▲ Johansens Recommended Inn or Restaurant

■ Johansens Recommended Country House or Castle

0	20	40	60	80	100 Kilometres

0	10	20	30	40	50 Miles

© Lovell Johns Ltd. Oxford

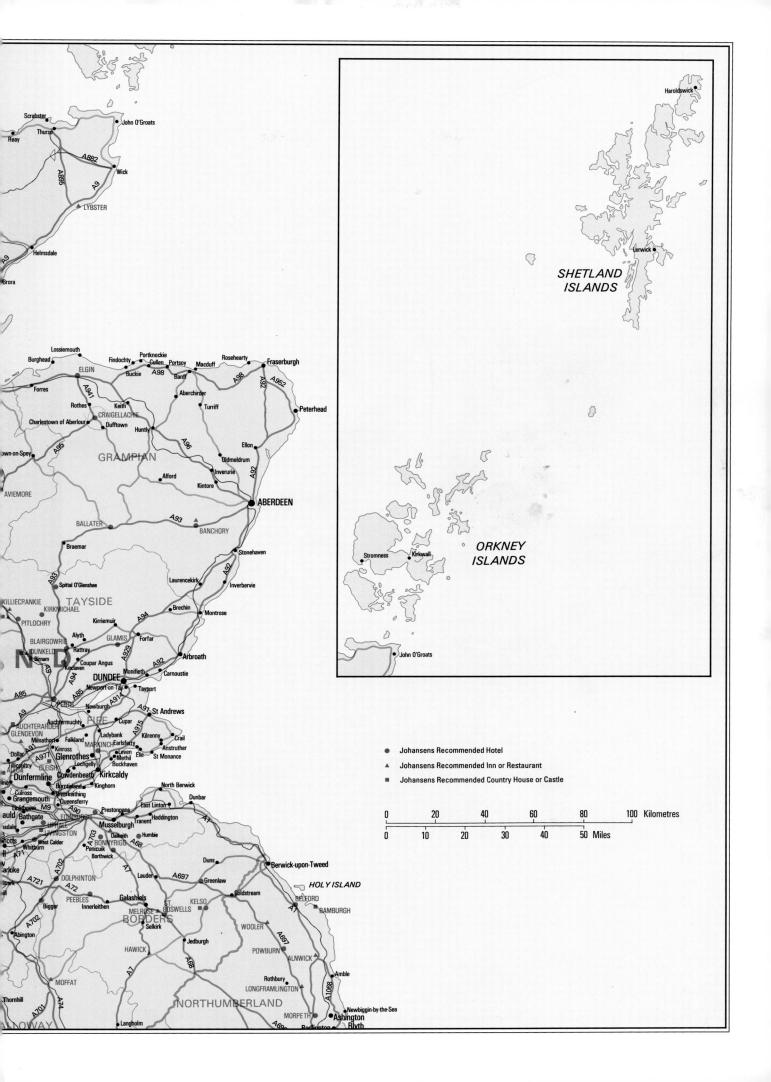

Scrabster
John O'Groats
Reay
Thurso
A882
Wick
A886
A9
LYBSTER
A9
Helmsdale
Brora

Haroldswick

Lerwick

SHETLAND ISLANDS

Lossiemouth
Burghead
Portknockie
Findochty
Cullen
Portsoy
Macduff
Rosehearty
Fraserburgh
ELGIN
Buckie
A98
Banff
A98
A92
A952
Forres
A941
Aberchirder
Rothes
Keith
Turriff
Peterhead
Charlestown of Aberlour
CRAIGELLACHIE
Dufftown
Huntly
own-on-Spey
A96
Ellon
A96
Oldmeldrum
GRAMPIAN
Alford
Inverurie
A92
AVIEMORE
Kintore
Kintore
ABERDEEN
A93
BALLATER
BANCHORY
Braemar
Stonehaven
KILLIECRANKIE
Spittal O'Glenshee
A92
Laurencekirk
Inverbervie
KIRKMICHAEL
TAYSIDE
Brechin
Montrose
PITLOCHRY
Kirriemuir
A94
BLAIRGOWRIE
Alyth
GLAMIS
Forfar
DUNKELD
Rattray
A929
N D
Coupar Angus
Kinclaven
A92
Arbroath
Birnam
A9
Monifieth
Carnoustie
A85
DUNDEE
Newport-on-Tay
Tayport
PERTH
A85
Newburgh
A914
A9
A91
St Andrews
AUCHTERARDER
Auchtermuchty
Cupar
FIFE
GLENDEVON
A915
Ladybank
Kilrenny
Crail
Milnathort
Falkland
MARKINCH
Anstruther
Dollar
Kinross
Earlsferry
A91
Glenrothes
Leven
Elie
St Monance
Tillicoultry
Lochgelly
Methil
BLEISH
Cowdenbeath
Buckhaven
Dunfermline
KIRKCALDY
North Berwick
Culross
Burntisland
Kinghorn
Grangemouth
Inverkeithing
Dunbar
M9
Queensferry
East Linton
auld
Bathgate
A90
Prestonpans
Tranent
Haddington
A1
adale
LIVINGSTON
EDINBURGH
Musselburgh
Humbie
otts
West Calder
A703
Dalkeith
Whitburn
Penicuik
BONNYRIGG
A68
arluke
Borthwick
Duns
Berwick-upon-Tweed
A702
DOLPHINTON
Lauder
A697
Greenlaw
HOLY ISLAND
A721
A72
Goldstream
BELFORD
PEEBLES
Galashiels
KELSO
BAMBURGH
Bigger
Innerleithen
MELROSE
ST.
BOSWELLS
A7
BORDERS
Selkirk
WOOLER
Abington
HAWICK
A697
A702
Jedburgh
POWBURN
MOFFAT
A68
ALNWICK
A7
Rothbury
Amble
Thornhill
LONGFRAMLINGTON
A1068
A701
A74
NORTHUMBERLAND
Newbiggin-by-the-Sea
LOWAY
Langholm
MORPETH
Ashington
A696
Blyth

ORKNEY ISLANDS

Stromness
Kirkwall

John O'Groats

● Johansens Recommended Hotel

▲ Johansens Recommended Inn or Restaurant

■ Johansens Recommended Country House or Castle

| 0 | 20 | 40 | 60 | 80 | 100 Kilometres |

| 0 | 10 | 20 | 30 | 40 | 50 Miles |

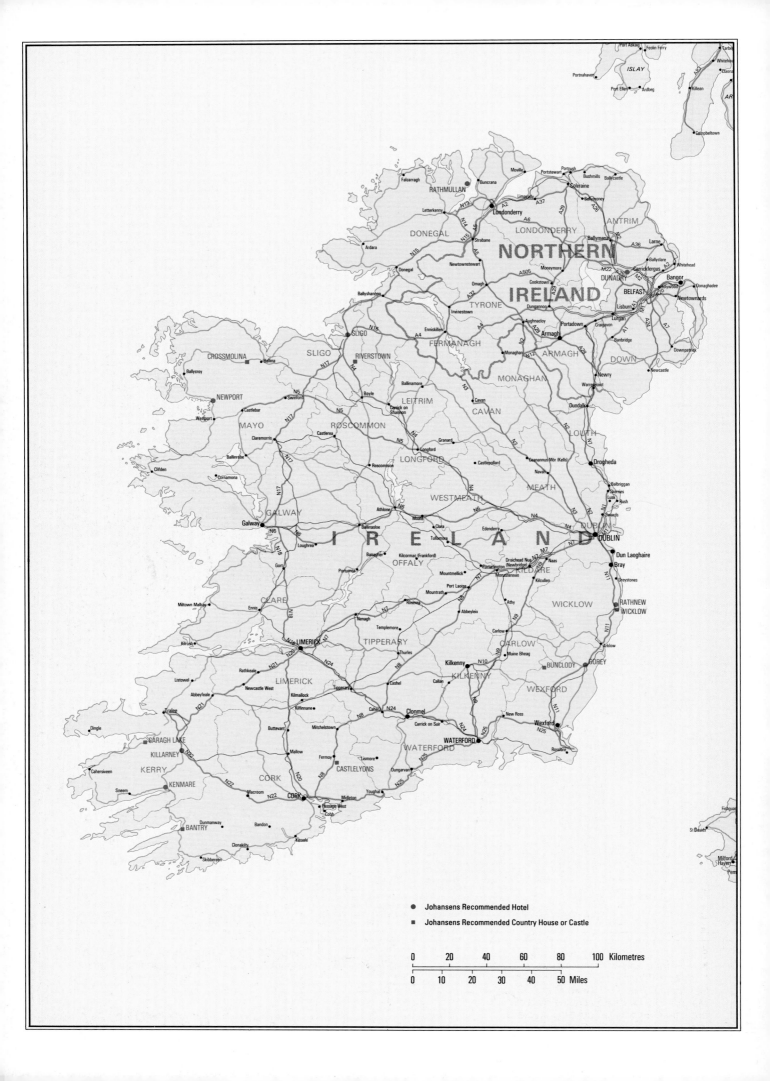

● Johansens Recommended Hotel

■ Johansens Recommended Country House or Castle

| 0 | 20 | 40 | 60 | 80 | 100 | Kilometres |

| 0 | 10 | 20 | 30 | 40 | 50 | Miles |

The Classic Breakfast

JOHANSENS
S E C R E T S

A series of Johansens Treasure Hunts is appearing in our new *Excellent Secrets* newsletter with bottles of champagne for published entries. To join the Johansens Treasure Hunt, write to us with your answers to the three questions below. Then make up three clues of your own on similar lines and include those (with answers).

1

1 **Which is the Johansens Recommended Hotel nearest to the Badminton Horse Trials?**

2

2 **Which Johansens Inn featured on television in *All Creatures Great and Small*?**

3

3 **In which Johansens Country House are the bedrooms named after musical composers?**

Send your answers and your own clues to: Johansens Ltd, Freepost, Bateman Street, Cambridge, CB2 1BR

Britain's Best Kept Secret?

Johansens recommendations have been described as 'Britain's best kept secret'. Johansens country house hotels, inns and private country houses offer unparalleled excellence and value-for-money. Throughout the year Johansens establishments also offer an amazing variety of special weekends – shooting; antiques; collecting modern art; music; racing; and murder mysteries – always with excellent cuisine and comfort at the right price. No secret!

And now we are launching *Excellent Secrets*, Johansens regular newsletter. Just complete the order form at the end of this book to receive your own copy, or write to us requesting it using our freepost address. We'll send it on your behalf to a friend or two as well, if you like. No secret, no charge!

So pass on *Johansens Excellent Secrets* by filling in one of the forms at the end of this book or by writing to:

Johansens Limited, Freepost, Bateman Street, Cambridge CB2 1BR

POTTER & MOORE · Gilchrist & Soames
LONDON

Potter & Moore and Gilchrist & Soames,
both traditional manufacturers of luxury toiletries, offer to the
select and discerning hotelier a wide variety of
high quality bath products.

The perfect touch to the perfect stay.

ENGLAND

The following pages contain hotel entries in England in alphabetical
order according to their placename.

Wales entries begin on page 365;
Scotland on page 403;
Ireland on page 475;
and the Channel Islands on page 485.

THE ALDERLEY EDGE HOTEL

MACCLESFIELD ROAD, ALDERLEY EDGE, CHESHIRE SK9 9BJ
TEL: 0625 583033 FAX: 0625 586343

This award-winning hotel, dating from 1850, was refurbished from attic to cellars in 1989 under the direction of the General Manager, John Buttery. The Alderley Edge now has a new conservatory, 21 executive de luxe rooms and 11 luxury suites (each with a whirlpool bath), offering a choice of traditional decor or cottage-style accommodation. Attention is given to the highest standards of cuisine; Alderley Edge was *Cheshire Life* Restaurant of the Year 1990. Fresh produce, including fish deliveries twice daily, is provided by top local suppliers. Specialities include light lunches of hot and cold seafood dishes with hot sweets served straight from the oven; afternoon tea includes pastries baked by the hotel's own pâtissier. Main meals are complemented by over 600 wines. There is a conference room for 120 people as well as a suite of meeting and private dining rooms. Secretarial services, fax and chauffered limousines are all available. The famous Edge walks are nearby, as are Manchester, Tatton and Lyme Parks, Quarry Bank Mill and Dunham Massey. Price guide: £120–£150. Directions: M6 to M565 Stockport. Exit Junction 6, take A538 to Wilmslow. Follow signs 1¼ miles through Alderley Edge, left at Volvo garage, hotel is 200 yards on right.

WHITE LODGE COUNTRY HOUSE

SLOE LANE, ALFRISTON, SUSSEX BN26 5UR
TEL: 0323 870265 FAX: 0323 870284

Exquisitely furnished with authentic period pieces and elegant drapery, White Lodge Country House is the place to enjoy the style and luxury of a bygone age, with every comfort and facility of the present day. Guests can enjoy the three comfortable lounges which are light and airy. The two restaurants provide a high standard of service and cuisine, and the pleasant cocktail bar is an ideal spot to relax in comfortable surroundings. Each bedroom has every facility the discerning guest would expect, with decor to match the quiet elegance of the rest of the hotel. The view is an attraction in itself; the hotel overlooks the wooded, tranquil Cuckmere Valley. Within easy reach of Brighton, Eastbourne and the port of Newhaven, with its frequent ferries to mainland Europe, the hotel is ideally situated for touring. Children over 9 are welcome. Price guide: £75–£110. Directions: White Lodge Country House lies 1 mile south from the A27 roundabout.

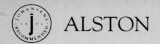

LOVELADY SHIELD COUNTRY HOUSE HOTEL

NENTHEAD ROAD, ALSTON, CUMBRIA CA9 3LF
TEL: 0434 381203 FAX: 0434 381515

Two and a half miles from Alston, England's highest market town, Lovelady Shield nestles in 3 acres of tranquil riverside gardens. Bright log fires in the library and drawing room enhance the hotel's welcoming atmosphere and owners Kenneth and Margaret Lyons take great care to ensure that staying at Lovelady Shield is a memorable occasion. The five course dinners created by Barrie Garton are varied and very substantial, rounded off by home-made desserts and a selection of English cheeses. Many guests first discover Lovelady Shield en route for Scotland. They then return to explore this beautiful and unspoiled part of England and experience the comforts of the hotel. Golf, fishing, shooting and riding are available locally. The Pennine Way, Hadrian's Wall and the Lake District are within easy reach. Conferences for up to 12. Closed January and February. Price guide: £96–£120 (including dinner). Directions: The hotel's driveway is by the junction of the B6294 and the A689 east of Alston.

KIRKSTONE FOOT COUNTRY HOUSE HOTEL

KIRKSTONE PASS ROAD, AMBLESIDE, CUMBRIA LA22 9EH
TEL: 05394 32232

Kirkstone Foot Country House Hotel is a superb 17th-century manor house set in 2 acres of tranquil landscaped gardens, overlooking Stock Ghyll which flows through the grounds. The hotel has been lovingly restored and has 16 bedrooms in the main house and 15, very comfortable, self catering cottages within the grounds. The restaurant provides the best of English traditional cuisine, using a wide variety of high quality local produce, and offers an extensive, imaginative wine list. For sports enthusiasts golf, sailing, horse-riding, private fishing, wind-surfing and water-skiing are close at hand, as is the magnificent scenery of the fells and lakes, a Mecca for walkers. The homes of Beatrix Potter and Wordsworth are just a short drive away. Guests staying in a cottage may take their dogs. Closed 9–20 December and 3–31 January. Price guide: £70–£95 including dinner. Directions: Kirkstone Foot lies on the Kirkstone Pass Road, off the A591 at the north end of Ambleside.

ROTHAY MANOR

ROTHAY BRIDGE, AMBLESIDE, CUMBRIA LA22 0EH
TEL: 05394 33605   FAX: 05394 33607

Situated half a mile from Lake Windermere, this elegant Georgian listed building, once the home of a prosperous merchant, stands in 1½ acres of grounds. The luxurious bedrooms include three beautifully furnished suites, two of which are in the lodge beside the manor and afford an unusual measure of space and privacy. One suite is equipped for five people and designed with particular attention to the comfort and relaxation of guests with disabilities; it has a ramp leading to the garden and an especially spacious shower. Care, consideration and comfort are evident throughout.

For the actively inclined, there is free use of the Lowood Leisure Centre, and permits are available for trout fishing. The Manor is ideal for private functions for up to 20 people. Nearby are golf, riding, stately homes, a steam railway and Wordsworth's cottage. Closed early January to mid-February. Represented in USA by Josephine Barr: 800-323-5463. Price guide: £90–£104. Special winter breaks are offered. Directions: ¼ mile out of Ambleside on the road to Coniston.

ANSTY HALL

ANSTY, NR COVENTRY, WARWICKSHIRE CV7 9HZ
TEL: 0203 612222 FAX: 0203 602155

This mellow red brick Caroline house stands in 8 acres of gardens on the edge of the village of Ansty. Comfort is the watchword here. All of the spacious, well-proportioned rooms overlook the gardens and farmland beyond. The decor throughout is soothing and the cuisine imaginative. Chef Robert McColl makes good use of the produce grown in the walled kitchen garden, and an admirable cellar complements his efforts. Ansty Hall is the perfect meeting place for businessmen, being conveniently placed for the M1 and M6 motorways, with London, Manchester and Bristol about 1½ hours drive away. Arrangements can be made for exclusive use of the establishment for conferences. It is also an ideal base for touring the Warwickshire countryside and visiting, for instance, Birmingham's National Exhibition Centre, Coventry with its cathedral, Stratford-upon-Avon and Shakespeare country, Warwick and Royal Leamington Spa. A Hidden Hotel. Price guide: £99.50–£109. Directions: At the edge of the village, 2 minutes from Junction 2 of the M6.

TUFTON ARMS HOTEL

MARKET SQUARE, APPLEBY-IN-WESTMORLAND, CUMBRIA CA16 6XA
TEL: 07683 51593 FAX: 07683 52761

This distinguished Victorian coaching inn, now a member of the Romantik Hotels group, has been completely refurbished to provide luxurious interiors and a high standard of comfort. The beautiful bedrooms successfully recapture the Victorian feel of the building, while providing all the facilities one expects in the 1990s. The kitchen is presided over by the owner's son, David, and guests can choose from a wide-ranging à la carte or a set menu, which changes daily. Whenever possible, fresh local produce is used, and the restaurant is noted for its fish dishes. The food is complemented by an extensive wine list which ranges from honest, fruity, country wines to mature and complex vintages.

Appleby, the historic county town of Westmorland, stands in beautiful countryside and is an ideal base for tours of the Lakes, Yorkshire Dales and North Pennines; it also makes an ideal stopping point en route to, and from, Scotland. Fishing and shooting can be arranged by the hotel. Other activities include walking, pony trekking, golf, bowls, birdwatching, clay pigeon shooting. Price guide: £46–£96. Directions: In the centre of Appleby, by the A66, 38 miles west of Scotch Corner, 13 miles east of Penrith (Junction 40, M6), 12 miles from Junction 38, M6.

AMBERLEY CASTLE

AMBERLEY, NR ARUNDEL, WEST SUSSEX BN18 9ND
TEL: 0798 831992 FAX: 0798 831998

Amberley Castle is over 900 years old and nestles in the lee of the lovely South Downs. Its mighty battlements afford breathtaking views while its massive, 14th-century curtain walls and mighty portcullis bear silent testimony to its fascinating history. Resident proprietors, Joy and Martin Cummings, have transformed this mediaeval fortress into a unique country castle hotel. They offer a warm, personal welcome and their hotel offers the ultimate in modern-day luxury while retaining an atmosphere of timelessness. Guests can choose from four-poster, twin four-poster or brass double-bedded rooms. Each room is individually designed and has its own jacuzzi bath. The exquisite, 12th-century Queen's Room

Restaurant provides the perfect setting for the traditionally-inspired, highly creative cuisine of head chef Nigel Boschetti and his team. Amberley Castle is a natural first choice for romantic or cultural weekends, sporting breaks or confidential senior management meetings (there are conference facilities for up to 30 delegates). It is ideally situated for opera at Glyndbourne, theatre at Chichester and racing at Goodwood and Fontwell. It is easily reached from London and the major air and channel ports. Price guide: £130–£175. Directions: Amberley Castle is on the B2139, off the A29 between Fontwell and Bury.

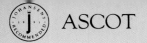

THE ROYAL BERKSHIRE

LONDON ROAD, SUNNINGHILL, ASCOT, BERKSHIRE SL5 0PP
TEL: 0344 23322 FAX: 0344 27100 TELEX: 847280

The home of the Churchill family for over a hundred years, The Royal Berkshire is now an elegant hotel ideally located between Ascot racecourse and the Polo Club. This Queen Anne mansion, built in 1705, is set in 15 acres of superb gardens and woodlands with tennis courts, putting green and croquet lawn for guests' enjoyment. Indoor facilities include a leisure complex with pool, whirlpool spa, sauna and squash court. The head chef produces a range of epicurean dishes that add a new dimension to the enjoyment of food. The wine list includes some excellent older vintages. The special 'Champagne Weekends' are good value for money. The hotel's proximity to Heathrow attracts the business traveller who will find a variety of rooms available for meetings or other company functions. *Egon Ronay* and *Good Food Guide* recommended. Dogs not allowed in public rooms. Price guide: £120–£170. Directions: 1 mile from Ascot on the corner of A329 and B383. Nearest M25 exit, Junction 13.

PENNYHILL PARK HOTEL AND COUNTRY CLUB

COLLEGE RIDE, BAGSHOT, SURREY GU19 5ET
TEL: 0276 71774 FAX: 0276 73217 TELEX: 858841 PHPARK G

Built in 1849, this elegant mansion bears traces of its passage through Victorian and Edwardian times, and although every modern amenity is provided, care has been taken to preserve the period atmosphere. It stands in 112 acres of tranquil grounds, including landscaped gardens, parkland and a lake. The bedrooms, each named after a shrub or flower, are individually decorated and furnished. Beautifully presented cuisine, comprising fresh British produce served in the traditional way, is offered in the splendid Latymer Restaurant. A relaxing atmosphere for business conferences or meetings for up to 30 people can be found in one of the oak-panelled Terrace Suites. Guests can take a sauna, or a light meal in the Orangery. The hotel has a 9-hole golf course, clay pigeon shooting and its own riding stables. Only 27 miles from central London, Pennyhill Park is a peaceful haven. Price guide: £105–£300. Directions: From the M3, off Exit 3, take A322 towards Bracknell. Left before lights into Bagshot Village. Through village; left onto A30 London Road. Go over lights; follow road for ¾ of a mile; right 50 yards past Texaco garage.

CALLOW HALL

MAPPLETON ROAD, ASHBOURNE, DERBYSHIRE DE6 2AA
TEL: 0335 43403 FAX: 0335 43624

Occupying a superb elevated position in woodland overlooking the valleys of the Bentley Brook and the River Dove, Callow Hall, lovingly restored over the last 6 years by the owners, David and Dorothy Spencer, is now a superb country house hotel. Mineral water and home-made biscuits are among the thoughtful touches to be found in the spacious period bedrooms. The elegant public rooms, with antique furniture and glorious views, are relaxing and comfortable. The restaurant boasts the use of fresh produce and the watchword here is 'home-made'. Bread, pastries, sausages and home-cured bacon are just a few of the items made on the premises. A private stretch of the Bentley Brook, a tributary of the River Dove, is mentioned in Izaak Walton's *The Compleat Angler* and is open for fly fishermen. The hotel is an ideal base for exploring the magnificent Derbyshire Peak District and Dales. Conference facilities for up to 20 people. Price guide: £80–£110. Directions: Take the A515 through Ashbourne towards Buxton. At the Bowling Green Inn on the brow of a steep hill, turn left, then take the first right, signposted Mappleton, and the hotel is over the bridge on the right.

HOLNE CHASE HOTEL

NR ASHBURTON, DEVON TQ13 7NS
TEL: 03643 471 FAX: 03643 453

A hunting estate in the 11th century, Holne Chase, commended by the BTA, is run in a very friendly yet professional fashion by the Bromage family. Most of the beautifully presented and comfortable bedrooms enjoy the same superb outlook over the Dart valley as the public rooms. The tranquil atmosphere of the public rooms, with luxurious sofas and easy chairs and panoramic views, makes them relaxing sanctuaries. A productive kitchen garden supplies the restaurant, where quality, regional cooking can be enjoyed in this recently refurbished, large and elegant room. Indoors are open fires and plenty of books; outdoors, a putting green, croquet lawn and a sporting cricket pitch. Fishermen are very welcome as the hotel boasts a mile of excellent fly-fishing on the River Dart. A good base for exploring the West Country, the hotel can offer guided walks on nearby Dartmoor. Price guide: £90–£110. Directions: To find the hotel, take the Ashburton turning off the A38, and follow the signs for Two Bridges. The hotel turning is on the right just after the road crosses the River Dart.

RIVERSIDE COUNTRY HOUSE HOTEL

ASHFORD-IN-THE-WATER, BAKEWELL, DERBYSHIRE DE4 1QF
TEL: 0629 814275 FAX: 0629 812873

Set in an acre of mature garden bordered by the River Wye, this is a rather special hotel, first opened to guests in 1982, and personally managed by owners Roger and Sue Taylor. A feature of the hotel is its cuisine produced by Jeremy Buckingham, head chef, who uses seasonally available game from the Chatsworth Estate. The fresh produce and the fine wines are served on antique tables set with gleaming silver, sparkling crystal and illuminated by candle light. All the pretty bedrooms have private facilities, and some have four-posters. Downstairs are oak-panelled interiors, an elegant lounge and inglenook fireplaces where log fires blaze. This BTA Commended hotel is ideally situated for visiting Chatsworth House, Haddon and Hardwick Halls. Fishing is available on the River Wye and the hotel has a croquet lawn. Conference facilities for up to 12. Price guide: £82.50–£88. The hotel offers 2 to 5-night bargain breaks. Directions: 1½ miles north of Bakewell on the A6 heading towards Buxton. Ashford-in-the-Water lies on the right-hand side of the river. The hotel is in the west end of the village next to the Sheepwash Bridge.

FAIRWATER HEAD COUNTRY HOUSE HOTEL

HAWKCHURCH, NR AXMINSTER, DEVON EX13 5TX
TEL: 02977 349

Set in an Ashley Courtenay award-winning landscaped garden on the borders of Dorset and Devon, this Edwardian country house enjoys panoramic views over the Axe valley. The restaurant features English cooking with a wide choice of menu. There are candle-lit dinners, with pianist, on Wednesday and Saturday evenings. The comfortable lounges look out on the surrounding countryside and the atmosphere is peaceful and relaxed. Guests may play croquet on the lawn and there is a billiards room. Nearby sporting facilities include golf (at reduced green fees), sailing, shooting and riding. Convenient for the coast at Lyme Regis, there are many historic houses and magnificent gardens in the area. Specialist holidays are available covering bridge, antiques and gardening. AA and RAC Hospitality Awards. RAC Restaurant Award. BTA Commended. Closed January and February. Dogs by arrangement. Price guide: £80–£95. Directions: The hotel is well signposted in Hawkchurch, reached by the B3165, Crewkerne–Lyme Regis road.

HARTWELL HOUSE

OXFORD ROAD, AYLESBURY, BUCKINGHAMSHIRE HP17 8NL
TEL: 0296 747444 FAX: 0296 747450 TELEX: 837108 HART H

Standing in 80 acres of gardens and parkland landscaped by a pupil of Capability Brown, Hartwell House has both Georgian and Jacobean facades. This beautiful house, sympathetically restored by Historic House Hotels, was the home, during his exile, of King Louis XVIII of France. The large, ground-floor reception rooms, which feature oak panelling and decorated ceilings, have been furnished with antiques and fine paintings to re-create the elegance of the 18th century. The grounds contain many restored ornamental buildings and statues and a lake where guests can fish for trout. The dining room at Hartwell House, designed after the style of eminent architect, Sir John Soane, is the setting for memorable meals produced by head chef Aiden McCormack. Situated in the Vale of Aylesbury the hotel is within an hour's drive of London and is only 20 miles from Oxford. Blenheim Palace, Woburn Abbey and Waddesdon Manor, are nearby. Final restoration of the coach house, stables and riding school by autumn 1991, will add a further 16 bedrooms and suites, plus meeting and leisure facilities, including a heated indoor swimming pool. Welcomes children over 12. Price guide: £147–£310. Directions: On the A418 Oxford Road, 2 miles from Aylesbury.

PETTY FRANCE
DUNKIRK, BADMINTON, AVON GL9 1AF
TEL: 045423 361 FAX: 045423 768

Situated amid typical Cotswold countryside, Petty France is a private hotel with a country home atmosphere. It affords beautiful views over open fields, with stone walls and mature trees. Its public rooms are full of antiques and decorated with fresh flowers. In winter the cosy atmosphere is enhanced by log fires burning, and sumptuous cuisine is prepared all year round by chef David James. The bedrooms are prettily furnished and those in the converted stable have special character and privacy. All have private bathrooms or shower rooms en suite. There are three conference rooms accommodating 10 to 25 people, all with air-conditioning, good natural daylight and full display presentation equipment. For lovers of nature, history and sport, this is an ideal location. The Cotswolds offer beautiful scenery, many relics of past ages, historic houses and castles, and excellent golf, riding and fishing. Price guide: £75–£110. Directions: M4 Junction 18: 5 miles north on A46. M5 Junction 13: A419 to Stroud, then 12 miles on A46 towards Bath.

DOWNREW HOUSE

BISHOPS TAWTON, NR BARNSTAPLE, NORTH DEVON EX32 0DY
TEL: 0271 42497/46673 FAX: 0271 23947

A beautiful Queen Anne house in 12 acres of grounds, Downrew House is immaculate in every detail and is run in a very personal way by the owners. The delightful and extremely comfortable bedrooms all have lovely bathrooms en suite, plus trouser press, iron and ironing board and 24-hour room service. Other features include a magnificent drawing room with log fire, an intimate bar with Delabole slate floor and a 17th-century cobb and stone wall. Renowned for fine English/French cuisine, served in the bow-windowed dining room with views over the grounds and countryside beyond. Extensive facilities on offer include a heated swimming pool, hard tennis court, approach golf, croquet, billiards and solarium. Children over 7 welcome. Price guide: £109–£133 including dinner. Directions: Downrew House is just 2 miles from new A361 North Devon link road (from M5). The house stands on Codden Hill just south of Barnstaple and the village of Bishops Tawton off the A377.

HALMPSTONE MANOR

BISHOPS TAWTON, NR BARNSTAPLE, DEVON EX32 0EA
TEL: 0271 830321 FAX: 0271 830826

This country house hotel set in 200 acres of Devonshire countryside is the ideal place to escape for both intimate meals or overnight stays. Jane and Charles Stanbury have created something unique at Halmpstone Manor achieving a delightful combination of the formal and informal. The standard of food, accommodation and service is luxurious, to say the least. Personal attention to detail, in the pursuit of excellence, creates an atmosphere of genuine interest in all of their guests' comfort.

Dinner is served in the unusual early 16th-century wood-panelled dining room where, in winter, a cosy open fire is lit. The exclusive four-poster bedded suites are truly a haven of peace and their ambience reflects an English country manor at its very best. Member ILA Group. AA Red Star Hotel. Dogs by arrangement. Price guide: £70–£90. Directions: A361 to Barnstaple; A377 to Bishops Tawton. At end of village, turn left opposite BP filling station. Go 2 miles, turn right at Halmpstone Manor sign.

KITTIWELL HOUSE HOTEL AND RESTAURANT

CROYDE, NORTH DEVON EX33 1PG
TEL: 0271 890247 FAX: 0271 890469

Kittiwell House is an enchanting 16th-century thatched Devon longhouse of great character, full of old-world charm and atmosphere. Guests can sleep in a four-poster in a room whose original features include exposed beams, uneven floors and intriguing nooks and crannies. A number of bedrooms open onto the garden or patio. The restaurant features two menus, table d'hôte, which is changed daily, and an extensive a`la carte list. Both are served at well-spaced tables and include a choice of dishes for vegetarians. The comprehensive, international wine list has something to suit most palates. Activity breaks offered throughout the year include, riding, clay pigeon shooting and golf. Superb golden sand beaches are within 2 miles of Kittiwell, providing safe bathing, sail-boarding and surfing. Closed mid-January to mid-February. Price guide: £90 including dinner. Directions: Take the A361 to Braunton, Croyde is signposted from there. The hotel is beside the main road in the village.

AUDLEYS WOOD THISTLE HOTEL
ALTON ROAD, BASINGSTOKE, HAMPSHIRE RG25 2JT
TEL: 0256 817555 FAX: 0256 817500 TELEX: 858273

Originally a Victorian country house, Audleys Wood is set in 7 acres of private gardens and lightly wooded parkland on the southern edge of Basingstoke, conveniently placed for the town centre and the M3 London-Southampton motorway. The restaurant is superbly restored with a minstrels' gallery, where guests are offered a creative and imaginative menu combined with an extensive wine list incorporating vintages of international repute. Each of the 71 bedrooms is individually decorated and has every modern luxury. The hotel is a perfect setting for senior-level management meetings and conferences for up to 25 delegates. It has five conference rooms, one of which, the Simonds Room, contains beautiful dark oak panelling from Tewkesbury Abbey. Audleys Wood provides putting, croquet and a golf driving net in the grounds and bicycles for guests who wish to explore the rolling Hampshire countryside. Winchester, Silchester, Watership Down and Jane Austen's childhood home at Alton are just a short drive away. Price guide: £95. Directions: Audleys Wood lies off the A339 south of Basingstoke.

CAVENDISH HOTEL

BASLOW, DERBYSHIRE DE4 1SP
TEL: 0246 582311 FAX: 0246 582312 TELEX: 547150 CAVTEL G

Built in the late 18th century, the original Peacock Hotel has been considerably upgraded and was re-opened as the Cavendish in 1975. Its location is unique as it is set on the Duke and Duchess of Devonshire's estate at Chatsworth. All of the comfortable, well-equipped bedrooms have a fine view over the estate's grounds and the largest rooms, in the original part of the hotel – The Inn Rooms – are furnished with antiques and fine art. A warm welcome is assured from proprietor Eric Marsh who greets every guest personally. The hotel's homely, relaxing atmosphere is enhanced by the crackling log fires in cooler weather. The hotel's Garden Room Restaurant – opened in 1989 – offers meals throughout the day in a more insouciant atmosphere than the other, more formal restaurant. Chef, Nick Buckingham, and his team have won many commendations for their creative cuisine: 'our reputation for good food is the envy of our peers', says the hotel's manager Neil Spencer. A footpath connects the hotel to the Chatsworth Estate where guests are welcome to stroll. Hardwick Hall, a late 16th-century 'prodigy house' and Haddon Hall are nearby too. Other places of interest include Treak Cliff Cavern (the Blue John Mine) and the Tramway Museum at Crich. Price guide: £94–£105. Directions: The hotel is on the A619 in Baslow, 9 miles west of Chesterfield; 15 miles from M1, Junction 29.

FISCHER'S

BASLOW HALL, CALVER ROAD, BASLOW, DERBYSHIRE DE4 1RR
TEL: 0246 583259

Built of Derbyshire stone with gables and mullioned windows, Baslow Hall looks every inch a period property. In fact it was not built until 1907. Now owned by Max and Susan Fischer, Baslow Hall is renowned for its cuisine. Stay here and you will wake to the smell of fresh-baked bread and croissants wafting up from the kitchens. All day the air is rich with the aroma of the home-made stocks and bases being prepared for lunch and dinner. Traditional British food – home-made steak and kidney pudding, for instance, – is always available at lunchtime but it is the dinner menu which reveals chef Max Fischer's culinary prowess. Fillet of venison on blackberry and bitter chocolate sauce, roast partridge served with its own sauce and garnishes or sea bass with tomato and root ginger are some of his creations. However, you must tear yourself away from the delicacies of the dining room occasionally to explore the beauties of the Peak National Park, Buxton and Matlock with their spa baths and Bakewell. Price guide: £82.50–£104.50. Directions: M1 from the south; A621 from Sheffield and the north.

APSLEY HOUSE HOTEL
NEWBRIDGE HILL, BATH, AVON BA1 3PT
TEL: 0225 336966

Reputedly built for the Duke of Wellington in 1830, Apsley House is one of Britain's finest small private hotels, offering the highest standards of comfort and cuisine. The elegant Georgian entrance hall and reception leads you to your own private luxurious bedroom suite, complete with all facilities and furnished and decorated in individual style. Apsley House stands only 5 minutes by car, or 20–30 minutes' walk, from the centre of Bath. Visitors can enjoy the unique splendour of the Roman Baths and the fine Georgian architecture of the Assembly Rooms, Royal Crescent, the Circus and Lansdown Crescent. The hotel is ideally situated for touring the nearby beauty spots and places of interest in the Cotswolds and the Mendip Hills. The hotel is considered unsuitable for children under 14. Price guide: £90–£120. Directions: The hotel lies 1 mile west of Queens Square on A431 to Kelston.

7 rms   BARCLAYCARD VISA   Access   AMERICAN EXPRESS   DINERS   OPEN ALL YEAR

COMBE GROVE MANOR

BRASSKNOCKER HILL, MONKTON COMBE, BATH, AVON BA2 7HS
TEL: 0225 834644 FAX: 0225 834961

Combe Grove Manor, an exclusive country house hotel is a beautiful 18th-century house set on a sunny hillside, 2 miles from the city of Bath. It is surrounded by 68 acres of formal gardens and woodland with views over the Limpley Stoke Valley to the White Horse of Westbury. In the à la carte restaurant, the cuisine is superb. There is also a private dining room plus a welcoming wine bar and restaurant with a terrace garden. After dinner, you can relax in the graceful drawing rooms. The bedrooms all have en suite facilities. The suites have jacuzzi baths and are all individually designed and furnished. Within the 68 acres of grounds are some of the finest leisure facilities in the country, including indoor and outdoor (heated) swimming pools, a spa bath and steam room, 4 all-weather tennis courts, squash courts, a 5 hole par 3 golf course and two-tiered driving range. There is also a jogging trail, Nautilus gym, aerobics studio, saunas and solaria. The Garden Lodge comprises 35 individually decorated rooms, most of which afford stunning views. Conference facilities for up to 40 delegates. ETB 5 Crowns. Price guide: £75–£160. Directions: Combe Grove Manor is SE of Bath on Brassknocker Hill, between Combe Down and Monkton Combe.

FOUNTAIN HOUSE HOTEL SUITES

9-11 FOUNTAIN BUILDINGS, LANSDOWN ROAD, BATH, AVON BA1 5DV
TEL: 0225 338622 FAX: 0225 445855 TELEX: 444905

An elegant Georgian mansion in the heart of one of England's most beautiful cities, Fountain House is Bath's first all-suite hotel. Each of the charming, comfortably appointed suites has a separate living room with colour TV and telephone, one, two or three bedrooms and a fully equipped kitchen. Much thought has gone into the attractive decor and meticulous arrangement of the suites in order to create an atmosphere of tranquillity and informality. A host of excellent restaurants are within walking distance of the hotel or, for dining in, a 'Gourmet Basket' is provided. Bath is a treasure house for the tourist. The Roman Baths, the Circus and the Assembly Rooms echo the novels of Jane Austen, and the shopping facilities are second only to London. Fountain House is an ideal base for exploring the West by car; the Cotswolds, Longleat, Castle Combe and Laycock are only a short drive away. Lock-up garages available. Price guide: £108. Directions: Take Exit 18 from M4, or the A4 from Chippenham, and look for Lansdown Road on your right. Fountain House is 50 yards along on the right.

CLOS DU ROY AT BOX HOUSE

BOX, NR BATH, WILTSHIRE SN14 9NR
TEL: 0225 744447 FAX: 0225 743971

Clos du Roy at Box House is a handsome Georgian mansion set in 7 acres of beautiful gardens and pastures. The Clos du Roy restaurant has a reputation built on superb cuisine, comfort and hospitality in elegant surroundings. Guests here can choose from imaginative à la carte, or set price, menus complemented by a list of personally selected wines. There are regular gourmet evenings when guests can choose from such delicacies as fillet of Gressingham duck stuffed with a game mousse and veal sweetbreads, garnished with potato cake and served in its own juices flavoured with elderflower. Then, to follow, Rêve Exotique – a timbale of chocolate mousse and coconut bavarois, served with a rum sauce. The nine bedrooms are individually designed, spacious, extremely comfortable and have the added benefit of splendid views. Box House is an ideal base for exploring the west country with its wealth of historical landmarks. Guests can swim in the hotel's outdoor, heated pool, play croquet on the lawn or play golf at a nearby course. Shooting, horse-riding and ballooning can be arranged. One and three day cookery courses are available too. Conference facilities for up to 16 delegates. Helipad available. Price guide: £95–£130. Directions: 15 minutes from M4, Junctions 17 and 18. Less than 2 hours' drive from London.

LUCKNAM PARK

COLERNE, NR BATH, WILTSHIRE SN14 8AZ
TEL: 0225 742777 FAX: 0225 743536 TELEX: 445648

Lucknam Park, a magnificent Georgian mansion built in 1720, is only 6 miles from the famous city of Bath and is set on the southern edge of the Cotswolds. It is furnished with fine antiques and a delicate sense of historical context, but with the luxury facilities demanded of a first-class country hotel. The Leisure Spa, set in the theme of a Roman villa, comprises an indoor heated swimming pool, sauna, solarium, steam room, whirlpool spa, gymnasium, snooker room, beauty salon and tennis courts. The elegant dining room is set with exquisite porcelain, silver and glass. Riding, shooting, hunting, fishing and hot air ballooning can be arranged. Helipad. Represented in USA by Prestige Hotels North America: Telephone 800-544-7570 toll free. Price guide: £120–£275. Directions: 15 minutes from M4, Junctions 17 and 18.

STON EASTON PARK

STON EASTON, BATH, SOMERSET BA3 4DF
TEL: 076121 631 FAX: 076121 377

Internationally famous, Ston Easton Park is a listed Grade I Palladian mansion. This beautifully run hotel provides a unique opportunity to live in one of England's great country houses, with the advantage of all the comforts and convenience of the 20th century. While Ston Easton Park offers every comfort expected of a hotel of this quality, it also provides friendly and unobtrusive personal attention to detail. The house has won innumerable awards for its decor, service and food. The grounds, landscaped in the 18th century by Humphry Repton, are being restored according to his Red Book; and the walled Victorian kitchen garden produces many of the vegetables, flowers and herbs used in the house. Cuisine prepared from only the finest quality produce and a cellar stocked with many rare wines and vintages help make Ston Easton Park the perfect place to relax in the peace and tranquillity of the classic English countryside. Boardroom-style meetings are possible for up to 24 people. A basement kennel is provided for dogs. Price guide: £115–£285. Directions: 11 miles south of Bath on A37 between Bath and Wells.

        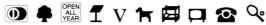

THE BRIDGE HOUSE HOTEL

BEAMINSTER, DORSET DT8 3AY
TEL: 0308 862200

The history of The Bridge House Hotel is uncertain. Its stone mullioned windows imply Tudor origins but their differing sizes and levels indicate they were added to upgrade an older building. Little blocked-up windows suggest an early Church connection, while the presence of a priest hole confirms previous ownership by a Roman Catholic family during the time of the Reformation. Whatever the truth of its development, as a hotel the building offers extremely comfortable, en suite accommodation and food cooked to order by proprietor Peter Pinkster. The emphasis is on fresh local produce and West Bay scallops, Poole mussels, Dorset lamb and local, farmhouse Cheddar are regulars on the menu. Meals are served in the panelled Georgian dining room or the garden conservatory restaurant and are complemented by an 'interesting, sensibly priced wine list'. Beaminster is 5 miles north of Bridport which makes the hotel an ideal base for the exploration of Hardy country. There are several golf courses nearby; fresh and salt water fishing, sailing and sea bathing are popular local pursuits. Special 3-night breaks available. Price guide: £75. Directions: Beaminster is off the A3066 at the junction with the B3163.

BEECHFIELD HOUSE

BEANACRE, MELKSHAM, WILTSHIRE SN12 7PU
TEL: 0225 703700 FAX: 0225 790118

Beechfield House, built in 1878 of mellow Bath Stone, nestles in 8 acres of gardens in the beautiful Wiltshire countryside. Each room, which is named after a species of tree in the gardens, is distinctively decorated and elegantly furnished with antiques; crystal chandeliers and open fires add to the appeal. The restaurant and private dining rooms feature modern English cuisine created by chef Shaun Ellis, and most of the fruit, vegetables and herbs are grown in the hotel's gardens. The high standard of the cuisine is guaranteed whether it is intended for a quiet dinner for two in the restaurant, or a barbecue for 102 around the heated outdoor swimming pool. The gardens are spectacular during the spring, summer and autumn seasons; there is a tennis court and a croquet lawn set amid the fragrant rose beds. The hotel is ideally situated to explore Bath, Bowood House and the National Trust village of Lacock. Fishing can be arranged on the River Avon which is within walking distance. A Hidden Hotel. Price guide: £90–£110. Directions: Situated 15 minutes' drive from M4, Junction 17, on the A350 north of Melksham.

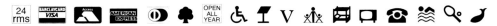

THE MONTAGU ARMS HOTEL

BEAULIEU, NEW FOREST, HAMPSHIRE SO42 7ZL
TEL: 0590 612324 FAX: 0590 612188

Situated at the head of the River Beaulieu in the heart of the New Forest, The Montagu Arms Hotel carries on a tradition of hospitality started seven centuries ago. As well as being a fine place for a holiday, the hotel is an ideal venue for small conferences. Each of the 24 bedrooms has been individually styled and decorated and has en suite facilities. Many feature four-poster or Victorian brass beds, and all rooms are equipped with colour television, radio, and direct-dial telephone. Dine in the oak-panelled restaurant, overlooking the garden, where you can enjoy excellent English cuisine prepared by award-winning chef John Mann. The menu is supported by an outstanding wine list. There is much to see and do around Beaulieu. Visit the National Motor Museum, Exbury Gardens or Buckler's Hard, or walk for miles through England's most beautiful New Forest. Price guide: £95–£175 (special break tariff on request). Directions: The village of Beaulieu is well signposted and The Montagu Arms Hotel commands an impressive position at the foot of the main street.

THE BLUE BELL HOTEL

MARKET PLACE, BELFORD, NORTHUMBERLAND NE70 7NE
TEL: 0668 213543 FAX: 0668 213787

Situated near the old Market Cross in the centre of the village of Belford, this renowned coaching inn has been tastefully refurbished in the Georgian style and retains all its original character and charm. The hotel's 3 acres of gardens supply fresh vegetables and fruit for the kitchen. The restaurant proffers a superb menu, relying also on fresh local produce, such as Cheviot lamb, Tweed salmon, Craster kippers, fresh lobsters and crabs and Northumbrian game, and thus provides seasonal variety. The Blue Bell is ideally situated as a base for discovering the historic coastal area of Northumberland; Farne Island, Lindisfarne and Berwick are but a few of the many interesting places to visit. For the sportsman, there are many fine golf courses nearby and sailing, fishing, shooting, climbing and walking are of the highest quality. Conference facilities for up to 80 participants. Price guide: £70–£86. Directions: From the A1, turn off at Belford/Woler junction B6349. The hotel is situated in the village centre.

NAILCOTE HALL HOTEL

NAILCOTE LANE, BERKSWELL, NR COVENTRY, WARWICKSHIRE CV7 7DE
TEL: 0203 466174 FAX: 0203 470720

Nailcote Hall is a charming Elizabethan country house of 15th-century origin, set in 8 acres of garden and parkland. Although a dwelling has existed on the site since the Norman Conquest, a Georgian wing was added in 1870, and in 1990 a further Georgian-style wing was built to create 16 bedrooms and comprehensive conference and banqueting facilities. The sympathetic restoration and extension has ensured that the character of the house has remained completely intact. The Hall is easily accessible by road, rail and air, and is ideally located for the National Exhibition Centre in Birmingham as well as Stratford-upon-Avon, Warwick and the Cotswolds, which makes it a welcome retreat for both business clients and tourists alike. The staff take pride in providing a personal service, and guests are assured of a high standard of cuisine. Both à la carte and table d'hôte menus are available. Children over 7 welcome. Dogs by prior arrangement. Price guide: £110–£125. Directions: Situated 5 miles west of Coventry on the B4101 Coventry to Knowle road.

PORTLEDGE HOTEL

FAIRY CROSS, BIDEFORD, DEVON EX39 5BX
TEL: 02375 262/367 FAX: 02375 717 TELEX: 9312132625 ANSWERBACK:PHG

If it is peace and quiet you are after, Portledge, a 17th-century manor house with features dating back to the 13th century, is the ideal place to stay. Set in 1,000 acres of park and farmland, the hotel has a private beach which you can laze on, or surf from. Colour co-ordinated interiors, the Armada Wing, ancestral portraits – family connections at Portledge go back to Norman times – together with ornate plaster ceilings and antique furniture, enhance the hotel's atmosphere of elegance. One bedroom also has a four-poster bed. Tennis, minigolf, a heated swimming pool plus a games room with space invader machines, a pool table and table tennis are all on the premises. As a Best Western Hotel, Portledge provides free accommodation for children sharing their parents' room. The hotel also hosts occasional whodunnit breaks, when you can spend the weekend with murder suspects. Alternatively you might prefer to be scared out of your wits on a horror weekend. Portledge can accommodate up to 70 conference delegates. The cuisine is imaginative and a six-choice, vegetarian menu has recently been introduced. Price guide: £60–£106. Directions: M5, exit Junction 27, follow A361 to Bideford, A39 signed to Bude and Camelford. Portledge is 4 miles on the right.

DURRANT HOUSE HOTEL

HEYWOOD ROAD, NORTHAM, BIDEFORD, NORTH DEVON EX39 3QB
TEL: 0237 472361 FAX: 0237 472361 TELEX: 46740

Originally a Georgian gentleman's home, Durrant House has been tastefully extended and modernised to provide a hotel of great comfort and warmth. An air of grandeur pervades the whole building. There are colonnades, oriental looking murals, and candelabra, gracing the tables in the silver service dining room which overlooks the courtyard, where illuminated fountains spray into a circular, carved stone pool. Maintaining the reputation built up by owners Vincent and Maria Borg for excellent food, chef Tony Johnson prepares mouthwatering dishes using fresh produce from local farms, rivers and the sea. The rooms are of a high standard and are tastefully co-ordinated in soft blues, pinks and creams. Leisure facilities include a sauna, solarium, and in the grounds, a swimming pool set attractively among green lawns and neat hedges. Conference facilities for up to 150 delegates. Durrant House is pleased to offer special interest holidays. For details, please contact the hotel. Price guide: £80. Directions: Exit M5 Junction 27 onto A361 to Barnstaple, then take A39 to Bideford. Just before Bideford, exit the roundabout for Northam.

JONATHANS' HOTEL AND RESTAURANT
16–24 WOLVERHAMPTON ROAD, OLDBURY, WARLEY, WEST MIDLANDS B68 0LH
TEL: 021–429 3757 FAX: 021–434 3107

This hotel can best be described as a Victorian extravaganza. Authentically furnished down to the last chamberpot, aspidistra, and teddy bear, Jonathans' is an intriguing maze of rooms on a multitude of levels. There are secret passages, archways, roof-gardens, and corners stuffed with bric-à-brac. Guests can take morning coffee or afternoon tea in the cosy sitting room and browse through books, munch a chocolate or two or listen to old 78s on the wind-up gramophone. The suites are charmingly arranged with comfortable wing chairs and open coal fires. Even the bathrooms boast rich drapes, gold taps, polished wood and hand-painted tiles. British chef Graham Bradley is renowned for serving the best meat cuts, unusual fowl and fish, fresh from Birmingham markets. Naughty puds with a Victorian heritage – spotted dick, trifle and treacle tart – make regular menu appearances. Few hotels are as charmingly quirky and distinctive as this one. Conference facilities for up to 35 people including a weekday Luncheon Club for business gatherings. Price guide: £80–£140. Directions: A mile from Junction 2 of the M5 at the intersection of A4123 and A456, 4 miles from the city centre.

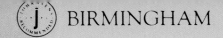

NORTON PLACE HOTEL

180 LIFFORD LANE, KINGS NORTON, BIRMINGHAM B30 3NT
TEL: 021–433 5656 FAX: 021–433 3048

Norton Place was completed in early 1990 to a design complementing its Victorian surroundings in the leafy suburb of Kings Norton. Each room has been individually decorated. The Suite provides four-poster bed, Louis XIV fireplace and luxury bathroom, together with its own conservatory. All rooms have marble bathrooms and a number feature *trompe l'œil* decoration. The sitting room also has its own conservatory. The Lombard Room Restaurant adjoining the hotel, which was established in 1987, is available for both residents and casual diners. The restaurant is proud of its reputation as one of the finest in the Midlands. Residents can enjoy the use of a small private fitness centre or visit Autoworld at the Patrick Collection, which includes a display of some 80 vehicles dating from 1904 to the present day. Norton Place is unique among small hotels within the Birmingham boundaries. Its gardens and lake afford guests a peaceful refuge from the hustle and bustle of the city. Price guide: £155–£250. Directions: Leave the M42 at Junction 3 and follow the Patrick Collection signs on the A435.

SWALLOW HOTEL

12 HAGLEY ROAD, FIVEWAYS, BIRMINGHAM B16 8SJ
TEL: 021–452 1144 FAX: 021–456 3442 TELEX: 333806

One of a new range of Swallow Luxury Hotels, this establishment has been designed in an Edwardian style to the highest standard, yet offers the ultimate in modern facilities. Fully air-conditioned in all public rooms and with individually controlled air-conditioning in the bedrooms, the hotel is keen to emphasise comfort at all times. Two restaurants are available: Langtry's, open throughout the day, and the Edward Elgar, offering English cuisine. The Swallow Leisure Club, designed around the theme of Ancient Egypt and including an indoor heated pool, an aerated pool and solarium, is truly luxurious and a must for any guest, whether at the hotel for business or pleasure. There is much to see in the area; Stratford-upon-Avon and Warwick Castle are nearby as well as the bustling city of Birmingham itself. The hotel offers excellent executive suites for those on business. Price guide: £97.50. Directions: 5 miles from Junction 1 of M5 and 5½ miles from Junction 6 of M6 on the A456 Hagley Road, just off Fiveways roundabout.

THE FOXFIELDS COUNTRY HOTEL
WHALLEY ROAD, BILLINGTON, NR BLACKBURN, LANCASHIRE BB6 9HY
TEL: 0254 822556 FAX: 0254 824613

This hotel is set in 11 acres of landscaped grounds, and all of the bedrooms afford views of the surrounding countryside: some overlook Pendle Hill; the others, the Ribble Valley. The ground floor suites have patios leading out into the gardens and one is purpose-built for guests with a disability. The air-conditioned boardroom seats up to 30 guests while the Pendle Suite has its own reception/bar areas and can accommodate up to 140 delegates for a conference or formal dinner, or 100 people for a dinner-dance. Nearby are Gawthorpe Hall, home to the Rachel Kay-Shuttleworth textile collections, and the seaside towns of Blackpool and Southport. Price guide: £80–£100. Directions: Turn off M6 at Junction 31. Take A59 to Clitheroe Whalley. Turn off at Langho roundabout. Hotel 1 mile further on right.

SINGLETON LODGE COUNTRY HOUSE HOTEL

LODGE LANE, SINGLETON, NR BLACKPOOL, LANCASHIRE FY6 8LT
TEL: 0253 883854

Personally managed by owners Alan and Ann Smith, Singleton Lodge is a country house built in 1702, and set in 5 acres of parkland and gardens. This charming 18th-century building has had a varied past, having been both a school for refined ladies and a vicarage! Guests will find the hotel equipped with comfortable, well-furnished bedrooms and relaxing public rooms. A well-presented menu combines traditional English food with a touch of French flair, prepared from the best local produce; vegetarian menus are always available. Conference facilities are available for up to 20 people. The many attractions of Blackpool are nearby, and for the sports enthusiast, there are eight golf courses within 15 minutes' drive, swimming, squash, badminton, indoor bowls, and coarse fishing on the hotel's own waters, as well as fishing in local rivers for trout and salmon and sea-angling. Dogs by prior arrangement. Price guide: £60. Directions: The village of Singleton lies on the B5269, just before it joins the A585, about 4 miles from the centre of Blackpool.

MAINS HALL COUNTRY HOUSE HOTEL

MAINS LANE, SINGLETON, NR BLACKPOOL, LANCASHIRE FY6 7LE
TEL: 0253 885130 FAX: 0253 894132

Privately owned and run, Mains Hall is a Grade II listed house overlooking the River Wyre. Built in the 16th century by an order of monks, it became a travellers' resting place. Under the Fitzherberts' ownership, it was a sanctuary for Prince George (later George IV), who illicitly courted Maria Fitzherbert. There is lavish use of oak panelling in the reception hall and an open log fire in the bar. Guests can relax in the elegant drawing room or browse in the library. All the bedrooms have en suite or private facilities. The garden conservatory and walled gardens make an ideal setting for private functions and weddings; the private river frontage allows both fishing and birdwatching. Badminton and croquet lawns are in the grounds, there is stabling nearby for guests' horses and there are 15 golf courses in the vicinity. Conference facilities for up to 50 are on offer, as are gourmet evenings and classic cordon bleu courses throughout the year. Price guide: £55–£95. Directions: Leave M55 at Junction 3 following signs to Fleetwood on A585 for 5 miles (ignore signs to Singleton). The hall is a ½ mile past second set of traffic lights on the right-hand side.

THE MILLSTREAM HOTEL
BOSHAM, CHICHESTER, WEST SUSSEX PO18 8HL
TEL: 0243 573234 FAX: 0243 573459

Situated in a yachtsman's paradise on the banks of Chichester harbour, the Millstream is a most attractive small hotel. The hotel buildings are comprised of a 16th-century malthouse and adjoining cottages linked to The Grange, a small English manor house, all restored to an exceptionally high standard of modern comfort. A stream meanders past the front of the hotel's pretty gardens, which are filled with traditional herbs used by the Millstream's chef de cuisine in his cooking. The excellent food comprises a mixture of English and French cuisine. In summer, an extensive buffet includes specialities like lobster, crab and salmon. What ever the season, care is taken to provide the best in fresh local produce, fish and game. The bedrooms are furnished with cane and pine, and decorated in period style in soothing pastels and pretty chintzes. Price guide: £85–£105. Directions: From A259 4 miles west of Chichester take Walton Lane to Bosham; hotel is situated on the right.

WOOLLEY GRANGE

WOOLLEY GREEN, BRADFORD-ON-AVON, WILTSHIRE BA15 1TX
TEL: 02216 4705 FAX: 02216 4059

Woolley Grange is set in 14 acres of formal gardens and paddocks. Standing on high ground, it provides magnificent views over the Wiltshire countryside and the historic White Horse at Westbury. The house is furnished with flair and the warm and welcoming atmosphere is enhanced by the cheerful glow of open fires. Chef Ian Mansfield makes much use of local farm produce and the organically grown fruit and vegetables from the Victorian kitchen gardens; Woolley Grange has developed its own sophisticated style of country house food. Children are particularly welcome at Woolley Grange; resident owners Nigel and Heather Chapman have four of their own children whose ages range from 1 to 8. In the Victorian coach house there is a huge games room and a well-equipped nursery with a full-time nanny available to look after guests' children 10am–6pm every day. For fine days there is a heated swimming pool, sandpit and climbing frame. Nearby are Bradford-on-Avon, Bath, Longleat and Stonehenge. The hotel offers 21 special breaks. Price guide: £85–£150. Directions: From Bath on A363, fork left at Frankleigh House after town sign. From Chippenham, A4 to Bath, fork left on B3109; turn left after town sign.

RELAIS &
CHATEAUX

FARLAM HALL HOTEL

BRAMPTON, CUMBRIA CA8 2NG
TEL: 06976 234/359 FAX: 06976 683

Farlam Hall dates back to the 17th century but was enlarged during Victorian times and is set in 4 acres of well-tended grounds which have a lake with resident ducks. John Wesley preached in the house and George Stephenson also stayed here. It is now home to the Quinion and Stevenson families and the warmth of their welcome is guaranteed. Each of the 13 bedrooms differs in size and shape and all are individually and comfortably furnished. Some have jacuzzi bathrooms and one has a large, antique four-poster bed. The award-winning restaurant serves cordon bleu cuisine with consistently high standards and makes full use of prime local meat, game, fish and dairy produce. The area is steeped in history with Hadrian's Wall close by and ancient attractions such as Naworth Castle and Lanercost Priory are just a short drive away. The hotel is surrounded by beautiful countryside but if you wish to soak up even more splendid scenery during your stay, the Lake District and Yorkshire Dales National Park are within an hour's drive. In this remote but accessible countryside, peace and solitude are to be found. Closed Christmas and all of February. Welcomes children over 5 and dogs by arrangement. Price guide: £140–£180 including dinner. Directions: Farlam Hall is 2½ miles east of Brampton on the A689, not in Farlam village.

MONKEY ISLAND HOTEL

BRAY-ON-THAMES, MAIDENHEAD, BERKSHIRE SL6 2EE
TEL: 0628 23400 FAX: 0628 784732

The name Monkey Island derives from the mediaeval Monk's Eyot. In about 1723 the island was purchased by Charles Spencer, the third Duke of Marlborough, who built the fishing lodge now known as the Pavilion, and the fishing temple, both now Grade I listed buildings. The Pavilion's Terrace Bar, overlooking acres of riverside lawn, is an ideal spot for a relaxing cocktail, and the Pavilion Restaurant, perched on the island's narrowest tip, has fine views upstream. Such imaginative dishes as braised duck with green lentils, and warm lamb fillet with a truffle vinaigrette and sweet coriander potatoes are served. The River Room, with panoramic windows and domed ceilings, is suitable for weddings or other large functions. The Temple houses not only the comfortable bedrooms, but also the Wedgwood Room with its amazing relief plaster ceiling, and the octagonal Temple Room below. The Regency-style boardroom is ideal for business or private functions for up to 16 guests. Monkey Island is 1 mile downstream from Maidenhead, and is within easy reach of Royal Windsor, Eton College, Henley and London. Price guide: £104.50–£154. Directions: Take the A308 out of Maidenhead towards Windsor, and turn left following signposts to Bray. On entering Bray, turn right down Old Mill Lane, which goes over the M4, and Monkey Island is on the left.

BRENTWOOD MOAT HOUSE

LONDON ROAD, BRENTWOOD, ESSEX CM14 4NR
TEL: 0277 225252 FAX: 0277 262809 TELEX: 995182

Brentwood Moat House, originally the home of Catherine of Aragon, was built in 1512 and is later mentioned in the diaries of Samuel Pepys. The original Tudor reception rooms retain their oak beams and panels, and open fireplaces. The de luxe garden suites face into an old world garden, and three luxury Tudor rooms are available complete with period four-poster beds and marbled bathrooms with spa baths. The restaurant is set in an impressive baronial hall. Dogs can be accommodated by prior arrangement. Close to the A12 and the M25, this is an ideal base for touring London. Price guide: £95.80–£155. Directions: The hotel is on the A1023 (Junction 28 of M25).

THE OLD VICARAGE HOTEL
WORFIELD, BRIDGNORTH, SHROPSHIRE WV15 5JZ
TEL: 07464 497 FAX: 07464 552

Originally a turn-of-the-century vicarage, the hotel is set in 2 acres of grounds and provides a haven of peace and quiet. All the bedrooms are individually decorated and furnished. In the coach house, there are four luxury rooms, all of which have jacuzzis, one room being specially adapted for disabled guests. The menu changes daily and owner Peter Iles says that 'two chefs serving a small number of guests guarantees exquisite quality'. The hotel stocks a range of British cheeses, including regional specialities, and you can choose from over 150 wines to complement your meal. You can enjoy a leisure break any time here. Stay any two or more consecutive nights and you will be charged one third less than the normal daily rate. There are also conference facilities for up to 14 delegates. During your stay, you can travel on the Severn Valley Railway which terminates at Bridgnorth, visit the Ironbridge Gorge – the birthplace of the industrial revolution – and explore the lovely Shropshire countryside. Closed at Christmas. Price guide: £69.50–£77.50. Directions: Leave M5 at Junction 6 Worcester North. From Kidderminster, follow signs for Bridgnorth or Telford (A442), then take the A454 towards Wolverhampton.

TOPPS HOTEL

17 REGENCY SQUARE, BRIGHTON, SUSSEX BN1 2FG
TEL: 0273 729334 FAX: 0273 203679

Situated in a quiet Regency square in the heart of Brighton, the Topps Hotel and Bottoms Restaurant is within 2 minutes of the main conference centres and shops, with the Lanes and Royal Pavilion close by. This charming hotel offers an attractive alternative to the more anonymous large hotels in the vicinity and is under the personal supervision of resident proprietors, Paul and Pauline Collins. The spacious bedrooms are all attractively furnished. Bottoms Restaurant in the basement serves delicious traditional English food at reasonable prices. There is ample NCP car parking opposite the hotel. Glyndbourne, Arundel, Chichester and the historic town of Lewes are all within easy reach and London is 1 hour away by train. Closed for Christmas and New Year. Price guide: £70–£90. Directions: Regency Square adjoins Kings Road, opposite the West Pier.

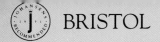

CHELWOOD HOUSE

CHELWOOD, NR BRISTOL, AVON BS18 4NH
TEL: 0761 490730 FAX: 0761 490730 ext 504

Chelwood House, built in 1681, is a listed building, retains original panelling, an impressive staircase and affords uninterrupted views as far as Bath, 10 miles away. The guest rooms are individually designed; three have four-poster beds of different styles – French, Victorian and Chinese. The hotel is furnished with proprietors Rudi and Jill Birk's own antique furniture, ornaments and paintings, which enhance the relaxed atmosphere. Bavarian Rudi Birk, himself a first-class chef, has set high standards of food and service in the restaurant. These same high standards have been maintained in the hotel's 'Restaurant in a Garden', which opened in April 1990. The conservatory-type dining room, with plants, fountain and gazebo is decorated with murals. Children over 10 are welcome. Closed Christmas to New Year. Price guide £72–£95. Directions: On A37 8 miles south of Bristol, between Pensford and Clutton. From Bath keep on A368 through Chelwood village. Turn left at Chelwood Bridge traffic lights.

HUTTON COURT

CHURCH LANE, HUTTON, NR WESTON-SUPER-MARE, AVON BS24 9SN
TEL: 0934 814343 TELEX: 449752 CHACOM G

Hutton Court dates back to the Normans, and the manor was mentioned in the *Domesday Book*. It was enlarged during Jacobean times, from which period several magnificent fireplaces remain. Set in 5 acres of secluded grounds in an area designated as one of outstanding natural beauty about 3 miles from the coast, the hotel is an ideal base for the fishing, riding and walking enthusiast. The bedrooms are spacious and tastefully furnished in character with the architecture of the building. The restaurant with its superb vaulted ceiling is renowned for its cuisine and lists over a 100 wines from 12 countries. There are three golf courses locally, horse-riding can be arranged, and the trout lakes of Blagdon and Chew are nearby. The cities of Bath, Wells and Bristol, Wookey Hole, Glastonbury, the Cheddar Gorge and the stately homes of Longleat and Montacute are easily accessible. The hotel welcomes children over the age of 10. Price guide: £75–£95. Directions: Hutton Court is 5 miles from Junction 21 of the M5, just off the A371 Banwell to Weston road.

DORMY HOUSE

WILLERSEY HILL, BROADWAY, WORCESTERSHIRE WR12 7LF
TEL: 0386 852711 FAX: 0386 858636 TELEX: 338275 DORMY G

This former 17th-century farmhouse has been beautifully converted to a delightful hotel which retains much of its original character. With its oak beams, stone flag floors, honey coloured, local stone walls and an ambience which exudes warmth and tranquillity, Dormy House has a wealth of comforts for the most discerning guest. Each bedroom is individually decorated; some have four-poster beds, and suites are available. The restaurant offers the creative cuisine of head chef John Sanderson. Table d'hôte and à la carte menus include several dishes which won the local environmental health department's Heartbeat Award for healthy living. To complement the high standard of cuisine, there is an extensive wine list. The hotel is surrounded on three sides by Broadway Golf Club. The surrounding countryside is an idyll for walkers and Stratford-upon-Avon and Cheltenham Spa are nearby. Hidcote Manor Garden and Sudeley Castle are within easy reach too. Closed Christmas and Boxing Day. Price guide: £108. USA representative: Josephine Barr, 519 Park Drive, Kenilworth, Illinois 60043, USA (0101 312) 251 4110. Directions: The hotel is situated ½ mile off the A44 between Moreton-in-Marsh and Broadway, taking the turning signposted 'Saintbury'.

THE LYGON ARMS

BROADWAY, WORCESTERSHIRE WR12 7DU
TEL: 0386 852255 FAX: 0386 858611 TELEX: 338260

The Lygon Arms, a magnificent Tudor building with numerous historical associations, stands in 'the prettiest village in England', in the heart of the Cotswolds. Over the years much restoration and building work has been carried out, but outstanding period features, such as original 17th-century oak-panelling and an ancient hidden stairway, have been retained. The bedrooms are individually and tastefully furnished and offer guests every modern luxury combined with the elegance of a bygone era. The Great Hall, complete with a 17th-century minstrels' gallery, and the smaller private dining rooms provide a fine setting for a well-chosen and imaginative menu. Conference facilities with all the latest communication devices are available for up to 80 participants. Guests can enjoy a superb range of leisure facilities including an all-weather tennis court, indoor swimming pool, gymnasium, billiards room, beauty salon and, by arrangement, golf nearby. Weekend and mid-week special breaks are available. Dogs welcome by arrangement. Nearby: Stow-on-the-Wold, Oxford, Shakespeare country. Price guide: £135–£185. Directions: Situated on the right-hand side of Broadway High Street on the A44 in the direction of London to Worcester.

CAREYS MANOR HOTEL

BROCKENHURST, NEW FOREST, HAMPSHIRE SO42 7RH
TEL: 0590 23551 FAX: 0590 22799

Careys Manor, an elegant country house, dates from 1888 on the site of what was once a royal hunting lodge used by Charles II. Situated in 5 acres of landscaped gardens and surrounded by thousands of acres of glorious New Forest countryside, the hotel is proud of the personal welcome and care it extends to its visitors. The bedrooms have all been comfortably and elegantly furnished to the highest standards. There is a Garden Wing, with luxury bedrooms opening directly onto the lawns or a balcony overlooking the glorious gardens. The restaurant offers traditional English and French cuisine, professionally prepared and superbly presented. The hotel boasts a superb sports complex consisting of a large indoor swimming pool (ozone) with jacuzzi, sauna, solarium, and a Turkish steam room. In addition, there is a professionally supervised gymnasium, and a treatment room for massage, sports injury and beauty treatment. Wind-surfing, clay pigeon shooting, fishing, golf and sailing are all within easy reach, as are Stonehenge, Beaulieu, Broadlands, Salisbury and Winchester. Business interests are catered for with excellent self-contained conference facilities. Price guide: £99–£119. Directions: From Junction 1 of M27 follow A337 to Lymington, Careys Manor is on the left after the 30mph sign at Brockenhurst.

For hotel locations, see Atlas on pages 14 – 20

NEW PARK MANOR

**LYNDHURST ROAD, BROCKENHURST, NEW FOREST, HAMPSHIRE SO42 7QH
TEL: 0590 23467 FAX: 0590 22268**

This beautiful manor house, totally refurbished, dates back to the days of King Charles, and retains many original rooms with massive beams, interesting carvings and superb fireplaces, in which log fires blaze in winter. The bedrooms have all modern facilities; the ground floor rooms also have verandas leading onto the garden. In the candle-lit restaurant with its open log fire, you can enjoy good food complemented by fine wines. Many types of outdoor pursuit can be undertaken in the New Forest area and New Park Manor has stables to which guests are welcome to bring their own horses. Polo is played every Saturday during the season and arrangements can be made for clay pigeon or game shoots. Four golf courses are just a short drive away. Business people are well provided for with three excellent conference rooms equipped with up-to-date audio-visual equipment, photocopying and secretarial services. Nearby: Beaulieu, Broadlands and gardens at Furzey, Spinners and Exbury. Price guide: £108. Directions: New Park Manor is ½ a mile off the A337 between Lyndhurst and Brockenhurst.

RHINEFIELD HOUSE

RHINEFIELD ROAD, BROCKENHURST, HAMPSHIRE SO42 7QB
TEL: 0590 22922 FAX: 0590 22800 TELEX: 477617

You will know when you are on the right road to Rhinefield House by the azaleas and rhododendrons which border the hotel's Ornamental Drive. Flexibility is a feature here: conferences, families of all ages and weddings can be catered for. Menus are wide-ranging: at one wedding, where only vegetarian food was served, a large selection of international dishes was prepared. Croquet is popular with many guests in summer, and so too, all year round, is the Atlantis Leisure Club with its indoor swimming pool, sauna, steam rooms and gymnasium. Outside, another swimming pool and tennis courts are available. Set in the New Forest, Rhinefield House was built as a family residence in 1889 by the daughter of a wealthy mine-owner. The original family's dining room is now the Armada Restaurant, named after the carving over the fireplace, and coffee is served in the Alhambra Room. This was designed by the original owner, Mabel Walker Munro, as a Christmas present for her husband. Price guide: £100. Directions: A35 from Lyndhurst, or along Rhinefield Road from Brockenhurst.

GRAFTON MANOR COUNTRY HOUSE HOTEL

GRAFTON LANE, BROMSGROVE, WORCESTERSHIRE B61 7HA
TEL: 0527 579007 FAX: 0527 575221

Dating from 1567, Grafton Manor is set in 11 acres of lovingly tended gardens leading to a lake. The hotel cleverly combines modern comfort and style with the distinct atmosphere of another age. 'There is an air of faded grandeur which is most attractive'. Pot pourris from the hotel's 19th-century roses scent the rooms and over 100 herbs are grown in a chessboard pattern garden. All the herbs are in regular use in the restaurant kitchen where it is the aim of chef/patron John Morris to 'produce only the best' for his guests. The elegant 18th-century dining room is the focal point of a visit to Grafton. The fully equipped bedrooms have been painstakingly restored and furnished in traditional style. Some have open fires in winter. The public rooms are warm and welcoming. Convenient for the motorway network, Grafton Manor is a very accessible base for the business visitor to the city of Birmingham or its National Exhibition Centre. It is an equally good base for exploring the Worcestershire countryside. Welcomes children over 8. Kennels available for dogs. Price guide: £95– £110. Directions: Grafton Lane is reached via Worcester Road at the south west end of Bromsgrove.

BUCKLAND MANOR

BUCKLAND, NR BROADWAY (WORCESTERSHIRE), GLOUCESTERSHIRE WR12 7LY
TEL: 0386 852626

Set in an idyllic Cotswold valley, this fine old house, parts of which date back to the 13th century, was tastefully converted in 1982 by the owners, Adrienne and Barry Berman, into an award-winning country house hotel. Amid an atmosphere redolent of bygone days, guests can unwind away from the hurly-burly of 20th-century living. There are antiques, blazing log fires and exquisitely furnished bedrooms, all with luxury bathrooms fed from the Manor's own spring water. All rooms are equipped with hair dryers and bathrobes; two have four-poster beds. The chef is Martyn Pearn – previously head chef of the Michelin starred *La*

Reserve at Bordeaux – who trained at the Connaught Hotel, London. Given sufficient notice, he will be happy to cook whatever guests require. Only fresh produce is used to meet the hotel's exacting standards. There is a heated outdoor swimming pool, tennis court, putting green, and croquet lawn plus some 10 acres of superb gardens. The Broadway Golf Course is nearby as are stables for guests wishing to ride. Closed for 3½ weeks from mid-January. Welcomes children over 12; conferences by arrangement. Price guide: £135–£210. Directions: Off B4632 (formerly A46).

THE BAY TREE HOTEL

SHEEP STREET, BURFORD, OXFORDSHIRE OX8 4LW
TEL: 099382 2791 FAX: 099382 3008

The Bay Tree has been cleverly refurbished so that it retains all its Tudor splendour while offering every modern facility. The oak-panelled rooms have huge stone fireplaces, and a galleried staircase in the raftered hall leads to the en suite bedrooms, three of which have four-poster beds. Two of the five suites have half-tester beds. In the summer, you can relax in the delightful walled gardens with landscaped terraces of lawn and flower beds. A relaxing atmosphere is enhanced by the staff's attentive service in the flagstoned dining room where head chef Stephen Fischer's creative cuisine is complemented by a comprehensive selection of fine wines. There is also a conservatory lounge with views over the gardens and a country-style bar, where light meals are available. Golf, clay pigeon shooting and horse-riding can be arranged. Burford, often called the gateway to the Cotswolds, is renowned for its antique shops and the Tolsey Museum. The hotel is an ideal venue for touring the Cotswolds and visiting Stratford-upon-Avon, Stow-on-the-Wold and Warwick Castle. There are conference facilities for up to 12 people. Price guide: £85–£130. Directions: Take the A361 Stow-on-the-Wold to Swindon road. From Burford High Street turn into Sheep Street, and the Bay Tree Hotel is on your right.

THE GOLDEN PHEASANT HOTEL

THE HIGH STREET, BURFORD, OXFORDSHIRE OX8 4RJ
TEL: 099382 3223 FAX: 099382 2621 TELEX: 849041

The Golden Pheasant is a charming historic hotel with all the comforts of the modern world. The Cotswold-stone exterior dates from the 14th century and there is a lovely, enclosed courtyard-garden. Inside, the special old-world atmosphere is enhanced by period decor throughout, with wonderfully preserved original features and furnishings like the four-poster beds, ceiling beams and log fires. The excellent cuisine and warm, intimate atmosphere reflect the personal interest and skill of every member of staff in this establishment. Three different table d'hôte menus are offered daily, including one specifically for vegetarians and one for the gourmet. Blenheim Palace and Oxford are within easy reach, as is Burford Wildlife Park. Price guide: £68–£88. Directions: The Golden Pheasant is in Burford High Street, near the A40 from London.

THE BROOKHOUSE HOTEL

ROLLESTON-ON-DOVE, NR BURTON-UPON-TRENT, STAFFORDSHIRE DE13 9AA
TEL: 0283 814188 FAX: 0283 813644

This attractive William and Mary Grade II listed residence was originally built in 1694 as a farmhouse. It was converted to a hotel in 1976 and is set in beautiful gardens beside a brook. Of particular interest are the lovely bedrooms, many of which have four-poster, half-tester or Victorian brass beds trimmed with Nottingham Lace. The use of soft wall lighting and candle light creates a romantic mood in the restaurant where fine foods and wines are complemented by fine silver and crystal. The public rooms are filled with antique furniture. Golf, shooting and fishing trips can be arranged by the hotel. The Shugborough Estate, Calke Abbey, Hadden and Kedleston Halls are all nearby, as are the Derbyshire Dales. For the businessman, The Brookhouse Hotel offers comfort plus the necessary facilities – fax, photo-copying, typing – to enable him to profit from his stay. There are conference facilities for up to 15 people. Welcomes children over 10. Dogs by arrangement. BTA Commended. Price guide: £70–£75. Directions: Rolleston is just outside Burton between the A50 to Stoke-on-Trent and the A38 to Derby.

KINGSHOTT'S

12 ANGEL HILL, BURY ST EDMUNDS, SUFFOLK IP33 1UZ
TEL: 0284 704088 FAX: 0284 763133

Kingshott's is a lovely small 18th-century town house hotel in the centre of Bury St Edmunds, 2 minutes from the historic 11th-century abbey and gardens. The resident proprietors, Dianne and Gary Kingshott, have created a beautifully elegant yet relaxed atmosphere which will immediately appeal to both the business traveller and the tourist. The soft furnishings throughout the hotel have been carefully selected from the finest fabrics. The hotel boasts an exceptionally good restaurant under the personal supervision of the chef-proprietor, and has already established an excellent local reputation. An imaginative and well-balanced wine list complements the restaurant which is situated in the 16th-century part of the hotel. There is a separate, small private dining room overlooking an Italian-style walled garden, ideal for private dinner parties. Kingshott's is just over an hour from London, which together with its close proximity to Newmarket and Cambridge, makes it ideal for a relaxing long weekend, with the opportunity to explore the beautiful Suffolk countryside. Price guide: £60–£75. Directions: The hotel is on the west side of Angel Hill in the town centre.

RAVENWOOD HALL

ROUGHAM, BURY ST EDMUNDS, SUFFOLK IP30 9JA
TEL: 0359 70345 FAX: 0359 70788

Dating from 1530 when Henry VIII was on the throne of England, this fine Tudor building with its elaborate oak carving is now an excellent country house hotel. While the period decor and furnishings reflect its history, the bedrooms are very comfortable and have private bathrooms. Fresh local produce forms the basis of the classic, modern English cooking which guests can enjoy in the impressive restaurant; it has a beamed ceiling and a massive fireplace. Facilities at the hotel include an outdoor heated swimming pool, an all-weather tennis court and a croquet lawn. Golfers are well catered for: there are two courses nearby. Fishing and riding are also available and resident director, Craig Jarvis, takes pride in organising a splendid day's game shooting for guests. With the support of his efficient staff, he does all he can to ensure the guests' wellbeing. Set amid landscaped lawns and mature woodland, Ravenwood Hall is convenient for horse-racing at Newmarket, and for visiting the historic, university city of Cambridge. The hotel also has original banqueting facilities for up to 200 people. Price guide: £85–£100. Directions: Situated 2 miles east of Bury St Edmunds off the A45.

HOWFIELD MANOR

CHARTHAM HATCH, NR CANTERBURY, KENT CT4 7HQ
TEL: 0227 738294 FAX: 0227 731535

This charming country manor, dating back to the 11th century, is set in 5 acres of secluded grounds with a formal English rose garden. A new wing tastefully blends with the old building, originally part of the Priory of St Gregory. The building has tremendous character with a wealth of beams and nooks and in the restaurant, an old well. The restaurant has attracted the culinary expertise of chef Andrew Leech whose reputation for imagination, originality and natural flair is well established. Guests relax and enjoy drinks in the charming bar which is decorated with *trompe l'œil* murals and has a priest hole. There is a library, a spacious lounge with an inglenook fireplace, a conservatory and a conference and banqueting suite. Just 2 miles from the cathedral city of Canterbury on the A28 Ashford road, the hotel makes an ideal base for touring this historic area and as a stopping-off point to and from the Continent. Welcomes children over 10. Price guide: £70. Dogs by arrangement. Directions: From A2 London–Dover road, turn right 2 miles before Canterbury signposted 'Chartham Hatch'. Straight on 2¼ miles. Hotel on left at junction with A28.

THE STRING OF HORSES INN

FAUGH, HEADS NOOK, CARLISLE, CUMBRIA CA4 9EG
TEL: 0228 70297 FAX: 0228 70675

The String of Horses is a former packhorse inn built in the late 1600s and situated in an officially designated area of outstanding beauty. It has a wealth of oak beams, open fires, copper and brass, and is an Aladdin's Cave for lovers of antiques. The bedrooms are luxurious, most appointed with Bonsack baths en suite and furnished with handpainted decorative furniture from all over the world. The restaurant offers an exciting range of speciality dishes and has a fine selection of wines. There is a leisure centre with sauna, solarium, American whirlpool and ergometer, and the outdoor heated swimming pool can be used all year round. Salmon fishing, wind-surfing and yachting can all be pursued nearby. Only a short distance away are the ancient fortifications of Hadrian's Wall, Roman remains and the northern lakes and fells immortalised by Wordsworth. Closed 3 days at Christmas. Dogs by arrangement. Price guide: £62–£96. Directions: Faugh is 3 miles from the A69 at Corby Hill (Exit 43 from M6).

THE NARE HOTEL

CARNE BEACH, VERYAN, TRURO, CORNWALL TR2 5PF
TEL: 0872 501279 FAX: 0872 501856

The Nare Hotel overlooks one of the finest views in the British Isles on the long sandy beach of Gerrans Bay facing south and sheltered by the Nare and St Mawes headlands. The hotel has been refurbished to a high degree of country house comfort and elegance, and is fast becoming one of Cornwall's leading hotels for discerning people. All the rooms are within 100 yards of the sea, many with patios or balconies. The restaurant, one of the most attractive in Cornwall, overlooks sea on three sides, with superb food and interesting wines – local sea foods a speciality.

Surrounded by sub-tropical gardens and National Trust land, the peace and tranquillity of The Nare makes a worthy setting to laze or explore the glorious Roseland Peninsula with its picturesque coastline and villages. Facilities include free golf, hotel boat, watersports, heated swimming pool and tennis. Guests arriving by train can be met at Truro by prior arrangement. Price guide: £84–£146. Directions: Follow road to St Mawes; 3 miles after Tregony Bridge turn left for Veryan. The hotel is 1 mile from Veryan.

AYNSOME MANOR HOTEL
CARTMEL, NR GRANGE-OVER-SANDS, CUMBRIA LA11 6HH
TEL: 05395 36653

This small hotel dates from the 16th-century and is run by the Varley family. It is the ideal retreat if what you really want is peace and quiet. You can stroll around the hotel's grounds, relax in its lounges where, on chilly days, log fires are lit, and enjoy its excellent cuisine. It is an ideal base for touring the Lake District or coastline. Newby Bridge, at the foot of Lake Windermere, is only 4 miles distant and nearby Holker Hall is a hive of activity in the summer months with ballooning, vintage car rallies, model aircraft shows and the annual Lakeland Rose Show. Every July in Flookburgh there is a steam fair and the village of Cartmel plays host to one of the biggest agricultural shows in the country. Two golf courses and swimming facilities are close by too. The hotel will arrange for cars to meet guests from Grange-over-Sands station. Closed January. Special winter/spring breaks available. Price guide: £82–£94 including dinner. Directions: The hotel is ¼ mile outside Cartmel, reached from the A590.

THE MANOR HOUSE

CASTLE COMBE, CHIPPENHAM, WILTSHIRE SN14 7HR
TEL: 0249 782206 FAX: 0249 782159 TELEX: 449931 MANOR G

The Manor House at Castle Combe has a setting of idyllic tranquillity: 26 acres of gardens and parkland, a gently flowing trout stream and the romance of a terraced Italian garden. Rooms have been lovingly restored in sympathy with their historical significance and many interesting features are now revealed, such as hidden stone fireplaces and a grain-drying kiln dating from the 14th century. The bedrooms are individually furnished to a luxurious 5-star standard, in keeping with the history of the house. A homely relaxed atmosphere, excellence of service, food and customer care are combined in a country house of exceptional charm. A stroll through the village of Castle Combe endorses the magical experience. Unchanged for almost 200 years and nominated 'England's prettiest village', it is possible to imagine oneself in a fairytale 'Land of make-believe'. Price guide: £95–£250. Directions: 15 minutes from Junctions 17 and 18 of M4. 20 minutes from M5/M4 intersection. 12 miles from Bath (central London 2 hours). Approached directly from A420 and B4039.

36 rms

EASTON COURT HOTEL

EASTON CROSS, CHAGFORD, DEVON TQ13 8JL
TEL: 0647 433469

Easton Court is a 15th-century, Grade II listed, thatched Tudor house with many historic connections, particularly literary ones. Both Evelyn Waugh and Patrick Leigh Fermor found inspiration here in this tranquil setting amid the glorious Devon countryside. The hotel has been lovingly restored and offers every comfort. However, it has retained its old-world charm and period features such as exposed stone walls, plentiful oak beams and an open fireplace complete with bread oven. For those of a literary bent, there is a superb library housing a fascinating collection of old books. The bedrooms have been very tastefully furnished. The extremely attractive restaurant uses fresh local produce for its traditional English cuisine so the menus vary from season to season. It also has an extensive and interesting wine list. Special diets can be catered for by prior arrangement. There is an 18-hole golf course just a short drive away, and riding, tennis, swimming and fishing facilities are available nearby. Castle Drogo, Dartmoor National Park and Fernworthy Reservoir are but a few of the places of interest to visit. Welcomes children over 14. Closed January. Price guide: £65–£75. Directions: From Exeter, take A30. At first roundabout, take A382 signposted Moreton Hamstead.

RELAIS & CHATEAUX

GIDLEIGH PARK

CHAGFORD, DEVON TQ13 8HH
TEL: 0647 432367/225 FAX: 0647 432574 TELEX: 42643

Gidleigh Park in Dartmoor enjoys an outstanding reputation among connoisseurs for its comfort and gastronomy. It has collected a clutch of top culinary awards for its imaginative cuisine (Egon Ronay hotel of the year, 1990), and the Gidleigh wine list is one of the best in Britain. The hotel's master chef, Shaun Hill, was one of the first British members of *l'Academie Culinaire de France*. Service throughout the hotel is faultless. The bedrooms, two of which are in a converted chapel, are nicely furnished and have private bathrooms. The house is set in 40 acres in the Teign Valley, 1½ miles from the nearest road. There are two croquet lawns, an all-weather tennis court and a splendid water garden in the grounds. You can swim in the river or explore Dartmoor on foot or horseback. There are 14 miles of trout, sea trout and salmon fishing, as well as golf facilities nearby. Price guide: £200–£350 (includes dinner). Directions: Approach from Chagford; go along Mill Street from Chagford Square. Fork right after 150 yards, down to factory crossroads. Cross into Holy Street and follow lane for 1½ miles.

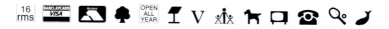

16 rms · BARCLAYCARD VISA · Access · OPEN ALL YEAR

TYTHERLEIGH COT HOTEL

CHARDSTOCK, AXMINSTER, DEVON EX13 7BN
TEL: 0460 21170 FAX: 0460 21291

This is a charming 14th-century listed building situated in the secluded village of Chardstock on the borders of Devon, Dorset and Somerset. The bedrooms are delightful, each individually designed and fully appointed. The restaurant is a Victorian-style conservatory overlooking a large ornamental pond with a wrought iron bridge, cascading with ivy and fresh flowers. The outstanding modern cuisine is all freshly prepared and accompanied by memorable wines for every taste. Pat and Frank Grudgings, the resident proprietors, maintain a most welcoming, friendly and relaxing atmosphere. Located in the idyllic, varied landscape of south west England, the Tytherleigh Cot is ideally situated for guests touring the countryside or visiting the many country houses in the area, including the *To The Manor Born* mansion at Cricket St Thomas. Many sporting activities are easily accessed. Conference facilities are available. Children over 14 are welcome. ETB 4 Crowns, Highly Commended. BTA Highly Commended. Shooting weekends. Price guide: £92–£114 (bargain breaks available). Directions: From Chard take A358 Axminster road; Chardstock signposted on right approximately 3 miles along.

THE GREENWAY

SHURDINGTON, CHELTENHAM SPA, GLOUCESTERSHIRE GL51 5UG
TEL: 0242 862352 FAX: 0242 862780

Ideally situated in the very heart of the world-famous Cotswold countryside, The Greenway, set in private parkland, is an oasis of peace and tranquillity. An elegant house, its splendid interiors combine elegance and 20th-century comforts. Roaring log fires in winter and lovely fresh flower arrangements throughout the year grace the public rooms. The panelled, candle-lit dining room, which leads into the conservatory dining room, overlooks the lily pond. The imaginative, well-balanced, menus are made with top quality ingredients. Fine antiques, stone mullioned windows and individual furnishings enhance the 18 delightful bedrooms. These include eight huge rooms formed from the old Coach House originally dating from 1816. A croquet lawn is also available for guests. A truly superb country house hotel, personally owned and operated by Tony Elliott. Closed 2 weeks after Christmas. Children over 7 welcome. From USA toll free (reservations only) 1-800-543 4135. Price guide: £115. Directions: 2½ miles south of Cheltenham on the A46 Cheltenham–Stroud Road.

WHITE HOUSE HOTEL

GLOUCESTER ROAD, STAVERTON, NR CHELTENHAM, GLOUCESTER GL51 0ST
TEL: 0452 713226 FAX: 0452 857590

Whether your visit is for business or pleasure, the White House will meet your requirements. With three conference suites and two syndicate rooms catering for up to 220 delegates, plus a full secretarial service, the hotel is ideal for business people wanting informal surroundings. The comfortable bar and lounge, where a pianist entertains on occasions, is the heart of the hotel and is equally popular with tourists and business guests. Food here is taken seriously and extensive light lunch and gourmet dinner menus are available. The cuisine is complemented by European and Australian wines. The bedrooms all have private bathrooms and two have four-poster beds. They combine practicality with touches of opulence having satellite TV, a hair dryer, trouser press and tea/coffee making facilities as standard. Only 5 minutes' from Cheltenham by car, the hotel is a good base for tours of the picturesque Cotswolds' villages. Price guide: £85. Directions: On the B4063, Cheltenham-Gloucester road.

HUNSTRETE HOUSE

HUNSTRETE, CHELWOOD, NR BRISTOL, AVON BS18 4NS
TEL: 0761 490490 FAX: 0761 490732 TELEX: 449540

This 18th-century house, with its outstanding gardens and a 92-acre deer park is set on the edge of the Mendip Hills and was converted to a hotel in 1978. The reception areas are handsomely furnished and the decor is restful. Collectors will admire the many antiques which reflect the interests of the owners. There are paintings, books, early pottery and porcelain, and flowers from the garden. The Terrace dining room overlooks the flower-filled courtyard. The chef, with the help of seven assistants, creates light, distinctive dishes using home-grown and local, fresh produce in season. The bedrooms vary in size and all are superbly furnished in the style of an elegant private country house. Hunstrete House affords an idyllic setting for wedding receptions, and Swallow Cottage, adjoining the Courtyard House, makes a perfect honeymoon suite. There is a heated swimming pool in a sheltered corner of the walled garden, and an all-weather tennis court and croquet lawn are also available. Hunstrete village has riding stables. Price guide: £150. Directions: From the A39 at Markesbury, take the A368, then first right towards Hunstrete. The hotel is on the left.

BROXTON HALL COUNTRY HOUSE HOTEL
WHITCHURCH ROAD, BROXTON, CHESTER CH3 9JS
TEL: 0829 782321 FAX: 0244 314798

Broxton Hall is situated south of the historic walled city of Chester with its Roman and mediaeval architecture. The Hall is set in 5 acres of beautiful grounds and extensive gardens and is positioned in some of the most picturesque countryside in Cheshire. The hotel is a Tudor, half-timbered building and offers the ambience of years gone by together with every modern comfort. On cool evenings, log fires are lit in the 17th-century fireplaces creating a warm, cosy atmosphere which enhances a pleasurable stay. Each of the 12 bedrooms has a bathroom en suite and tea/coffee making facilities. Price guide: £55–£85. Directions: The hotel is situated on the A41 Whitchurch–Chester road, within easy travelling distance of Chester, Wrexham and also Manchester International Airport.

CRABWALL MANOR

PARKGATE ROAD, MOLLINGTON, CHESTER, CHESHIRE CH1 6NE
TEL: 0244 851666 FAX: 0244 851400 TELEX: 61220 CRAWAL G

The history of Crabwall Manor goes back to Saxon England, but the present Grade II listed building, set in 11 acres, dates from the early 19th century. Carl Lewis has created one of the finest country house hotels in England. The ambience is distinguished and relaxed, enhanced by staff who show guests genuine friendliness and care. There is a choice of richly furnished suites or luxury double rooms, all of which are individually decorated. Chef Michael Truelove, formerly of The Box Tree Restaurant in Ilkley, combines French modern classic cooking with the best traditional English dishes, using only the finest natural fresh produce. An outstanding wine cellar complements these dishes. The hotel has its own helipad and is 30 minutes by road from Manchester and Liverpool airports. Nearby are the historic city of Chester (just 2 miles away) and five championship golf courses. Welcomes children and provides professional baby-minding service. Price guide: £99–£115. Directions: The hotel is situated off the A540 Chester/Hoylake road.

FROGG MANOR

FULLERS MOOR, NANTWICH ROAD, BROXTON, CHESTER CH3 9JH
TEL: 0829 782629

Built in 1734, Frogg Manor is a superb Georgian manor house decorated in traditional style with period furniture to combine modern comfort with the grace of the Georgian era. From its elevated position in the Broxton Hills, the hotel affords magnificent views of Cheshire to Wales and is a haven of country seclusion. Within the gardens, there is a tennis court and an indoor swimming pool. Each of the bedrooms has been individually furnished to provide excellent quality and comfort. The public rooms overlook 9 acres of landscaped gardens and woods.

Traditional English-style cuisine, freshly prepared under the supervision of the proprietor, is served in the dining room. For small meetings, or for those who wish to dine in a more intimate atmosphere, a private room is available. Frogg Manor is an ideal location whether your stay is for business or leisure. AA 'Selected Hotel', RAC 3 Star, ETB 4 Crowns. Price guide: £60–£99.50. Directions: 15 minutes from Chester. Follow the A41 south towards Whitchurch, then A534 in the direction of Nantwich.

SOUGHTON HALL COUNTRY HOUSE HOTEL

NORTHOP, NR MOLD, CLWYD CH7 6AB
TEL: 035286 811 FAX: 035286 382 TELEX: 61267 SOWTON

Built as a bishop's palace in 1714, Soughton Hall is set in 150 acres of parkland, and is approached via a spectacular avenue of lime trees. The 12 period bedrooms have bathrooms fitted with hand-painted suites. Antique furniture, baroque marble fireplaces, French tapestries and Persian carpets adorn a house of unique history and architecture. Recent awards for the superb cuisine include Welsh Lamb Chef of the Year (Egon Ronay); Welsh Restaurant of the Year (British Stilton); and Wales' Best New Hotel (AA, 1989/90). The South Parlour, furnished with sumptuous, fully upholstered dining chairs, provides a private dining room for parties of up to 22 people. By day, it also doubles up as an ideal setting for executive meetings. The personal welcome of the Rodenhurst family, who say 'our guests arrive as customers and leave as friends', and the attentiveness of their dedicated staff ensure that your stay will be worth remembering. From the hotel, you can explore North Wales and visit historic Chester. Also, the hotel provides an exclusive full-colour guide which highlights selected holiday drives in the area. Children over 12 are welcome. Price guide: £100–£140. Directions: From the M56 take the A55 towards North Wales, then the A5119 to Northop. Cross the traffic lights; the Hall is 1 mile along the road, on the left.

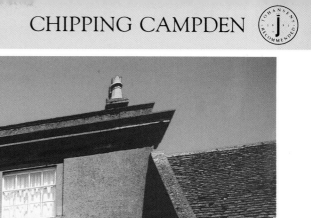

THE COTSWOLD HOUSE

CHIPPING CAMPDEN, GLOUCESTERSHIRE GL55 6AN
TEL: 0386 840330 FAX: 0386 840310

Dating back to the 17th century and recently restored to its original splendour by proprietors Robert and Gill Greenstock, Cotswold House takes pride of place on Chipping Campden's historic High Street. The bedrooms all combine luxury with an air of warmth and friendliness. A recent addition is the Colonial room which features a turn-of-the-century four-poster bed and a pineapple-inspired decor. (The pineapple was the symbol of welcome and hospitality in Colonial America.) The hotel's elegant interior boasts antique furniture, paintings and a magnificent Adam spiral staircase. Mouthwatering English food, with fresh seasonal delicacies, is served in the restaurant, which overlooks the delightful old-world gardens. The hotel provides conference and private dining for up to 20 people. Picturesque Chipping Campden is an ideal base for exploring Shakespeare country and the Cotswolds. Cheltenham, Stratford-upon-Avon and Oxford are close by. Local sporting facilities include golf, fishing, tennis, riding, hunting and cycling. The hotel is closed Christmas and Boxing Day. Children over 8 are welcome. Price guide: £82.50–£143.50. Directions: Chipping Campden lies 2 miles east of the A44 on the B4081.

CHARINGWORTH MANOR

CHARINGWORTH, NR CHIPPING CAMPDEN, GLOUCESTERSHIRE GL55 6NS
TEL: 038678 555 FAX: 038678 353 TELEX: 333444

The ancient Manor of Charingworth was first mentioned in the *Domesday Book*, and the present building dates back to the 14th century. It has welcomed many famous visitors including T S Eliot, who wrote *Burnt Norton* during one of his stays and now has a room named after him. The Manor is set in 50 acres of gardens and grazing land and has superb views over the surrounding countryside. Maps of local walks are provided to encourage guests to explore. The public rooms are cosy with log fires in cooler weather, and the bedrooms are individually furnished with antique furniture and fine fabrics; all are appointed with luxurious bathrooms. Some have four-poster beds and there are suites with separate sitting rooms. The restaurant provides a well-chosen menu and an extensive wine list. There is much to see and do in the area. Hidcote Manor Gardens, Batsford Arboretum and the delightful Cotswold villages are close by, while Stratford, Oxford and Cheltenham are within easy reach. Children are welcome. Reservations require £50 deposit or credit card confirmation. Price guide: Double/twin rooms from £95; four-poster rooms and junior suites from £145. Two night short breaks including dinner, bed and breakfast £132–£168 per day, for double occupancy. Directions: On the B4035 midway between Chipping Campden and Shipston-on-Stour.

CHISELDON HOUSE

CHISELDON, NR MARLBOROUGH, WILTSHIRE SN4 0NE
TEL: 0793 741010 FAX: 0793 741059

This charming early Regency country house set in 3 acres of mature gardens, is an ideal retreat in which to enjoy the luxury of being waited on. The new owners have tastefully converted and restored this former private house, once the home of the Borrelli family. The original stables and staff quarters are now a restaurant, bar and brasserie. The restaurant overlooks a heated outdoor swimming pool set in a delightful walled garden. The late Victorian rear wing has been remodelled to provide 21 luxury bedrooms. There are extensive facilities for the businessman: three meeting rooms, private dining rooms and function rooms; and for history buffs the ancient sites of Avebury and Stonehenge are nearby. Salisbury, Bath and Cirencester are a short drive away, while for walkers, ramblers and cyclists, the nearby Ridgeway and Wansdyke are popular venues. Closed Christmas. Price guide: £89. Directions: 1 mile from M4 Junction 15, off the A345 between Swindon and Marlborough.

CRUDWELL COURT HOTEL

CRUDWELL, NR MALMESBURY, WILTSHIRE SN16 9EP
TEL: 06667 7194/5 FAX: 06667 7853

Crudwell Court is a beautiful 17th-century rectory, set in 3 acres of Cotswold walled gardens. Completely refurbished, the hotel achieves a comfortable and relaxed country house atmosphere with books to read and log fires. The good-sized bedrooms overlook the gardens; the public rooms have plenty of comfortable sofas and chairs, and the lovely panelled dining room, where imaginative food is freshly prepared to order, gives a view of the neighbouring Saxon church. For the sports enthusiast, fishing, golf, sailing, riding and tennis are available nearby. The hotel has conference facilities for up to 15 people. An ideal centre to visit the West of England, especially Roman and Georgian Bath, Bristol, Lacock Abbey, and the picturesque stone villages of the Cotswolds. The hotel is 3 miles from Malmesbury and 5 miles from Cirencester. Price guide: £70–£100. Directions: Crudwell Court is on the A429. Travelling towards Cirencester, when you reach the village of Crudwell turn right (signposted Oaksey) opposite the Plough pub, and the hotel is on the left.

WOODLANDS MANOR

GREEN LANE, CLAPHAM, BEDFORD MK41 6EP
TEL: 0234 363281 FAX: 0234 272390 TELEX: 825007

A Victorian manor house set in several acres of well-tended grounds, Woodlands Manor has been managed by the owners for the past 13 years. The warm character of a country house has been preserved. Designed to provide comfort and relaxation, extensive personal facilities can be found in the bedrooms. Guests can enjoy drinks and light refreshments in the comfortable lounge, which is furnished with deep, easy chairs. The elegantly proportioned dining room is gracefully furnished, and provides an agreeable and relaxing venue for meals. The menu is traditionally English, with a touch of French flair. The hotel is only 2 miles from the county town of Bedford, with its riverside park and the Bunyan Museum. Other places of interest nearby include Woburn Abbey, the RSPB at Sandy and the Shuttleworth Collection of aeroplanes. Facilities for golf, 1 mile away. Children over 7 welcome. Price guide: £71.40–£94.50. Directions: Take the A6 out of Bedford towards Rushden and Kettering. Woodlands Manor is to the right in the village of Clapham.

THE WYNDHAM ARMS
CLEARWELL, NR COLEFORD, GLOUCESTERSHIRE GL16 8JT
TEL: 0594 33666 FAX: 0594 36450

This lovely 14th-century village inn, converted and extended into a 17-bedroomed hotel, has been in John and Rosemary Stanford's ownership since 1973. Every immaculate bedroom has all of the creature comforts expected in a fine hotel today. Chef de cuisine Paul Cooke started here in 1977 and offers a most extensive à la carte and table d'hôte menu in the award-winning restaurant. The welcoming stone-built bar with its inglenook fireplace offers traditional ale as well as all the more contemporary drinks, and there are over 20 malt whiskies to choose from! This is the perfect centre for visiting the Royal Forest of Dean and Wye Valley. There are golf courses at Chepstow, Coleford, Ross-on-Wye and Monmouth, horseracing at Chepstow, Hereford and Cheltenham, some of the finest salmon fishing in Britain on the River Wye, and 27,000 acres of royal forest almost on the doorstep. With six ground-floor bedrooms, elderly and disabled people are most welcome. Children accommodated free of charge in parents' rooms. Price guide: £70 (weekend breaks available). Directions: Clearwell is on the B4231, 2 miles from Coleford.

BAILIFFSCOURT

CLIMPING, NR LITTLEHAMPTON, WEST SUSSEX BN17 5RW
TEL: 0903 723511 FAX: 0903 723107 TELEX: 877870

It looks like a mediaeval manor, it is furnished in mediaeval style and up to 80 people can banquet here. However, Bailiffscourt is a 1930s replica of a 13th-century courthouse tended by bailiff monks. Constructed from pieces of derelict mansions, farmhouses and cottages salvaged from all parts of southern England, the hotel continues the mediaeval theme with four-poster beds in eight bedrooms and open log fires in nine. Yet there is nothing mediaeval about the hotel's facilities. It has an outdoor swimming pool, tennis courts, golf practice area, croquet lawn and exercise room plus a helicopter landing pad. The restaurant offers a varied menu and summer lunches can be taken outdoors in a fragrant rose clad court-yard or the walled garden. The hotel is within easy reach of Brighton, Chichester and Goodwood and companies can hire it as their 'country house' for 2/3 days. The hotel welcomes children over 8, dogs and horses. The hotel may be closed for building works during 1991. Price guide: £90–£180. Directions: The hotel lies just off the A259 between Bognor and Littlehampton.

NORFOLK MEAD HOTEL

COLTISHALL, NORWICH NR12 7DN
TEL: 0603 737531

On the fringe of the Norfolk Broads, standing in 12 acres of gardens and parkland gently sloping to the River Bure, the Norfolk Mead is a true country house hotel, personally supervised by the owners, and combining Georgian charm with a warm and inviting atmosphere. During its restoration great care was taken to provide every comfort for guests (including a two-berth jacuzzi in one of the pretty bedrooms) while retaining the attractive features and character of a house of this period. The restaurant offers an imaginative menu of beautifully presented modern British cooking complemented by a full wine list. The 2-acre fishing lake is well-stocked with coarse fish and rowing dinghies are available for 'messing about on the river'. Golf, sailing and horse-riding are all available nearby; also some beautiful National Trust properties, the unspoiled North Norfolk coastline and the lovely historic city of Norwich. Guests may arrive by car, boat or helicopter. The hotel has no facilities for children under 3 years old or pets. Closed Christmas. Price guide: £65–£85. Directions: Coltishall lies on the B1150 between Norwich and North Walsham.

COULSWORTHY HOUSE HOTEL

COMBE MARTIN, NORTH DEVON EX34 0PD
TEL: 0271 882463

This charming small hotel stands at the western edge of the Exmoor National Park in a region of outstanding natural beauty. There are magnificent views across country to the sea from the hotel's 6 acres of grounds. The hotel, parts of which are 600 years old, is family-owned and family-run to provide the relaxing ambience of a friendly house party. Alison Osmond's country cooking is of a very high standard. The table d'hôte menus offer a wide choice and are changed daily. In the bar guests can sip wines or spirits or try some real ale and a locally made cider. Golf, clay pigeon shooting and fishing (river, lake and sea), are all available nearby and there are many fine houses, gardens and other places of interest to be visited. The hotel is closed mid-December to mid-February. Price guide: £90–£135 including dinner. Directions: From A39 at Blackmoor take Combe Martin road; hotel is signposted after 2 miles.

TREGLOS HOTEL

CONSTANTINE BAY, NR PADSTOW, CORNWALL PL28 8JH
TEL: 0841 520727 FAX: 0841 521163

Twenty-five years of the same ownership have established high standards in this superb hotel overlooking Constantine Bay and Trevose Golf Course. The friendly and attentive staff are well known to the many guests who return year after year. The bedrooms, some of which have a private lounge, are luxurious, with lovely coastal views. There are five spacious, comfortable lounges, cheered by traditional glowing log fires on chilly days. The delicious cuisine has earned the restaurant wide recognition. Both the table d'hôte and à la carte menus offer a wide range of dishes, with the emphasis on fresh local seafood and meats, and vegetables from the hotel's own kitchen gardens, while home-made desserts with Cornish cream form another speciality. Guests may choose from the hotel's wide selection of fine wines. Amenities include an indoor heated swimming pool and jacuzzi, while within easy reach of the hotel lies a footpath passing through miles of ruggedly beautiful Cornish countryside, and a variety of National Trust properties. Open March to November. Price guide: £95–£105 including dinner. Directions: Constantine Bay and Treglos signposted from St Merryn (B3276 from Padstow).

MORTONS HOUSE HOTEL

CORFE CASTLE, DORSET BH20 5EE
TEL: 0929 480988 FAX: 0929 480820

Built in the 16th century in the shape of an E to honour Queen Elizabeth I and linked by underground tunnels to Corfe Castle, Mortons offers both the history and the charm of a private country house. The entrance hall, which contains the original stone fireplace, leads into the magnificent oak-panelled drawing room, lined with exotic friezes carved by Indonesian sailors. The quality of the traditional British cooking is one of the chief concerns of the owners of Mortons. Prepared with flair and imagination are such dishes as collops of venison with wild mushrooms, walnuts and a port cream sauce and paupettes of sea trout filled with spinach and smoked salmon. Vegetarian dishes always feature on the menu. Nearby are sandy beaches, golf, fishing, tennis, horse-riding and hill walking facilities. Also worth a visit are Lulworth Cove, Durdle Door, the homes of Thomas Hardy and T E Lawrence, Kingston Lacy Estate and Compton Acres, one of the finest Japanese gardens in Britain. Price guide: £70–£100. Directions: Mortons House Hotel lies in East Street, the main road through Corfe Castle.

CORSE LAWN HOUSE HOTEL

CORSE LAWN, GLOUCESTERSHIRE GL19 4LZ
TEL: 045278 479/771 FAX: 045278 840 TELEX: 437348

Corse Lawn, though only 6 miles from the M5 and M50, is a completely unspoiled, typically English hamlet in a peaceful Gloucestershire backwater. The hotel, an elegant Queen Anne listed building set back from the village green, is situated in 12 acres of gardens and grounds, and retains the charm of its historical pedigree. Visitors can be assured of the highest standard of service and cuisine. Baba Hine and head chef Tim Earley are famous for the dishes they produce, while Denis Hine, of the Hine Cognac family, is in charge of the wine cellar. The service here is faultlessly efficient, friendly and personal. As well as the renowned restaurant, there are three comfortable drawing rooms, a large lounge bar, a private dining-cum-conference room for up to 40 persons, and a similar smaller room for up to 20. A tennis court, heated swimming pool and croquet lawn adjoin the hotel, and most sports and leisure activities can be arranged. Corse Lawn is ideal for exploring the Cotswolds, Malverns and Forest of Dean. Price guide: £85–£95. Directions: Corse Lawn House lies 5 miles south west of Tewkesbury. Take A438 towards Ledbury for 4 miles, turn left onto B4211 by Corse Lawn sign, go 1 mile and the hotel is on the right.

KENNEL HOLT COUNTRY HOUSE HOTEL

CRANBROOK, KENT TN17 2PT
TEL: 0580 712032 FAX: 0580 712931

This Elizabethan manor house, set in 6 acres of landscaped gardens with a duck pond, croquet lawn and paddock, combines period charm with modern facilities. The two spacious sitting rooms are extremely comfortable and feature large open log fires. The alcove dining room contains an original fireplace, and the informal bar contributes to the relaxed, private house atmosphere. The cuisine is cordon bleu and is made with fresh, seasonally available produce from the kitchen garden. A well-balanced wine list complements the food. Entrance to a local 18-hole golf course is available for guests. Sissinghurst Castle with its famous garden, Hever Castle and Chartwell are interesting places to visit. Conference facilities are available for up to 30 delegates, boardroom-style. Children over 6 and dogs are welcome. Price guide: £150 including five-course dinner. Directions: The hotel is on the A262, 1 mile west of the junction with A229, close to Cranbrook.

CRATHORNE HALL HOTEL

CRATHORNE, NR YARM, CLEVELAND TS15 0AR
TEL: 0642 700398 FAX: 0642 700814 TELEX: 587426

Crathorne Hall was the last of the Edwardian country houses to be built. Completed in 1906, it remained the home of the Dugdale family until 1979 when it was converted into a splendid country house hotel, situated in 15 acres of woodland overlooking the River Leven and the Cleveland Hills. The Hall can accommodate a variety of events for up to 300 guests; whether for conferences, seminars, training courses, product launches, wedding receptions or a quiet weekend break for two, the hotel will provide professional, efficient and courteous service. This part of the north east is often referred to as Herriot country, but was also Captain Cook's birthplace. The historic cities of Durham and York, the North Yorkshire Railway and the Beamish Open Air Museum are nearby. Price guide: £90–£112. Directions: The Hall lies 1 mile from the A19 trunk road, 7 miles from Teesside International Airport and 8 miles from Middlesbrough.

CRICKLADE HOTEL AND COUNTRY CLUB

COMMON HILL, CRICKLADE, WILTSHIRE SN6 6HA
TEL: 0793 750751 FAX: 0793 751767

Set in 30 acres of private grounds in the heart of rural Wiltshire, this comfortable private hotel offers a diverse range of attractions for its guests; from quiet seclusion to the most modern sporting facilities. The leisure complex includes 9-hole golf, *en tout cas* tennis, indoor swimming pool, a gymnasium, hot spa bath, solarium and full-sized snooker tables. Ideal for business meetings or plain relaxation, the public rooms are luxuriously appointed and full of atmosphere. A conservatory has recently been added, affording fine views over the Marlborough Downs. The bedrooms are smartly modern and tastefully furnished; each is more than well-equipped, with teletext TV, hair dryer and trouser press. Up to 120 people can be accommodated in the suite of conference rooms; there is even a helipad for the busiest traveller. Dining at the Cricklade is a pleasure with a varied and interesting menu to suit all tastes, the emphasis being on fresh local produce and careful presentation. The hotel is well placed for visits to the Cotswolds and the historic centres of Cirencester, Bath and Gloucester. Children over 14 welcome. Fishing by arrangement. Price guide: £80–£90. Directions: On the B4040 Cricklade–Malmesbury road; Junction 15/16 M4, Junction 11 on M5.

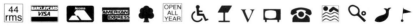

OCKENDEN MANOR

**OCKENDEN LANE, NR HAYWARDS HEATH, CUCKFIELD, WEST SUSSEX RH17 5LD
TEL: 0444 416111 FAX: 0444 415549**

Built in the 16th century, this lovely manor house in 9 acres of gardens has become a hotel of great character. The bedrooms all have their own individual identity; climb your private staircase to Thomas or Elizabeth, see the lovely Sussex countryside from Victoria's bay window or choose Charles with its handsome four-poster. The restaurant with its striking painted ceiling, heavy drapes and stained-glass windows is a wonderful setting for Ockenden's famous modern English cuisine. Herbs used by the chef are grown in the hotel garden. There is an outstanding wine cellar (300 bins) with an excellent choice of first-growth clarets. The Ockenden Suite, with french windows on to the lawns, welcomes private lunch and dinner parties. An ideal centre from which to explore Sussex and Kent, the Garden of England. Price guide: £90–£165. Directions: Ockenden Manor is in the centre of Cuckfield, on the A272.

HALL GARTH COUNTRY HOUSE HOTEL

COATHAM MUNDEVILLE, NR DARLINGTON, CO DURHAM DL1 3LU
TEL: 0325 300400 FAX: 0325 310083

This charming, rambling, informal hotel, dating from 1540, is situated in 67 acres of splendid grounds and is well placed for touring the north: Raby Castle, Washington Hall, Durham Cathedral, Herriot Country and the Dales. Skilfully converted by the present owners, and lovingly furnished with interesting antiques, the hotel has 40 comfortable bedrooms. Five have antique four-posters and there are three suites. In the restaurant, excellent food is served using fresh vegetables and fruit from the walled garden. A fine selection of wines complement the menu.

Bar food and a variety of real ales are available in the Stables Bar, a few yards from the main house. The function suite and conference centre can accommodate up to 250 people theatre-style. The staff are friendly and obliging; they do everything possible to create a warm, relaxing atmosphere. Facilities include 3-hole minigolf, a putting green, croquet lawn, grass tennis court, sauna and solarium. Opening on the premises in 1991 is a fully equipped leisure club. Price guide: £80–£95. Directions: The hotel is ½ mile from the A1(M) junction with the A167.

HEADLAM HALL

HEADLAM, NR GAINFORD, DARLINGTON, COUNTY DURHAM DL2 3HA
TEL: 0325 730238 FAX: 0325 730790

This magnificent Jacobean mansion is set in 3 acres of formal gardens in quiet rural Teeside. Originally built in the 17th century, the hall was home for 150 years to the Brocket family and more recently to Lord Gainford. The grounds include a small private trout water enclosed by ancient yew and beech hedges. The hotel has a tennis court, croquet lawn, a new swimming pool, sauna, exercise area and snooker room. All the bedrooms are individually furnished, and the restaurant provides the best of traditional English cuisine. The main hall features a magnificent carved oak fireplace and open staircase, while the Georgian drawing room opens onto a stepped terrace overlooking the lawns. Fishing and golf are nearby and Barnard Castle and Durham are only a short drive away. Conferences for up to 40. Free bedroom and champagne breakfast are provided for newly weds holding their reception here. Closed over Christmas. Dogs by prior arrangement. Price guide: £55–£72. Directions: Headlam is 2 miles north of Gainford off the A67, Darlington to Barnard Castle.

FINGALS AT OLD COOMBE MANOR

DITTISHAM, NR DARTMOUTH, SOUTH DEVON TQ6 0JA
TEL: 080422 398 FAX: 080422 401

This 17th-century manor house, with its elegant Queen Anne facade still intact, provides the archetypal country retreat for guests looking for the highest standards of modern comfort. The rooms look out over the garden onto some delightful country scenes. In the gardens are incorporated a grass tennis court, croquet lawn, and also a stream-side, heated, mosaic-tiled swimming pool and a jacuzzi. Indoors, the decor remains faithful to the building's origins with antique furniture and Old Masters hanging against the panelled walls. Relaxation is assured in the elegant lounge and library, or in the games room with its Victorian snooker table. The old panelled dining room at Fingals provides the most atmospheric of surroundings in which to enjoy the gourmet cuisine. A new wing has been added using traditional barn building techniques giving extra facilities for small management meetings and mini-conferences. For those wanting other activities, there are craft courses available next door and horse-riding, fishing and boating close by. Price guide: £65–£80. Directions: Fingals is situated between the two historic towns of Dartmouth and Totnes. Turn left off the Dartmouth road, 3 miles before Dartmouth at the Sportsmans Arms. Drive through Dittisham and, 1 mile past the village, take the second left signposted Fingals.

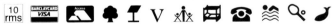

YALBURY COTTAGE

LOWER BOCKHAMPTON, DORCHESTER, DORSET DT2 8PZ
TEL: 0305 262382

Yalbury Cottage is situated in the heart of Thomas Hardy's Wessex, in the undulating and unspoiled Dorset countryside. This small country house hotel, once the home of the local shepherds and keepers of the water meadows, has been tastefully refurbished while retaining the architectural features of past centuries. The thatched roof, the beamed ceilings and the inglenook fireplaces in the public rooms invite guests to relax and enjoy the tranquillity. The restaurant provides an imaginative menu offering the best of English cuisine, made with fresh local produce. The bedrooms, all with magnificent views, are tastefully furnished and appointed with every modern comfort. Golf, fishing, sailing and riding are available close by. The fine houses of Parnham and Athelhampton and The Kingston Lacy Estate are but a short drive away. For the more energetic, there are visits to the Cerne Abbas Giant, Maiden Castle, Eggardon Hill and many coastal path walks. Vegetarian meals by prior arrangement. Price guide: £68–£80. Directions: Approaching Dorchester from Puddletown (A35), pass the lay-by and turn left into the lane signposted Higher Bockhampton/Lower Bockhampton. Proceed ¾ mile – Yalbury is the first cottage on the left.

IZAAK WALTON HOTEL

DOVEDALE, NR ASHBOURNE, DERBYSHIRE DE6 2AY
TEL: 033529 555 FAX: 033529 539 TELEX: 378406 IZAAK W

Originally built as a 17th-century farmhouse, it was here that Izaak Walton often stayed to fish and collect material for the *Compleat Angler*. It has been lovingly restored to create a hotel offering guests every luxury while retaining its historic charm. Some of the double/twin-bedded bedrooms have adjoining children's rooms. There are also four-poster and executive rooms. The Regency-style restaurant overlooks extensive gardens and offers a superb menu, relying on local fresh produce, combined with an extensive wine list. Morning coffee, light lunches and afternoon teas are available in the Buttery – a converted dairy. The hotel affords superb views of Dovedale, Thorpe Cloud and the rolling Derbyshire hills on all sides and is an ideal place to retreat from the hubbub of city life. Fishing, walking, hill climbing and cycle hire are all available locally. Alton Towers, the Wedgwood Visitor Centre, Chatsworth House and the Heights of Abraham are nearby. Price guide: £68.50–£75.50. Directions: From Ashbourne, take A515 (Buxton Road). Follow signs for Dovedale; the hotel stands at the foot of Thorpe Cloud.

DUNSFORD MILLS COUNTRY HOUSE HOTEL

DUNSFORD, NR EXETER, DEVON EX6 7EF
TEL: 0647 52011 FAX: 0647 52988

Situated on the edge of the River Teign in the beautiful Teign Valley, and inside the Dartmoor National Park, the hotel is ideally placed for exploring one of England's last wildernesses and visiting the historic city of Exeter. The fully restored mill, set in 10 acres of grounds, offers 11 spacious, en suite, luxury bedrooms, all furnished to a very high standard. The comfortable lounge bar, overlooking the river, has a large stone open fireplace, oak beams and relaxing setting throughout. The restaurant is located within the original working area of the flour mill. Here the water flows under the building through the original, 15 foot working waterwheel, now enclosed in a glass and oak beam case, setting the scene and atmosphere of the whole hotel. Our young, imaginative chef, Andrew, provides high-quality cuisine. An excellent wine list, continually being improved, will complement your meal, and the hotel guarantees postprandial pleasure and a memorable stay. This country hotel is among the best in the area. Horse-riding and golf nearby. Children aged up to 2, and over 12, welcome. Price guide: £80–£120. Directions: Situated west of Exeter on the B3212, 5 miles from East Moretonhampstead.

GRINKLE PARK HOTEL

EASINGTON, SALTBURN-BY-THE-SEA, CLEVELAND TS13 4UB
TEL: 0287 40515 FAX: 0287 41278

Grinkle Park Hotel, a splendidly refurbished 19th-century mansion, is surrounded by 35 acres of parkland and gardens containing many varieties of azalea and rhododendron. The hotel's lake is home to local wildfowl and peacocks strut the grounds. The gracious and elegant public rooms are beautifully decorated; guests can enjoy tea taken in the charming camellia room, play croquet, billiards or snooker, or simply relax in the majestic entrance hall lounge. For the more energetic, there is a purpose-built jogging track. Each of the specially designed bedrooms is named after local flowers and birds, and every comfort and luxury the discerning guest would expect, is provided throughout. Friendly, efficient service and extensive menus give lovers of good food and wines a treat in the charming candle-lit dining room. The hotel's location between the unspoiled coastline and North York Moors National Park ensures a wide choice of outdoor activities: climbing, freshwater and sea fishing, swimming, golf and moorland walks. Price guide: £72–£85. Directions: Grinkle Park Hotel is situated 9 miles from Guisborough, signed left, off the main A171 Guisborough to Whitby road.

SUMMER LODGE HOTEL
SUMMER LANE, EVERSHOT, DORSET DT2 0JR
TEL: 0935 83424

The Summer Lodge is a charming Georgian building, formerly the Dower House of the Earls of Ilchester. Now an intimate, luxurious hotel, it has a unique atmosphere blending perfectly with its idyllic location in the heart of Hardy country. The 4-acre grounds have an air of tranquillity, especially the lovely walled bower. Every comfort is provided and the rooms have garden views or overlook the village rooftops across the meadowland. The unspoiled countryside and National Trust properties make the surrounding area fascinating. There are stables, numerous excel-lent golf courses and trout lakes nearby to complement the hotel's own facilities. The classic cordon bleu cuisine and an interesting selection of wines are the ideal complement to guests' outdoor pursuits in this fine hotel. Closed first 2 weeks in January. Conference facilities are available for up to 12 people. Children over 8 welcome. Price guide: £95–£135. Directions: The turning to Evershot leaves the A37 half-way between Dorchester and Yeovil, and once in village turn left into Summer Lane and hotel entrance is 150 yards on the right.

THE EVESHAM HOTEL

COOPERS LANE, OFF WATERSIDE, EVESHAM, WORCESTERSHIRE WR11 6DA
TEL: 0386 765566 FAX: 0386 765443 TELEX: 339342

National awards for 'friendly eccentricity' suggest that a stay at the Evesham Hotel will be memorable. Originally a Tudor farmhouse, the hotel was extended and converted into a Georgian mansion house in 1810. More recent additions have given the hotel 40 comfortable bedrooms which come complete with a teddy bear and toy duck for the bath. The peace and tranquillity of the 2½ acre garden belies the fact that the hotel is only 5 minutes' walk from the town. In the gardens, there are six 300 year-old mulberry trees and a magnificent cedar of Lebanon, planted in 1809. The hotel offers prompt service, excellent food and a relaxed atmosphere. The restaurant offers unusual dishes and very unusual wines. The hotel's director, John Jenkinson, says the eclectic wine list 'enjoys great notoriety', and that the hotel boasts a very wide range of drinks. The recently built indoor swimming pool has a seaside theme. The Evesham is a good base from which to explore the South Midlands, Cotswolds, Stratford-upon-Avon or the Severn and Wye Valleys. Price guide: £70–£76. Directions: Coopers Lane lies just off Waterside (the River Avon).

THE ROYAL BEACON HOTEL

THE BEACON, EXMOUTH, SOUTH DEVON EX8 2AF
TEL: 0395 264886/265269 FAX: 0395 268890

This hotel faces south and affords views across the gardens down to the beach and the beautiful Devon coastline. Originally a Georgian posting house, The Royal Beacon maintains a tradition of hospitality, good fare and comfort, while its friendly atmosphere ensures guests a relaxing visit. Overlooking the sea, the hotel's Fennels Restaurant offers both table d'hôte and à la carte menus. Traditional Devon cream teas are served every day and light snacks are always available in the bar and lounge. Packed lunches can be arranged for guests who want to take a day trip. Exmouth is an ideal centre from which to explore this lovely area of South Devon and there are plenty of opportunities for windsurfing, birdwatching and fishing as well as visits to the theatre. Dogs accommodated at the management's discretion. Price guide: £72. Directions: Leave M5 at Junction 30, then take A376 to Exmouth.

THE MARSH COUNTRY HOTEL

EYTON, NR LEOMINSTER, HEREFORDSHIRE HR6 0AG
TEL: 0568 3952

An attractive 14th-century timbered house, lovingly restored by the owners Jacqueline and Martin Gilleland into a beautiful and relaxing country hotel, it offers a perfect retreat from the pressures of modern living. The bedrooms are individually furnished to create a warm, comfortable atmosphere and afford fine views over the garden and surrounding countryside; all have en suite facilities. The variety of fresh ingredients and the attention to detail make dining at The Marsh an experience to be savoured and remembered with great pleasure. Meals are complemented by a fine selection of wines. Nearby there are great houses, famous gardens, pretty villages and breathtaking walks across open countryside. Also, there are several golf courses in the vicinity. The Marsh is convenient for visiting the cathedral cities of Hereford and Worcester and the festival towns of Hay-on-Wye, Malvern and Ludlow. Leominster is well known as a centre for antiques; it has over 25 specialist shops. The hotel is also convenient for the Wye Valley and the Malvern and Shropshire Hills. Price guide: £93–£110. Directions: Located 2 miles north west of Leominster, signposted Eyton, off the B4361 Richard's Castle road.

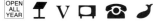

BUDOCK VEAN GOLF AND COUNTRY HOUSE HOTEL

MAWNAN SMITH, FALMOUTH, CORNWALL TR11 5LG
TEL: 0326 250288 FAX: 0326 250892

Budock Vean, originally Eglos-Budock-Vean (little Budock church), was a small religious centre dedicated to St Budock, a Breton saint. It became a manor early in the Middle Ages, and passed through many owners until, in the early 18th century, a fine new house was built. Having faced near-dereliction in the recent past, Budock Vean has been substantially extended, renovated and refurbished to provide a fine country house hotel. For golfers the hotel's challenging parkland course provides a 9- or 18-hole layout; its 7th hole is the longest in the county. Other sporting facilities include all-weather tennis courts and a spectacu-

lar indoor swimming pool, opening out onto the terrace in summer, and with its own log fire in the winter. Seafood is a speciality of the menu, with local lobsters and oysters, and the extensive wine list incorporates a fascinating selection of 'wines of the world'. As well as en suite facilities, some of the stylish bedrooms have a separate sitting room and stunning views over the Helford River. Price guide: £92–£143 including dinner. Directions: Take the A39 towards Falmouth, then the A394 Helston road. After about 1 mile, follow the signs to Mabe and Mawnan Smith.

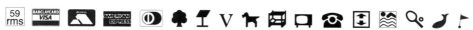

MEUDON HOTEL

MAWNAN SMITH, FALMOUTH, CORNWALL TR11 5HT
TEL: 0326 250541 FAX: 0326 250543 TELEX: 45478 MEUDON G

The two 300 year-old former coastguards' cottages in the grounds are a reminder of the pirates and wreckers who used to haunt this coastline. Meudon today is a haven of peace and tranquillity. Formerly a mansion set in its own magnificent grounds with a private beach, the hotel is now owned and run by the Pilgrim family. Originally laid out by Capability Brown, the breathtaking gardens are an exceptional example of a Cornish hanging garden. The original mansion now houses the reception area, three lounges, a well-stocked cocktail bar and a glass-walled restaurant. The bedrooms, all with lovely views of the gardens, are situated in a modern wing connected to the house, thus ensuring peace and quiet. Among the many services is a well-equipped hairdressing salon. Outdoor activities available include free golf at a nearby course, tennis, riding, fishing, skin-diving and windsurfing. Closed January and February. Children over 5 welcome. Dogs by arrangement. Price guide: £110–£150 including dinner. Directions: From Truro take the A39 for 7 miles, then the A394 for 1 mile. Cross the Helston road and follow signs to Mawnan Smith. Bear left at the Red Lion public house, hotel is 1 mile further, on the right.

TRELAWNE HOTEL

MAWNAN SMITH, NR FALMOUTH, CORNWALL TR11 5HS
TEL: 0326 250226 FAX: 0326 250909

A very friendly welcome awaits guests who will be enchanted by the beautiful location of Trelawne Hotel, on the coast between the rivers Fal and Helford. Large picture windows in the public rooms, including the freshly decorated, spacious lounge, ensure that guests take full advantage of the panoramic views of the ever-changing coastline. The bedrooms are charming; many afford views of the ocean. The soft colours of the decor, the discreet lighting and the attention to detail provide a restful atmosphere, in harmony with the delightful Wedgwood, fresh flowers and sparkling crystal in the restaurant. The menu changes daily and offers a variety of fresh, local produce. The hotel has a putting green and a games room with snooker, table tennis and darts. The Royal Duchy of Cornwall is an area of outstanding beauty, with National Trust and English Heritage properties to visit, and a variety of leisure pursuits to enjoy. Trelawne Hotel offers its own golf package at no less than ten superb courses. Open 1 March to 30 December. A Hospitality Hotel of Cornwall. Price guide: £66–£73. Directions: From A39 take A394 Helston road. After 1 mile follow sign for Mabe/Mawnan Smith.

NANSIDWELL COUNTRY HOUSE

MAWNAN, NR FALMOUTH, CORNWALL TR11 5HU
TEL: 0326 250340 FAX: 0326 250440

Nansidwell Country House, run by proprietors Jamie and Felicity Robertson, is an unspoiled country mansion set in 9 acres of subtropical gardens leading down to the sea and surrounded by glorious National Trust coastland. The grounds are filled with unusual and interesting plants and flourishing shrubs, bearing testimony to the mild climate. The bedrooms are most tastefully furnished offering guests every comfort. Chef Anthony Allcott places an emphasis on fresh local produce, particularly the best of fresh seafood such as lobster, mussels and oysters, offering generous portions and an interesting wine list. For the sports enthusiast there are no fewer than five 18-hole golf courses within a short drive, together with excellent sea fishing and reservoir trout fishing. Wind-surfing, sailing, riding and bowls are all within easy reach. There are several National Trust houses easily accessible and the hotel is surrounded by coastal walks through areas of unsurpassed and unspoiled beauty. Price guide: £88–£110. Directions: From A39 take A394 Helston Road. After 1 mile follow sign for Mabe-Mawnan Smith.

THROWLEY HOUSE (FORMERLY BARON'S HOTEL)

ASHFORD ROAD, SHELDWICH, FAVERSHAM, KENT ME13 0LT
TEL: 0795 539168 FAX: 0795 535086

A warm, family atmosphere is nurtured in Throwley House. A handsome mansion in the Georgian style with Adam features, it stands in 16 acres of mature parkland on the edge of the North Downs. The Baron's Dining Room is the heart of the house where highly individual dishes are served: hot salmon mousse with truffle on a dry Vermouth and dill sauce; saddle of lamb in filo pastry with wild mushroom and sherry sauce; warm apple tartlet with apple brandy ice cream. Throwley House is a natural choice for a family stay, offering an informal atmosphere and fully equipped nursery. While children enjoy high tea and the resident Throwley Bear, parents can totally relax and partake of high table. A Honeymoon Special, Champagne Break and special weekend rates are all offered by the hotel, as are conference facilities for up to 25 delegates. Canterbury, Ashford, Faversham and some delightful countryside are all close at hand. Price guide: £90–£100. Directions: Located on A251 between Faversham and Ashford, 2 miles from Junction 6 of the M2. Hotel is opposite the church in Sheldwich; the entrance is the first beyond the hotel, signposted to the right.

BRANDSHATCH PLACE

ASH GREEN, FAWKHAM, KENT DA3 8NQ
TEL: 0474 872239 FAX: 0474 879652

Twelve acres of gardens and woodland surround this elegant Georgian house, whose owners' intention is that their guests shall enjoy life as it used to be in those days of old, but with 20th-century comforts. All the bedrooms are comfortable with en suite bathrooms and colour television. Food is of an exceptional standard under chef Mark Fosh and is complemented by fine wines, all served in an elegantly furnished dining room. There is a popular sports club in the grounds which is also available for the use of hotel guests and includes squash, tennis and badminton courts, indoor heated swimming pool, snooker, gymnasium, spa whirlpool bath, sauna, and solarium. For business, this peaceful setting makes an ideal venue for conferences for up to 120 delegates in the purpose-built conference rooms. A Hidden Hotel. Price guide: £100. Directions: From M25 at Junction 3 follow A20 south, then signs to Fawkham Green on the left. The hotel is ½ mile before the village of Fawkham.

FELMINGHAM HALL COUNTRY HOUSE HOTEL

FELMINGHAM, NORTH WALSHAM, NORFOLK NR28 0LP
TEL: 069269 631 FAX: 069269 320

This peaceful, secluded Elizabethan manor house is set in 15 acres of grounds in the heart of the North Norfolk countryside. The 18 bedrooms are en suite and guarantee a good night's rest. The public rooms are intimate and cosy with crackling log fires in cooler weather, and the cellar bar and elegant Victorian conservatory are ideal for functions. The menu for the stately, candle-lit restaurant which is in the original 17th-century dining room, is changed daily. The kitchen uses only the freshest of ingredients; including vegetables from the hotel's own garden. The conference suite can accommodate up to 15 delegates. Extra study bedrooms, conference, syndicate and leisure facilities, will be available in converted farm buildings in late 1991. There is an outdoor swimming pool in a secluded, sunny corner, and shooting, horse-riding, golf, sailing and tennis are all available locally. River trips, complete with a picnic hamper, can be arranged as can day trips to nearby Blickling Hall. Other places of interest include Felbrigg Hall, the Broads and Norwich. Price guide: £110 including dinner. Special rates on application. Directions: Off the B1145 (Aylsham–North Walsham). Turn by the church, continue under railway bridge then take first right. Hotel is ½ mile on left.

FLITWICK MANOR

CHURCH ROAD, FLITWICK, BEDFORDSHIRE MK45 1AE
TEL: 0525 712242 FAX: 0525 419422 TELEX: 825562

A delightful 17th-century English manor house set in 50 acres of parkland containing an ironstone church, a grotto and a lake, the whole in a ring of woodland. For guests' enjoyment there is also an all-weather tennis court, two croquet lawns and a putting green. The bedrooms all have wonderful views of the park. The restaurant has an excellent reputation lauded by the major food guides. The finest ingredients, including local venison, fish and home-grown herbs, are prepared with skill and dedication. The vaulted cellars hold a comprehensive selection of the finest wines.

A collection of silver and pewter dish covers, mahogany furniture and family portraits all add to the sybaritic atmosphere. The library is used as a private dining room and for small meetings. Flitwick lies in an enviable position 40 miles from the centre of London, equidistant from Oxford and Cambridge, with Woburn to the west. Motor racing, golf and water sports are available nearby. Price guide: £95–£180. Directions: Flitwick is on the A5120 just north of the M1, Junction 12.

LANGSHOTT MANOR

LANGSHOTT, HORLEY, SURREY RH6 9LN
TEL: 0293 786680 FAX: 0293 783905

This beautifully restored Grade II listed Elizabethan manor house, dating from the 16th century, is tucked away down a quiet country lane in 3 acres of gardens and ponds and is just 8 minutes from Gatwick Airport. There is a croquet lawn, woods and country walks all around. Langshott Manor was bought by its present owners Patricia and Geoffrey Noble in 1986. Their loving restoration and old-fashioned hospitality are reflected in the warm atmosphere and character of this lovely old house, with its five finely furnished bedrooms. Guests have use of four oak-panelled reception rooms, all with log fires. Excellent traditional English cuisine is served in either the dining room, at one table, or in the privacy of the Gallery. Small business or social occasions for up to 20 people can be arranged and the hotel has full business communications. Free car parking (2 weeks) and luxury courtesy car to airport. Price guide: £104. Directions: From A23 in Horley take Ladbroke Road (Chequers Hotel roundabout) to Langshott. The manor is 3¼ miles on the right.

THE WIND IN THE WILLOWS

DERBYSHIRE LEVEL, GLOSSOP, DERBYSHIRE SK13 9PT
TEL: 0457 868001 FAX: 0457 853354

The phrase 'a warm and friendly welcome' can be a meaningless cliche, but at this charming small hotel, on the edge of the Peak National Park, it is something of an understatement. Guests here will find a relaxing combination of friendliness and professionalism. The hotel has benefited from the continuity provided by proprietors Anne and Peter Marsh, a mother and son team who have been running The Wind in the Willows for the past ten years – and each of these years has seen a careful upgrading of the interior. The quiet, peaceful and totally relaxed atmosphere is further protected by their own 5 acres of land and gardens on three sides and the golf course on the other. Food is superb – home cooking at its best in a private dining room which now occasionally lets in non-residents. The extremely pretty bedrooms and private shower/bathrooms have lovely, individual features. Ideal for the businessman or holiday maker looking for the truly personal touch. Price guide: £63–£95. Directions: One mile east of Glossop on the A57, 400 yards down the road opposite the Royal Oak pub.

MICHAELS NOOK

GRASMERE, CUMBRIA LA22 9RP
TEL: 09665 496 FAX: 09665 765 TELEX: 65329 POETIC G

A gracious stone-built Lakeland home, with a wealth of mahogany woodwork, the hotel is quietly tucked away overlooking the Grasmere Valley and is surrounded by well-kept lawns and beautiful trees. It was opened as a hotel in 1969 by Reg and Elizabeth Gifford. Reg is also a respected antique dealer, and the hotel's interior reflects his appreciation of English furniture, rugs, prints and porcelain. There are nine individually designed bedrooms, all with en suite bathrooms, and two magnificent suites, one twin-bedded. In the restaurant polished tables gleam, set with fine crystal and porcelain, and only top-quality ingredients are used for dishes memorable for their delicate flavours and artistic presentation. The panelled Oak Room, with its handsome stone fireplace and gilt furnishings, can be booked for private parties and executive meetings. Leisure facilities at the nearby Wordsworth Hotel are all available for guests at Michaels Nook, which is, above all else, a home where comfort is the watchword. Price guide: £145–£285 including dinner. Directions: Approaching Grasmere on the A591 from the south, continue until you see the Swan Hotel on the right. Turn right and Michaels Nook is 400 yards on right.

WHITE MOSS HOUSE

RYDAL WATER, GRASMERE, CUMBRIA LA22 9SE
TEL: 09665 295

This hotel has been described by a German gourmet magazine as 'probably the smallest most splendid hotel in the world'. Proprietors Peter and Susan Dixon have given White Moss House an intimate family atmosphere with a marvellous degree of comfort and attention to detail. The attractive 18th-century house overlooks beautiful Rydal Water and was once owned by Wordsworth. The five bedrooms in the main house and the two in the Brockstone Cottage Suite are individually furnished with taste and style, and all have lake views. The comfortable public rooms, furnished with antiques, have a homelike and friendly atmosphere. The restaurant is deservedly famous for English food cooked with imagination and style – 'the best English food in Britain' said *The Times* – and offers an extensive wine list of over 250. Peter Dixon is a superb chef who has won worldwide acclaim. The Lake District offers many attractions and sports enthusiasts will find many facilities nearby. The hotel is closed December to March. Children by arrangement. Price guide: £115–£160 including dinner. Directions: The hotel is situated off the A591, between Rydal Water and Grasmere, on the right as you drive north towards Grasmere.

THE WORDSWORTH HOTEL

GRASMERE, AMBLESIDE, CUMBRIA LA22 9SW
TEL: 09665 592 FAX: 09665 765 TELEX: 65329

In the very heart of English Lakeland, The Wordsworth combines four-star sophistication with the magnificence of the surrounding fells. It provides first-class, year-round facilities for both business and leisure travellers, and has acquired a reputation as one of Lakeland's finest and most welcoming hotels. Attractive and comfortable bedrooms have well-equipped bathrooms, television, radio and direct-dial telephone, and there are two luxury suites with whirlpool baths. Peaceful lounges overlook landscaped gardens and a suntrap terrace; there is a superb indoor heated pool pool with jacuzzi, a mini-gym, saunas and sunbed. In the Prelude Restaurant, the finest fresh produce is skilfully presented on the à la carte and table d'hôte menus, and each course is a delight. A specially mixed cocktail or favourite aperitif can be enjoyed in the cocktail bar. Conference and banqueting facilities are particularly good, with thoroughly professional and experienced support. Price guide: £84–£110. Directions: The Wordsworth is next to the church in the centre of Grasmere.

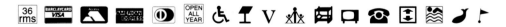

For hotel locations, see Atlas on pages 14 – 20

THE BRAMLEY GRANGE HOTEL

HORSHAM ROAD, BRAMLEY, NR GUILDFORD, SURREY GU5 0BL
TEL: 0483 983434 FAX: 0483 893835 TELEX: 859948 BRAMGH G

The Bramley Grange Hotel, a superb Victorian building, is set in 7 acres of tranquil landscaped gardens and woodland. For the health conscious a croquet lawn and putting green are available within the private grounds. The tastefully decorated bedrooms offer guests every modern luxury. The elegant restaurant features traditional French cuisine, combining a well-chosen menu, based on fresh local produce, with an extensive wine list. Bramley Grange has ideal facilities for meetings and senior-level management meetings in three conference rooms. Clandon Park, Guildford Cathedral, Polesden Lacey and the renowned race courses of Epsom and Ascot are but a short drive away. Price guide: £95–£120. Directions: Take A281 from Guildford to Bramley – about 10 minutes' drive.

WEST LODGE PARK

COCKFOSTERS ROAD, HADLEY WOOD, BARNET, HERTFORDSHIRE EN4 0PY
TEL: 081–440 8311 FAX: 081–449 3698 TELEX: 24734

Only 12 miles from Piccadilly Circus, West Lodge Park stands in 34 acres of Green Belt parkland containing a putting green, croquet lawn, arboretum and a lake with a rowing boat. The Beale family has run the hotel for over 40 years. It was originally a gentleman's country seat and was rebuilt in 1838 on the site of a 16th-century keeper's lodge in Royal hunting country, filled with Old Master paintings and period furnishings. All the bedrooms have a private bathroom, remote control colour TV with teletext, radio and telephone; each affords views of the countryside. In addition there are four private reception rooms for conferences and banquets. The hotel has its own helicopter landing pad and extensive car parking. Available nearby are facilities for golf and riding in Trent Park, Hadley Wood, a squash court and two swimming pools. AA and RAC 4 Stars. BTA Commended Country House Hotel Award. Price guide: £99.50. Directions: The hotel is situated on the A111 between Cockfosters station and Junction 24 of the M25 motorway.

HATTON COURT

BULLINGTON END, HANSLOPE, MILTON KEYNES, BUCKINGHAMSHIRE MK19 7BQ
TEL: 0908 510044 FAX: 0908 510945

Hatton Court is a splendid Victorian country house set in 7 acres of beautiful Buckinghamshire countryside. The house has been skilfully restored to blend the original character with every modern luxury while retaining fine architectural features such as the oak-panelled dining room. The latter provides an elegant setting for classic English cuisine, prepared from fresh local produce by the award-winning chef. The 20 bedrooms, individually and tastefully decorated, offer guests all modern comforts and magnificent views. Hatton Court is an ideal venue for senior-level management meetings combining peaceful surroundings and a convenient location with all necessary facilities. Silverstone motor racing circuit, Woburn Abbey with its safari park and golf and country club and Towcester racecourse are but a short drive away. London, Milton Keynes and Northampton are also within easy reach. Price guide: £92–£110 including complementary newspaper. Directions: Turn off the M1 at Junction 14, take the A509, turn right at the A4146; drive through Haversham, drive on for another 2 miles, the hotel is on your right.

GRANTS HOTEL

SWAN ROAD, HARROGATE, NORTH YORKSHIRE HG1 2SS
TEL: 0423 560666 FAX: 0423 502550

Stay at this friendly hotel and you could go up, up and away on one of its special Champagne balloon trips over the Yorkshire Dales. If you prefer to keep your feet firmly on the ground, take a walk around Harrogate, a favourite spa of the Victorian gentry. The Royal Pump Room Museum and Baths Assembly Rooms where you can soak up history, and soak yourself in the traditional turkish baths, are a few minutes' walk from the hotel. Harrogate is six times winner of the British Tourist Authority's 'Britain in Bloom' accolade and there are 22 beautiful gardens in and around the district to enjoy. There are also excellent shopping facilities and a choice of theatres. After a hard day's sightseeing or business – Grants is only 5 minutes' walk from the conference centre – return to the luxury of Grants' air-conditioned Chimney Pots restaurant where the 'New English' cuisine includes 'Old English' Yorkshire pudding. Or enjoy a drink and a snack in the cocktail bar where light meals are available at all times. Price guide: £80–£95. Directions: Swan Road is in the centre of Harrogate off the A61 to Ripon.

NIDD HALL

NIDD, HARROGATE, NORTH YORKSHIRE HG3 3BN
TEL: 0423 771598 FAX: 0423 770931

A long, curling, tree-flanked driveway leads to this imposing country mansion, set in 45 acres of grounds. Nidd Hall has something to delight every guest. Although extensively refurbished and equipped with every modern convenience, none of the grandeur and ambience of this 19th-century house with its fine marble fireplaces and carved mahogany doors has been lost. All the bedrooms have been individually designed and provide a high standard of comfort. Of the two restaurants, the elegant Lancaster Room is the more formal and affords fine views across the terrace, while the Cellar provides a more relaxed setting. The hotel is proud of its 200-bin wine list and tasting sessions can be arranged in the 14th-century vaulted cellars. In addition to the tennis courts and fishing lake in the hall's grounds, the leisure club's extensive facilities are available free to guests. There is much to see nearby, including the Yorkshire Dales and the North Yorkshire Moors, Harrogate and the historic city of York. Dogs by arrangement. Price guide: £125–£140. Directions: A61 Harrogate to Ripon. At Ripley, B6165 to Knaresborough. Hotel is 1 mile on the left.

HOB GREEN HOTEL AND RESTAURANT

MARKINGTON, HARROGATE, NORTH YORKSHIRE HG3 3PJ
TEL: 0423 770031 FAX: 0423 771589 TELEX: 57780

Hob Green is a small country house hotel set in 870 acres of farm and woodland. The hall and drawing room are furnished with a mixture of antique and modern furniture and guests will feel welcomed and warmed by the crackling log fires. The menu is regularly changed and incorporates home-grown vegetables. The grounds include a croquet lawn and the gardens have regularly won awards in the Harrogate District Best Kept Garden Competition. This is the perfect spot for horse enthusiasts. The Yorkshire Riding Centre, run by two former Olympic Dressage Team members is in the village and has the best riding facilities in Europe. It offers private or group lessons, courses for instructors and hacking. Golf, fishing, cricket and racing are within easy reach. Conferences for up to 12 people. Within easy reach are Fountains Abbey, Markenfield Hall and Ripley Castle. The cathedral cities of York and Ripon are a short drive away. Price guide: £78–£115. Directions: From A61 at Wormald Green take turning to Markington. Hob Green is 1 mile beyond Markington.

LYTHE HILL HOTEL

PETWORTH ROAD, HASLEMERE, SURREY GU27 3BQ
TEL: 0428 651251 FAX: 0428 644131 TELEX: 858402

This hotel is not just an enchanting Tudor building in 14 acres of parkland; it is a whole ancient hamlet that has long lain cradled by the rolling foothills of Surrey – parts of the timbered farmhouse date from the 14th century. The original farm buildings now house luxurious bedrooms and suites with views across the countryside. In keeping with this style it is no surprise to find that there is a choice of two splendid restaurants, one providing traditional but imaginative English cooking and the other, superb French classic cuisine. Its situation, within easy reach of London, Gatwick and Heathrow, together with excellent facilities make this an ideal venue for senior executive business meetings. Facilities include tennis and croquet, with clay pigeon shooting also available and fishing in the lake. Golf and riding are available nearby. The area abounds in interesting places to visit, along with racing at Goodwood, polo at Cowdray or walks in the surrounding woodland. Price guide: £85–£160. Directions: Lythe Hill lies east of Haslemere on the B2131.

FARTHINGS COUNTRY HOUSE HOTEL

HATCH BEAUCHAMP, SOMERSET TA3 6SG
TEL: 0823 480664

In true country-house tradition, Farthings is a captivating Georgian building situated in tranquil gardens of 3 acres. Since it lies only 2½ hours from London and Birmingham, it is the perfect place for tourists as well as executives in search of a get-away-from-it-all weekend or a convenient mid-week retreat from everyday pressures – a haven where guests may relax and enjoy delicious food, based on fresh local produce and a comprehensive wine list. The bedrooms are thoughtfully and elegantly furnished in individual style: one of the most popular has a hand-carved spiral staircase that leads up to its luxurious bathroom. Great attention is paid to detail and an exemplary standard of service is provided. In the vicinity is an abundance of stately homes and National Trust properties, all, of course, surrounded by the inimitable West Country scenery, while nearby facilities for recreation include golf, racing, polo, riding and hunting. Dogs by arrangement. Price guide: £90–£115 (no service charge). Directions: Hatch Beauchamp lies just off the A358 between Taunton and Ilminster (M5 Junction 25), and A303 (Horton Cross).

ROOKHURST GEORGIAN COUNTRY HOUSE HOTEL

WEST END, GAYLE, HAWES, NORTH YORKSHIRE DL8 3RT
TEL: 0969 667454

The front gate of this part Georgian, part Victorian country house opens onto the 250-mile long Pennine Way. Situated in the heart of the Yorkshire Dales National Park, it is a real family home and guests are welcomed as friends. The bedrooms contain either half-tester or four-poster beds. The Georgian Bridal Suite and the master four-poster rooms are especially ornate. Proprietor Iris Van Der Steen specialises in traditional, home-cooked English cuisine, made with fresh, locally grown produce, and guests dine by candle light in the restaurant – whatever the time of year – at 7.30 pm.

The sitting room and bar is made cosy by a wood burning stove and guests can relax here with a drink. Often referred to as Herriot country, since the TV series *All Creatures Great and Small*, the countryside is a delight for both serious walkers and those who prefer to stroll. Also nearby is the Hardraw Waterfall, which has the longest drop of any falls in England, Bolton Castle, where Mary Queen of Scots was imprisoned, and the Carlisle–Settle railway. Price guide: £68. Directions: Gayle adjoins Hawes on the A684.

THE BEL ALP HOUSE

HAYTOR, NR BOVEY TRACEY, SOUTH DEVON TQ13 9XX
TEL: 0364 661217/8 FAX: 0364 661292

Peace and quiet are guaranteed at The Bel Alp House with its beautiful views from the edge of Dartmoor, across the panorama of the South Devon landscape to the sea 20 miles away. Built as an elegant country retreat, Bel Alp has been lovingly restored by Roger and Sarah Curnock, whose personal attention will ensure your enjoyment and comfort in the atmosphere of a large private home. Sarah does the cooking herself and the five-course menu is changed daily. She uses only the best local produce and her meals are complemented by Roger's well-chosen and comprehensive wine list. Of the nine en suite bedrooms, two still have their original Edwardian basins and baths mounted on marble plinths, and all afford views over the gardens. An abundance of house plants, open log fires and restful colours complement the family antiques and pictures to create the perfect environment in which to relax. Bel Alp is ideally situated for exploring Devon and parts of Cornwall. Plymouth, famed for Drake and the Pilgrim Fathers, Exeter with its Norman Cathedral plus National Trust properties, such as Castle Drogo and Cotehele manor house, are within an hour's drive. Price guide: £102–£126. Directions: Bel Alp House is off the B3387 Haytor Road, 2½ miles from Bovey Tracey.

HOLLY LODGE HOTEL

LYNN ROAD, HEACHAM, NR KING'S LYNN, NORFOLK PE31 7HY
TEL: 0485 70790

This 16th-century listed building is of great historic interest as it was once a dormitory for visiting monks, and retains an atmosphere of great peace and tranquillity. It also has a strong feeling of a private home to which guests return again and again. A gracious staircase sweeps up to the individual and elegant bedrooms. The drawing rooms are comfortable and cosy with open fires in winter, and the candle-lit restaurant is romantic and relaxing. Miles of nearby sandy beaches provide opportunities for riding, sailing, wind-surfing, water-skiing and swimming.

Championship golf links are within easy reach. As well as fields, woods, and tracks for walking, there are several important stately homes nearby including the Halls at Houghton, Blickling and the Queen's Sandringham residence. Norwich, Ely and Cambridge are all within an hour's drive. The hotel is closed for January and February. Price guide: £75. Directions: From King's Lynn turn left off the A149 into Heacham village at the Norfolk Lavender crossroad. Holly Lodge is on the right-hand side after ½ mile.

THE CARLTON HOTEL

ALBERT STREET, HEBDEN BRIDGE, WEST YORKSHIRE HX7 8ES
TEL: 0422 844400 FAX: 0422 843117

The Carlton is an unusual town house hotel centrally situated on the first and second floors of the old co-operative society (1876). A lift will transport you from the beautiful, yet austere exterior to the comfortable, elegant interior. The Carlton is owned and run by Bob Graham and his staff led by Glen Mills and Helen Siddall. The 18 en suite rooms are colour co-ordinated and have every modern facility and comfort. Imaginative menus are available in the relaxed restaurant, while conferences and dinners for 120 can be arranged in the function room. Behind the hotel in Crown Street, the Crown Bar provides light lunches together with the charm of a local pub. Set at the head of the beautiful Calder Valley, Hebden Bridge offers rural peace, many antique and craft shops and a base from which to explore *Last of the Summer Wine* and Brontë country. Free golf is available at Mount Skip Golf Course as well as boating on the Rochdale Canal. Price guide: £75. Directions: Entering Hebden Bridge on the A646, turn down Hope Street, a one-way street nearly opposite the Marina which runs into Albert Street. The hotel is just on the left.

THE FEVERSHAM ARMS HOTEL

HELMSLEY, NORTH YORKSHIRE YO6 5AG
TEL: 0439 70766 FAX: 0439 70346

This historic coaching inn, rebuilt in 1855 by the Earl of Feversham, has been owned and managed by the Aragues family since 1967. Set in over an acre of walled gardens and luxuriously modernised in keeping with its character, the hotel offers its guests every modern convenience. All the bedrooms are individually and tastefully furnished, some having special features such as four-poster beds and de luxe bathrooms. Roaring log fires are lit in winter. The attractive candle-lit restaurant serves English, French and Spanish cuisine and, by relying on fresh local produce, offers seasonal variety. There is an excellent fish and shellfish menu. The hotel also boasts a superb wine list which includes a wide range of Spanish wines and clarets. Situated in the North York Moors National Park, central to many golf courses, this comfortable and welcoming hotel is ideal for sporting activities and for touring the Moors, Dales, East Coast and the mediaeval city of York. Dogs by arrangement. Price guide: £70–£80. Directions: A1 Exit: A64, York north bypass (A1237) then B1363, or, A1 exit: A168 Thirsk, then A170.

THE PHEASANT

HAROME, HELMSLEY, NORTH YORKSHIRE YO6 5JG
TEL: 0439 71241/70416

The Pheasant Hotel is rich in oak beams and open log fires and has additional accommodation, separate from the main building, in a charming 16th-century thatched cottage. Built, owned and managed by the Binks family, the atmosphere is one of traditional Yorkshire warmth and welcome. The bedrooms are bright and attractively decorated. Traditional English cuisine is the speciality of the restaurant, and many dishes are created from fresh fruit and vegetables grown in the hotel's grounds. Swimming, riding, golf and fishing are all close by. York is just a short drive away as are the Abbeys of Byland and Rievaulx, Castle Howard – of *Brideshead Revisited* fame – Pickering, and North York Moors National Park. Dogs by arrangement. Children over 12 are welcome. Closed January and February. Price guide: £98 (includes dinner). Directions: Leave Helmsley on A170 in the direction of Scarborough, after ¼ mile turn right for Harome.

12 rms 🌳 ♿ ⚐ V 🐕 ▭ ☎

HOAR CROSS HALL

HOAR CROSS, NR YOXALL, STAFFORDSHIRE DE13 8QS
TEL: 028375 671 FAX: 028375 652

Hoar Cross Hall is a health resort in a stately home. This Grade II listed building, situated in formal gardens and wooded grounds, has all the grace and charm expected of a luxurious country house. However, this is also a first-rate health spa specialising in hydrotherapy. At Hoar Cross Hall a complete bathing centre is combined with leisure facilities and a top quality hotel balancing physical fitness and mental relaxation. All the bedrooms are furnished with either four-poster, half-tester or crown-tester beds. Public rooms retain many original features such as panelling and mouldings. Dinner can be taken in the restaurant overlooking the pools or in the dining room with its gilded ceilings and crystal chandeliers. Guests who want to lose weight can opt for calorie-counted meals. There are badminton, tennis, croquet, boules and golf improvement facilities in the grounds. There are three conference rooms for up to 30 delegates. Price includes dinner, B&B, lunch, beauty treatment and use of spa. Price guide: £180. Directions: Turn off A51 on to A515 towards Ashbourne. Go through Yoxall, turn left to Hoar Cross. The spa resort is on the left beyond the church.

NUTHURST GRANGE
HOCKLEY HEATH, WARWICKSHIRE B94 5NL
TEL: 0564 783972 FAX: 0564 783919

The most memorable feature of this delightfully secluded, friendly country house hotel is its outstanding restaurant. Chef/proprietor David Randolph and his team have won many accolades for the hotel's imaginative menus described as 'English, cooked in the light French style', and the two adjoining rooms which comprise the restaurant are the heart of Nuthurst Grange. From here, diners can enjoy superb food and superb views of the 7½ acres of landscaped gardens to the rear of the building. The rest of the house is no less charming – the eight spacious bedrooms have a country house atmosphere and are provided with extra luxuries such as exhilarating air-spa baths, as well as a trouser press, hair dryer and safe. For that special occasion, one room has a four-poster bed and a marble bathroom. Conferences for up to 20 can be arranged, and there are plenty of sporting activities close by: golf, canal boating and tennis. Price guide: £99–£125. Directions: The hotel is in Nuthurst Grange Lane, off the A3400 Stratford Road ¼ mile south of Hockley Heath.

ALSTON HALL

ALSTON CROSS, HOLBETON, NR PLYMOUTH, DEVON PL8 1HN
TEL: 075530 555 FAX: 075530 494

Alston Hall is a substantial Edwardian manor house set in formal gardens, with stunning views over Newton Ferrers and the Mew Stone. Plymouth is just 20 minutes' drive away. The oak-panelled great hall, with its balustraded minstrels' gallery and stained-glass windows, acts as an elegant drawing room in which to relax with a drink or after-dinner coffee. The Peony Room, with its award-winning brigade of chefs, serves a mixture of traditional and international cuisine using freshly caught seafood and local farm produce. Refurbished throughout, the hotel represents the best in gracious living with 20 comfortable bedrooms, impressive public rooms, conference facilities and a leisure club. Situated in an outstanding area of natural beauty between the Yealm and Erme Rivers, one of the most beautiful parts of Devon, Alston Hall offers peace, tranquillity and the perfect opportunity to unwind. Price guide: £85–£125. Directions: Take road to Holbeton from A379 between Modbury and Yealmpton. Pass sign to Holbeton and the hotel (signposted) is on your right.

COURT BARN COUNTRY HOUSE HOTEL

CLAWTON, HOLSWORTHY, DEVON EX22 6PS
TEL: 0409 27219

This lovely Victorian manor house was built on the site of an original 14th-century building known as The Sanctuary. It later belonged to the estate of James I. The present Court Barn was rebuilt as the manor house to Clawton village in 1853, and is set in 5 acres of informal grounds. The hotel affords beautiful views across the croquet lawn to the 12th-century village church. The hotel is BTA Commended for 'outstanding cuisine and relaxed atmosphere', and Robert and Susan Wood received the *Mercier Corps d'Elite* Award 1989, and the *Prix d'Elite* Award 1988 for their wine list of over 300 varieties. The restaurant is luxuriously furnished with antique furniture and is the ideal setting in which to enjoy the delicious food and fine wines. The comfortable bedrooms offer rural views and, on request, a television can be provided. The relaxing public rooms have no-smoking areas. The hotel is well situated for exploring Dartmoor and North Devon. Price guide: £86–£95 including dinner. Directions: Clawton is on the A388 between Holsworthy and Launceston.

COMBE HOUSE

GITTISHAM, NR HONITON, DEVON EX14 0AD
TEL: 0404 42756 FAX: 0404 46004

Peace and seclusion reign at this 14th-century Elizabethan mansion situated in its own country estate. It is hard to believe that the main A30 Exeter – London road is only 2 miles away. Finely proportioned public rooms are enhanced with antiques and original oil paintings. Modern English cuisine is a feature of the two dining rooms, one of which features a superb Italian fireplace, the other a mirrored overmantle and carved pine doorcases. Extremely friendly and helpful staff serve dinner by candlelight; a real house party atmosphere prevails at Combe House. Perfectly placed for touring, visitors are sure to find Combe, a secluded retreat away from the hustle and bustle of the 20th century, the ideal place to re-charge their batteries. Closed Sundays and Mondays during January and February. Price guide: £85.50–£110.50. Directions: Gittisham lies 2 miles from the A30 – the hotel is signposted from the A30.

PETERSFIELD HOUSE HOTEL

LOWER STREET, HORNING, NR NORWICH, NORFOLK NR12 8PF
TEL: 0692 630741 FAX: 0692 630745

Set slightly back from the banks of the River Bure and surrounded by 2 acres of landscaped gardens, Petersfield House Hotel occupies one of the choicest positions in the heart of Broadland. The charming location of the hotel and its private moorings is away from the hustle and bustle of everyday life. It has the advantage of being a quiet, peaceful retreat with easy access to many local attractions and Norfolk's beautiful coastline. Varied fixed price, and extensive à la carte menus are offered in the restaurant each day and a regular Saturday night dinner-dance attracts many guests and non-residents. To enhance your meal, there is a choice of over 60 different wines from a comprehensive list. The bedrooms are comfortable and most offer views over the well-tended gardens which feature a delightful lily pond and fountain. There is also a moon gate built of flint stone which links the gardens to a small woodland glade. The Petersfield is family owned and managed; you can be assured of personal attention at all times. Price guide: £70. Directions: From Wroxham/Hoveton take the A1062 to Horning – located in centre of village.

FOXDOWN MANOR

HORNS CROSS, NR CLOVELLY, NORTH DEVON EX39 5PJ
TEL: 0237 451325

Foxdown Manor nestles in 20 acres of woodland and gardens through which a stream meanders. Guests are drawn back again and again by the beauty of the setting, the stateliness of the hotel, the quality of the food and the warmth of the welcome from resident proprietors Sally and Clifford Johnson. The Victorian building is filled with period furniture which contributes to the comfortable, family home atmosphere. The bedrooms are all en suite and two have four-poster beds. The restaurant offers a choice of ten starters and main courses (four for vegetarians) each day and is as popular with the locals as it is with guests. The hotel's sporting facilities include a heated outdoor swimming pool, indoor spa pool, sauna, solarium, all-weather tennis court and an 18-hole putting green. Fishing, golf, shooting (game and clay) and sailing are available nearby and the area is ideal for ramblers. Closed February. Price guide: £65–£75. Directions: Hotel is signposted 6 miles west of Bideford on A39.

CISSWOOD HOUSE

LOWER BEEDING, NR HORSHAM, SUSSEX RH13 6NF
TEL: 0403 891216 FAX: 0403 891621

Built in 1928 as the country house for the then Chairman of Harrods, Sir Woodman Burbidge, Cisswood was a family home until 1979 when Othmar and Elizabeth Illes converted it into a dignified, but friendly, hotel where the emphasis is on quality. Othmar Illes has worked as a chef in Europe and England and his experience shows in the quality of his cuisine. He handpicks the meat, fish and vegetables he uses from London markets and local nurseries as well as making good use of home-grown produce. All of the bedrooms at Cisswood have different decors and they are all en suite, some having spa baths. Also, there are two large suites with private sitting rooms, dining areas and jacuzzi baths. Mr Illes says these suites have proved especially popular for small business meetings. The Courtyard Suite is a banqueting and conference centre which can accommodate up to 125 people. It can be divided into the smaller Beech, Oak and Maple Rooms. Set in 12 acres of beautiful gardens, there is a helipad in the hotel's grounds. Welcomes children over 12. Price guide: £80–£125. Directions: Lower Beeding is on the A279 south west of Crawley, and 12 miles from Gatwick Airport.

SOUTH LODGE

LOWER BEEDING, NR HORSHAM, WEST SUSSEX RH13 6PS
TEL: 0403 891711 FAX: 0403 891766 TELEX: 877765

Rare shrubs abound in the 90 acres of gardens and parkland which surround this elegant country house built in 1883 by Lord Godman, a noted explorer and botanist; the grounds also contain perhaps one of the finest Victorian rock gardens in England. The house has been carefully and extensively renovated to provide a luxurious country house hotel while retaining the ambience of the original family home. Light and spacious bedrooms offer every comfort, with fine views of the rolling Sussex Downs, and the beautifully proportioned reception rooms with their ornate ceilings, wood panelling and open fires create a feeling of comfort and elegance. For small executive meetings the original drawing room and billiard room have been set aside. The extensive grounds provide leisure and sporting facilities with many delightful walks, croquet and tennis. Golf is available close by and fishing, riding and clay pigeon shooting can be arranged. Nearby attractions include Glyndbourne, Chartwell and the gardens of Leonardslee, with racing at Goodwood, Plumpton and Brighton. Price guide: £115–£220. Directions: South Lodge is situated on the A281 at Lower Beeding, south of Horsham.

OLD BRIDGE HOTEL

1 HIGH STREET, HUNTINGDON, CAMBRIDGESHIRE PE18 6TQ
TEL: 0480 52681 FAX: 0480 411017 TELEX: 32706

An attractive Georgian hotel in a riverside setting, the gardens lead down to the River Ouse and the hotel looks out across meadows and parkland. The individually designed bedrooms are tastefully appointed with every modern facility. The public rooms, too, are bright and comfortable, with delightful murals by Julia Rushbury in the terrace. The elegant restaurant, with its original panelling, has an excellent reputation for its food; the imaginative traditional dishes are complemented by an outstanding wine list which won the Egon Ronay 'Cellar of the Year 1989' award. The Old Bridge also boasts a small, exclusive business and conference centre. Price guide: £70. Directions: Situated off the inner ring road in Huntingdon (signposted from A604/M11 and A1).

ROMBALDS HOTEL

WEST VIEW, WELLS ROAD, ILKLEY, WEST YORKSHIRE LS29 9JG
TEL: 0943 603201 FAX: 0943 816586 TELEX: 51593

This splendid 150 year-old Georgian hotel, under the personal supervision of Ian and Jill Guthrie, is on the very edge of Ilkley Moor. The restaurant is a special feature and serves excellent, freshly prepared food, using seasonally available produce from local suppliers. Sundays at the hotel are famous: this is the day when guests are treated to a prize-winning 'Edwardian Breakfast' and, in the evening, a splendid roast dinner. The list of 40 wines includes something for every taste. New conference facilities for up to 50 delegates have been opened in the coach house, which was awarded, in 1989, the White Rose Award for Excellence and Innovation by the Yorkshire and Humberside Tourist Board. The bedrooms are being upgraded for 1991. There is wheelchair access to all public rooms. Nearby are the Yorkshire Dales National Park and Brontë country; Bolton, Fountains and Rievaulx Abbeys; Castle Howard and Harewood House stately homes. BTA Commended. Price guide: £80–£95. Directions: At the traffic lights on the A65 in the centre of town, turn into Brook Street, cross The Grove to enter Wells Road. The hotel is 600 yards up Wells Road on the left-hand side.

THE PHEASANT HOTEL

SEAVINGTON ST MARY, NR ILMINSTER, SOMERSET TA19 0QH
TEL: 0460 40502 (3 lines) FAX: 0460 42388

Noted for its distinctive charm and character, this beautifully converted 17th-century hotel, standing in landscaped gardens and lawns in a superb setting, is just the place for a weekend or longer holiday. The Pheasant features individually designed and superbly furnished bedrooms, while the restaurant serves excellent food. Oak-beamed ceilings and the soft gentle decor add to the relaxing atmosphere of both the lounge bar and the restaurant. In winter, cosy log fires crackle in the large open inglenooks. Just the place to enjoy fabulous dinners complemented by a fine range of wines and to appreciate such unique warmth and hospitality. Recom-

mended by all the major hotel and restaurant guides, and well known as the best in the area, staying at The Pheasant is not only a special pleasure, but one to be remembered and often repeated. An ideal stopping place when visiting or touring the West Country. Facilities nearby for golf and horse riding. Price guide: £60–£80. Directions: The Pheasant is just 1 mile from the South Petherton beginning of the Ilminster bypass A303, follow signs to Seavington St Michael; or 4 miles from the Horton roundabout of the Ilminster bypass, follow signs for local services.

THE COMMODORE HOTEL

MARINE PARADE, INSTOW, NORTH DEVON EX39 4JN
TEL: 0271 860347 FAX: 0271 861233

Overlooking the beach from its attractive garden setting, The Commodore commands a panoramic vista of sea and sand. Situated between the market towns of Barnstaple and Bideford and only minutes from the North Devon Link Road, the hotel is ideally placed for touring. The restaurant maintains a high reputation for service and cuisine with extensive à la carte and table d'hôte menus. Guests can enjoy an equally varied choice of excellent bar meals. The spacious en suite rooms are furnished to a luxurious standard and many have sea-facing balconies. Open throughout the year, The Commodore is owned and managed by Mr and Mrs Bruce Woolaway and family. Open to non-residents. Price guide: £73–£80. Directions: Turn off North Devon Link Road to Instow at the Torridge Bridge. The Commodore is 1½ miles further on.

BELSTEAD BROOK HOTEL AND RESTAURANT

BELSTEAD ROAD, IPSWICH, SUFFOLK IP2 9HB
TEL: 0473 684241 FAX: 0473 681249 TELEX: 987674

Belstead Brook's origins lie in Saxon times but additions during the reign of King James and around the time of World War I, have bequeathed to later generations a fascinating blend of old and new. The most recent addition is a fine wing in a secluded part of the garden which offers guests a choice of private suites. The hotel is sited in 6 acres of gardens and woodlands and resident peacocks strut across the lawns. Inside, oak panelling and, on the stairs, herringbone brickwork are complemented by plush carpeting and pretty pine furniture. Food here is first-rate. A characteristic menu might include fillet of oak smoked trout with a light lime and horseradish cream, fillet of beef glazed with Stilton cheese on a light port and fresh herb sauce or Suffolk glazed ham. There are two conference rooms and a special, larger, functions room. The Suffolk coastline is within easy reach, as are the castles at Orford and Framlingham. The festival town of Aldeburgh is only a short drive away. There will be another 55 rooms available from the end of November, 1990. Price guide: £70–£90. Directions: Facing Ipswich station, turn left and then right up Willoughby Road, turn right up Belstead Road. The hotel is 1½ miles on the right.

CASTLETOWN GOLF LINKS HOTEL

FORT ISLAND, DERBYHAVEN, ISLE OF MAN
TEL: 0624 822201 FAX: 0624 824633 TELEX: 627636 GOLFER G

The location of this hotel is quite superb. Occupying one of the prime positions on the Isle of Man, renowned for its beautiful views and scenery, it is surrounded by sea on three sides and a famous Championship golf links, which gives the hotel its *raison d'être*, on the other. The course is one of the most challenging in the British Isles and must be one of few in the world with sea in sight from every green. Leisure facilities include an indoor pool, sauna, solarium and two full-size snooker tables. Most of the guest rooms, delightfully and individually furnished, have sea views; the comfort of the guests is clearly a top priority. L'Orangerie, the à la carte restaurant at the hotel, has earned a reputation as one of the best on the island, with its gourmet cuisine presided over by Chef Pepper. Every visit to this outstanding restaurant is a truly memorable experience. A courtesy car is available to take guests to the Palace Casino and Night Club where they enjoy complementary membership. Price guide: £75–£85. Directions: Follow the promenade east out of Castletown for approximately 1½ miles. Turning on the right leads to hotel.

THE GRAND ISLAND HOTEL

BRIDE ROAD, RAMSEY, ISLE OF MAN
TEL: 0624 812455 FAX: 0624 815291 TELEX: 629849 GIHMAN G

Originally a Georgian country manor house, this hotel is perfectly situated with palm-fringed lawns sweeping down to the sea. All rooms feature antique furniture, and in the bedrooms, the liberal use of pretty chintz fabrics helps create a country house atmosphere. Guests may enjoy superb cuisine in the elegant Bay Room or more informal fare in the Country Kitchen. The hotel is the headquarters of the island's Croquet Association and has five croquet lawns of its own. There is also a putting green and a fully equipped health club with jacuzzi, sauna, solarium and steam room, multi-gym, a resident beautician and a hairdresser. The hotel is within 30 minutes' drive of seven golf courses and can arrange special packages for enthusiasts. AA/RAC 4 Star, Egon Ronay, Ashley Courtenay, Signpost, Premier Hotels of GB and Michelin recommended. IOM Merit Award 1988. Price guide: £74–£94. Directions: Situated 1 mile north of Ramsey centre.

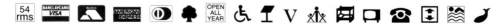

WINTERBOURNE HOTEL

BONCHURCH, ISLE OF WIGHT PO38 1RQ
TEL: 0983 852535 FAX: 0983 853056

Winterbourne, once the home of Charles Dickens during the period he wrote *David Copperfield*, is situated in its own beautiful sheltered grounds with a stream, waterfall, colourful borders and ornamental pools. The rarely crowded shingle and sand beach is reached by steps and private path from the foot of the garden. Without doubt, this has to be one of the most beautiful settings on the island. Nearly all bedrooms enjoy superb views of the sea at Bonchurch; additional bedrooms and a luxurious suite are available in the Coach House, which is in the hotel's grounds a few yards from the main entrance. The Regency dining room offers excellent cuisine using the best fresh produce available. There is a 40-foot swimming pool which has been skilfully landscaped into the contours of the garden, with a spacious terrace for sunbathing and taking lunchtime drinks and snacks. The pool is heated from May–October. Closed December, January and February. Children over 4 welcome. Price guide: £100 including dinner. Directions: The hotel is 100 yards from Bonchurch duck pond.

ST MARTIN'S HOTEL

THE ISLAND OF ST MARTIN'S, ISLES OF SCILLY TR25 0QW
TEL: 0720 22092 FAX: 0720 22298 TELEX: 94015906

The first and only hotel on this idyllic island opened in March 1989. St Martin's Hotel has been designed as a cluster of cottages overlooking a beautiful white sand beach and the crystal clear water of Tean Sound. The 24 individually designed rooms and suites are named after local legends, places or events; the colours, fabrics and furnishings give the hotel a restful atmosphere. Excellent food, including freshly caught *fruits de mer*, is served in the restaurant, and after dinner guests can relax and enjoy the stunning sea and island views from the Sunset Lounge. First-class facilities are backed by thoughtful, efficient service from the friendly staff. St Martin's is also the perfect setting for conferences, business meetings and exclusive corporate events, an unusual venue which is a world apart but not a world away. Sports facilities include an indoor heated swimming pool and snooker room; arrangements can be made for yachting, diving, windsurfing, sailing and many other interests. Dogs by arrangement. Price guide: £130–£196 including dinner. Directions: By air from Gatwick, Heathrow, Exeter, Bristol, Newquay, Plymouth or Penzance; by sea from Penzance.

BRUNDHOLME COUNTRY HOUSE HOTEL

BRUNDHOLME ROAD, KESWICK, CUMBRIA CA12 4NL
TEL: 07687 74495

This secluded country house hotel, set in 3 acres of mature gardens, has played host to many celebrated figures, including William Wordsworth. Elegantly furnished and redolent of the Georgian era, the Brundholme Country House Hotel offers every modern luxury and a mouthwatering menu of superbly presented dishes. In the summer months, guests can dine in the Victorian conservatory. The hotel is owned and run personally by Ian and Lynn Charlton. Ian, an experienced fell runner, is the chef who produces delicious food using fresh local produce and home-grown herbs. For recreation, there is a croquet lawn in the grounds. Mountain bikes are available and golf courses and squash courts are easily accessible. Conference facilities are available for up to 20 people. Closed Christmas to end of January. Children over 12 are welcome. AA 3 Stars; RAC 3 Stars Recommended. Price guide: £80–£100. Directions: From A66 roundabout, take Keswick turning and first left into Brundholme Road, then left again and the hotel is on the right.

BROCKENCOTE HALL

CHADDESLEY CORBETT, NR KIDDERMINSTER, WORCESTERSHIRE DY10 4PY
TEL: 0562 777876 TELEX: 333431

Lying just outside Chaddesley Corbett, the Brockencote Estate consists of 70 acres of landscaped grounds surrounding a magnificent hall. There is a gatehouse, half-timbered dovecote, lake, some fine specimens of European and North American trees and an elegant conservatory. The interior combines classic architectural style with modern day creature comforts. The bedrooms have antique-style furniture, colour TVs and videos. The friendly staff provide a splendid service. The menu is based on traditional French and English cuisine with occasional regional and seasonal specialities. Brockencote Hall is ideal for private dinner parties of up to 40 people, small business meetings and conferences. Positioned just south of Birmingham, it is convenient for business people and sightseers alike – tours of Worcestershire can start here. Closed Boxing Day to 20 January. Price guide: £74–£110. Directions: Brockencote Hall is beside the A448 at Chaddesley Corbett between Bromsgrove and Kidderminster.

STONE MANOR HOTEL

STONE, KIDDERMINSTER, WORCESTERSHIRE DY10 4PJ
TEL: 0562 777555 FAX: 0562 777834 TELEX: 335661

Stone Manor stands in 25 acres of grounds with well-kept gardens, ponds, fountains and beautiful lawns. Attractively furnished bedrooms with views of the gardens and surrounding countryside offer every facility. The cosy Residents' Lounge, with its inglenook fireplace, is an ideal setting for a quiet coffee or drink. For conferences and other functions the hotel offers a choice of fine venues, including the atmospheric Manor Suite, converted from the stable block and courtyard and seating up to 200 people; the Garden Room, for up to 150; the Patio Suite, for up to 90 (both with access to the gardens and private bars); and the small Wing Room for business meetings. The charming restaurant, Fields, gives scenic views, and the menu offers many speciality dishes cooked at your table. Stone Manor is only 40 minutes from Birmingham, and is well situated to explore the Malvern Hills, the Severn Valley Railway and the city of Worcester. Golf is available in Kidderminster, while the hotel has its own putting green and croquet lawn. Dogs by arrangement. Price guide: £60–£100. Directions: Stone Manor is in the village of Stone, just outside Kidderminster on the A448 towards Bromsgrove.

MEADOW HOUSE
SEA LANE, KILVE, SOMERSET TA5 1EG
TEL: 027874 546

Meadow House is set in 8 acres of landscaped gardens containing a croquet lawn, stream and meadow in the foothills of the Quantocks. The hotel stands only a few minutes' walk from an unspoiled beach famous for its fossil formations, and the views extend as far as the Welsh coast beyond the Bristol Channel. Public rooms are well-proportioned and all rooms have been tastefully furnished with a host of extras, including mineral water, fresh flowers and Continental biscuits. French windows open onto the large south-facing terrace overlooking the garden, while in winter log fires blaze in the drawing room and billiards room. The small, but ever-changing menus are backed by an exceptional wine list of over 300 bins. The dining room has recently been extended to include a conservatory. Children over 9 welcome. Conference facilities for up to 16 people. Price guide: £100–£120 including dinner. Directions: Sea Lane runs from the A39 at Kilve to the sea. The hotel is on the left.

CONGHAM HALL COUNTRY HOUSE HOTEL

GRIMSTON, KING'S LYNN, NORFOLK PE32 1AH
TEL: 0485 600250 FAX: 0485 601191 TELEX: 81508 CHOTEL G

Built as a Georgian manor house, the Hall nestles serenely in 40 acres of paddocks, orchards and gardens, with its own cricket ground. The conversion from country house to luxury hotel has been done with careful regard to its original classic interior, but with additional modern luxuries such as a jacuzzi spa bath for guests. The elegant restaurant and boardroom for private dinner parties and conferences are both under the special care of Mr Clive Jackson whose enthusiasm for the finest cuisine is evident. The kitchen gardens provide most vegetables, and the herb gardens are internationally renowned. The choice of wines will delight even the most discerning palate. The hotel has a tennis court, swimming pool and croquet lawn within the grounds, and golf links nearby. An ideal base for visiting Sandringham and the nature reserves of West Norfolk. AA 3 Red Stars and Rosette, RAC 3 Stars, Blue Ribbon Award and BTA Commended. Kennels available. Price guide: £95. Directions: Congham Hall lies just off the A148 north-east of King's Lynn, on the road to Grimston.

KNIGHTS HILL HOTEL

KNIGHTS HILL VILLAGE, SOUTH WOOTTON, KING'S LYNN, NORFOLK PE30 3HQ
TEL: 0553 675566 FAX: 0553 675568 TELEX: 818118 KNIGHT G

Knights Hill is a community within a community. It is a restored farm complex set in 11 acres of parkland, surrounded by the rural and coastal beauty of West Norfolk, and is one of only three of its type in the country. Originally a 16th-century hunting lodge, the aptly named Rising Lodge became the centre of a thriving farm. The original cottage still adjoins the main house. Today Knights Hill provides a range of modern facilities, sympathetically developed from existing buildings. There is a rustic pub, The Farmer's Arms; a conference, exhibition and banqueting centre in the Knights Barn and a superb health and leisure club with temporary membership for hotel guests. The lodge and master bedrooms in the main house, the courtyard apartments and coach-house-style accommodation, complete a quadrangle of rooms around the duck pond. All types offer en suite facilities and the master bedrooms afford views over the gardens and across King's Lynn to the Wash. There is also a cricket pitch, an all-weather tennis court and a jogging circuit. Nearby are Sandringham, Holkham and Houghton Halls, wildlife reserves, golf courses and several fishing villages. Conference facilities for 50 people in the small barn and 400 in the great barn. Price guide: £79–£90. Directions: At intersection of A148 King's Lynn/Cromer roads and A149 King's Lynn/Hunstanton roads.

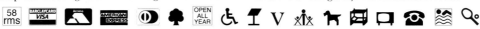

MILL HOUSE HOTEL

KINGHAM, OXFORDSHIRE OX7 6UH
TEL: 0608 658188 FAX: 0608 658492 TELEX: 849041 SHARET G TVH 003

Sparing no attention to detail, owners John and Valerie Barnett have lavished great care on this delightful former mill, to make it one of the more attractive hotels in the Cotswolds. It is set in 7 acres of gardens bordered by a trout stream. All the bedrooms are elegantly appointed, and most offer a superb view of the Cotswolds. There is a comfortable lounge with deep armchairs and sofas, open log fires and beamed ceiling. The restaurant provides cuisine of the highest standard; the menus are changed daily to take advantage of the very best of fresh, seasonal produce. The hotel is enhanced by beautiful flower arrangements and fragrant pot pourri which scents the rooms and hallways. With the whole of the historic Cotswolds at your doorstep, Mill House makes an ideal place from which to explore the multitude of quaint villages in this region, as well as Blenheim Palace and Stratford-upon-Avon. BTA Commended and AA 3 Stars. Welcomes children over 5. Price guide: £73–£103. Directions: From the A40/M40 westbound towards Cheltenham, turn right at roundabout towards Burford, through Chipping Norton. The hotel is then signposted.

BUCKLAND-TOUT-SAINTS

KINGSBRIDGE, DEVON TQ7 2DS
TEL: 0548 853055 FAX: 0548 856261

Buckland-Tout-Saints, a 17th-century manor house built in 1690 by Sir John Southcote, stands in a tranquil setting of 6 acres of gardens and woodland, with panoramic views of the magnificent Devonshire countryside. This gracious house is one of the finest examples of Queen Anne architecture to be found in the south west of England. The manor house has been lovingly restored, retaining period features such as oak panelling and polished wooden floors. The bedrooms are individually and tastefully furnished, many with fine antiques. Some have four-poster beds.

The elegant restaurant serves the best of modern British cuisine complemented by an extensive wine list. This award-winning hotel is an ideal base for touring Devon: Dartmouth, Totnes and Dartmoor are some of the notable places of interest to visit. The hotel has a helipad, croquet lawn and putting green; birdwatching, riding, fishing, clay pigeon shooting, ballooning and helicopter safaris can all be arranged. Children over 8 are welcome. Price guide: £110–£175. Directions: Buckland-Tout-Saints is signposted from the A381 between Totnes and Kingsbridge.

FALLOWFIELDS

SOUTHMOOR, KINGSTON BAGPUIZE, OXON OX13 5BH
TEL: 0865 820416 FAX: 0865 820629 TELEX: 83388

Originally part of the Kingston Estate, Fallowfields was once the home of the Begum Aga Khan and dates back over 300 years. It has been in private hands for about a century and has been extended during that time. Now it presents an early Victorian Gothic southern aspect and a formidable late Victorian northern elevation. It is set in 12 acres of grounds, two of which are given over to formal gardens and prolific vegetable and herb gardens. Proprietor, Mrs Alison Crowther, makes good use of their produce for her imaginative, home-produced fare. Personal attention is assured in this intimate establishment which has a small heated outdoor swimming pool plus a croquet lawn and tennis facilities.

Horse-riding, fishing, golf and, for the more adventurous, wind-surfing and water-skiing are available nearby. Situated 10 miles to the west of Oxford, Fallowfields is an ideal centre for touring. It is convenient for Stratford, the Cotswolds, Bath and Bristol. The surrounding Vale of the White Horse, named after the White Horse at Uffington, carved out of the chalk downs in pre-Saxon times, is worth exploring too. October to March – weekend houseparties of four or more people only. Dogs by prior arrangement. Price guide: £54–£58. Directions: Entrance from A420 Oxford to Swindon at Kingston Bagpuize west end.

COBWEBS COUNTRY HOUSE & RESTAURANT

LECK, COWAN BRIDGE, NR KIRKBY LONSDALE, LANCASHIRE LA6 2HZ
TEL: 05242 72141 FAX: 05242 72141

Cobwebs is a delightful country house fronted by a cobbled forecourt and set in 4 acres of beautiful countryside between the Lake District and the unspoiled Yorkshire Dales. Anyone staying at Cobwebs is guaranteed a warm welcome from hosts Yvonne and Paul Kelly, with personal old-fashioned courtesy. Guests may dine table d'hôte in the 20-seater conservatory dining room, which overlooks the fells. Yvonne firmly believes in using the very best ingredients carefully prepared, to create exciting and inventive menus. Paul has a well-stocked cellar offering a selection of wines from reasonably priced houses to the finest vintages from the world's greatest vineyards. The five en suite bedrooms are each individually furnished to provide both comfort and style and all have views of the surrounding Leck Fell. Cobwebs' highly successful Gourmet Evenings, which include a seven-course dinner and five classic wines, take place once a month. Salmon fishing and golf are just two of the many pursuits available in the area. Welcomes children over 12. Closed January and February. Price guide: £85 including dinner. Directions: Leck is just to the north of the A65 at Cowan Bridge.

HIPPING HALL

COWAN BRIDGE, KIRKBY LONSDALE, LANCASHIRE LA6 2JJ
TEL: 05242 71187

Set in 4 acres of walled gardens, 17th-century Hipping Hall lies 2 miles from Kirkby Lonsdale on the edge of the Dales and South Lakeland. It has five double rooms and two cottage apartments. There is an informal bar in the conservatory and guests dine together at one table, looked after by the owners Ian Bryant and Jocelyn Ruffle in the style of an informal country-house party. All dishes are freshly prepared by Jocelyn from home-grown and local produce. Open as a hotel from 1 March–17 November, Hipping Hall is available for private house parties in Spring and Autumn for groups of up to 14 people. Each party is planned to suit the guests' needs and ends with a Champagne brunch. The Hall is ideally situated for exploring the Lake District, the Yorkshire Dales and the Forest of Bowland. Welcomes children over 12. Price guide: £58–£68. Directions: Hipping Hall lies on the A65 (M6/Junction 36) 2 miles from Kirkby Lonsdale towards Settle.

THE OLD RECTORY

CLAUGHTON, LANCASTER LA2 9LA
TEL: 05242 21455

Set in the heart of the picturesque Lune Valley, this 17th-century listed building is bordered by sweeping lawns and a sparkling brook. Of the 12 en suite rooms, five are split-level studios with spiral staircases and ten have jacuzzi baths. In the Regency dining room, connoisseurs will appreciate the freshly prepared international cuisine with lightly cooked vegetables and meats cooked till just pink (just tell the owners if you prefer your food well-done). The Old Rectory can cater for all types of residential or day conferences combining an ideal location with elegant surroundings. Banqueting facilities are also available where guests can dine in splendour. The hotel arranges regular Champagne breaks and gourmet evenings. Local facilities include clay pigeon shooting and fishing. Brontë country, and the historic city of Lancaster are nearby too. RAC 3 Star 'R' Merit, ETB 4 Crowns. Children over 8 are welcome. Price guide: £65–£75. Directions: Five miles from Junction 34 off M6, on A683 to Kirkby Lonsdale.

HOPE END HOTEL

HOPE END, LEDBURY, HEREFORDSHIRE HR8 1JQ
TEL: 0531 3613

Set in 40 acres of wooded parkland, this very individual small Georgian hotel (the childhood home of Elizabeth Barrett Browning) provides total peace and an opportunity to relax and unwind in lovely rural surroundings. There are nine furnished bedrooms, all fully en suite and tranquil in the absence of TV. Antiques and interesting paintings abound. You will be tempted by the award-winning English country cooking of proprietress Patricia Hegarty. The menu is based on superb organically grown produce from the hotel's 1 acre walled garden, and local fish and meat. Choose from an outstanding wine list of over 150 labels. Who can resist the delicate sauces, the wealth of fresh vegetables and mouthwatering traditional puddings? Nearby: the Cotswolds and Wales; three beautiful rural counties full of pretty villages. An ideal centre for touring. Closed from end of November to end of February. AA Rosette. Price guide: £106–£132. Directions: 2 miles north of Ledbury, just beyond Wellington Heath.

HALEY'S HOTEL AND RESTAURANT

SHIRE OAK ROAD, HEADINGLEY, LEEDS, WEST YORKSHIRE LS6 2DE
TEL: 0532 784446 FAX: 0532 753342

This hotel is located on a tree-lined lane in a quiet suburb of Leeds within walking distance of the Yorkshire Cricket Club's home ground. A Victorian house which opened as a hotel in July 1990, the interior has been skilfully fashioned by a leading interior designer. All 22 rooms are individual and, in addition to offering the facilities expected in a high standard of hotel, Haley's provides more personal touches: a supply of Harrogate toffee, a shoe-cleaning service and suppers for latecomers. Modern English cuisine comes courtesy of up-and-coming chef, Andrew Foster, who prepares a daily choice of table d'hôte, à la carte and menu gastronomique. The staff play an important part in setting the high standard in this hotel, working to promote an elegant atmosphere reminiscent of the Victorian age, combined with the personal attention of a prestigious club. Conference services for up to 20 are offered in the air-conditioned Bramley Room. Leeds city centre is 2 miles distant. Price guide: £108. Directions: Shire Oak Road is off the main Otley road (A660) which forms the main route from the city centre to Otley, Ilkley and Leeds/Bradford Airport.

TIME OUT HOTEL

15 ENDERBY ROAD, BLABY, LEICESTER LE8 3GD
TEL: 0533 787898 FAX: 0533 771154

This early Victorian doctor's house, converted into a modern comfortable hotel, provides an ideal venue for the business traveller or those seeking peace and tranquillity. The croquet lawn, lily pond and regular summer barbecues entice guests into the gardens while the bar and lounge are havens for a convivial drink or relaxing read. The bedrooms are all delightfully furnished and extremely cosy. There is a wonderful choice of seasonal, fresh produce on the menu with an extensive, yet reasonably priced, wine list to complement your meal. The surroundings and decor make the function rooms ideal for receptions, meetings and conferences with seating for up to 40. The hotel has excellent leisure facilities including a pool, sauna, solarium, gym and jacuzzi plus snooker and a television lounge. In the surrounding region guests can explore Belvoir Castle, Charnwood Forest and Leicester Cathedral. Sporting interests catered for include football, cricket, top-class rugby, horse-racing and motor-racing. Special weekend Leisure Breaks available. Price guide: £72. Directions: Ideally situated 4 miles from Leicester, 2 miles from the M1 (Junction 21) on B582.

THE QUORN COUNTRY HOTEL

66 LEICESTER ROAD, QUORN, LEICESTERSHIRE LE12 8BB
TEL: 0509 415050 FAX: 0509 415557 TELEX: 347166

The privately owned Quorn Country Hotel stands in 4 acres of landscaped gardens and parkland leading to the River Soar. A magnificent reception hall, with a Minster fireplace, panelled walls, mahogany staircase and oil paintings, is a clear indication of the standard and comfort of this fine hotel. The public rooms are spaciously welcoming, furnished with well-chosen antiques. The bedrooms are equipped with a great attention to detail. Particular emphasis is given to the enjoyment of food, with both the Orangery and the Shires Restaurants enjoying an enviable reputation with the local community. The pride, care and attention associated with the cuisine is matched by the quality of the glazed elegance of the Orangery Restaurant where the subdued lighting and hand-painted murals make it the place to be . . . and be seen. Alternatively the cosy atmosphere of the Shires Restaurant with its traditional alcoves and low beamed ceilings provides a perfect setting for that more intimate occasion. RAC Merit awards for excellence, comfort, service and cuisine. Price guide: £97–125. Directions: The hotel is situated alongside the A6 between Loughborough and Leicester, just five miles off the M1.

CHILSTON PARK COUNTRY HOUSE

SANDWAY, LENHAM, MAIDSTONE, KENT ME17 2BE
TEL: 0622 859803 FAX: 0622 858588 TELEX: 966154 CHILPK G

Chilston Park Country House, a magnificent Grade I listed mansion in its own secluded 250 acres of Kent parkland, is one of the most luxurious hotels in England. Built originally in the 13th century, remodelled in the 18th century and now elegantly and sensitively refurbished, the hotel retains the graciousness of a bygone era, enhanced by the lighting, at dusk each day, of 200 candles. The elegant marble hall and drawing room offer guests the opportunity to relax while admiring the treasure trove of antiques that fill the entire building. All the bedrooms are luxuriously and individually furnished, and the three dining rooms serve the best of English cuisine complemented by an outstanding wine list. There are facilities available for senior-level management meetings for those participants requiring peace and security. In keeping with the traditions of a country house, a wide variety of sporting activities are available nearby. Price guide: £93.50–£176. Directions: Take Junction 8 off the M20, then A20 to Lenham Station. Turn left into Boughton Road. Over the crossroads and M20; Chilston Park is on the left.

LEWTRENCHARD MANOR
LEWDOWN, NR OKEHAMPTON, DEVON EX20 4PN
TEL: 0566 83256 FAX: 0566 83332

This attractive 17th-century manor house, set in 11 acres of magnificent grounds which include a lake, has been sensitively and imaginatively restored. Warm oak panelling and vast fireplaces ensure the manor is cool in summertime and warm and friendly in winter. Comfortable chairs, antique furniture and paintings provide an ideal atmosphere of peace and relaxation. Spacious and elegant bedrooms lead off an enormous and beautiful gallery and give magnificent views over the Devon countryside. The splendid panelled restaurant overlooking the wisteria-clad courtyard, has a fine reputation throughout the West Country for its French classic-style cuisine. Trout fishing, shooting and clay pigeon shooting are available on the 1,000-acre Lewtrenchard Estate. Nearby leisure facilities include horse-riding or even flying microlight aircraft. Dartmoor is close by, as well as Lydford Gorge, Plymouth and Exeter. The hotel has conference facilities for up to 60 delegates. Children of 8 and over are welcome; dogs by arrangement. Price guide: £90–£130. Directions: The hotel is clearly signposted from the A30 at Lewdown between Okehampton and Launceston.

HORSTED PLACE

LITTLE HORSTED, UCKFIELD, EAST SUSSEX TN22 5TS
TEL: 0825 75581 FAX: 0825 75459 TELEX: 95548

In the past, the Queen and members of the Royal Family have been frequent guests at Horsted Place. This is a truly grand hotel, splendidly furnished. The three bedrooms and 14 suites all have king-sized beds, bathrooms to the highest standards, and are fully equipped. Every room has outstanding views across the gardens to the Sussex Downs. The finest English and French cuisine, artistically presented, is served in the Pugin dining room and there is an extensive wine cellar. The staff provide a mixture of genuine friendliness and impeccable, unobtrusive service. Horsted Place is now able to offer its guests reduced rate green fees for the two new and prestigious courses at the adjacent East Sussex National Golf Club, where North American playing conditions are available to the keen golfer. Closed first week in January. Children over 7 welcome. Price guide: £125. Directions: On the A26, between Lewes and Uckfield.

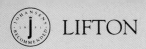

THE ARUNDELL ARMS

LIFTON, DEVON PL16 0AA
TEL: 0566 84666 FAX: 0566 84494

A 250 year-old former coaching inn near Dartmoor, The Arundell Arms is one of England's best-known sporting hotels. Americans travel 3,000 miles to fish the hotel's 20 miles of private waters on the River Tamar for salmon, trout and sea trout. The Arundell has a resident fishing instructor, a former Welsh Open fly-casting champion, Roy Buckingham. Also famous as a shooting lodge, European guests book for the shooting season a year ahead. The hotel takes great pride in the cuisine prepared by French-trained chef, Philip Burgess, formerly with *L'Ecu de France*, London. The extensive menu covers three pages, the wine list more! The Arundell exudes considerable old-world charm, and is a splendid base for visits to the historic houses and gardens, the moors and the quaint fishing villages of Devon and Cornwall. Yet, only 45 minutes' drive from Exeter and Plymouth, it is ideal for the business executive; there is a self-contained conference suite available. Price guide: £83. Directions: Lifton is on the A30 between Okehampton and Launceston.

ROWLEY MANOR

LITTLE WEIGHTON, NR HULL, NORTH HUMBERSIDE HU20 3XR
TEL: 0482 848248 FAX: 0482 849900

This gracious Georgian Manor built in 1621 was once the rectory to St Peter's Church. It was bought in 1928 by a shipping magnate who installed panelling by Grinling Gibbons in the study and a unique water temple in the garden. The croquet lawn and giant outdoor chess board further add to guests' enjoyment of the 15 acres of grounds. All rooms enjoy superb views and the restaurant offers delightful country cooking supported by a comprehensive wine list. Owners: Mario and Christine Ando. Price guide: £60–£80. Directions: Located between North Cave and Beverley near the M62.

THE ABBEY COURT

20 PEMBRIDGE GARDENS, LONDON W2 4DU
TEL: 071–221 7518 FAX: 071–792 0858 TELEX: 262167 ABBEYCT

The Abbey Court in Kensington is a Victorian town house that has been sympathetically renovated and restored to its former splendour. Its 22 bedrooms, furnished with antiques, are individually designed to cater for the varied tastes of their guests; they range from a four-poster in an imposing room to a single room with the feel of a country cottage. Italian marble bathrooms with whirlpool baths, showers and heated towel rails are standard features, as is the trouser press, hair dryer and towelling robe. A full secretarial service is available. There is a small reception room but no restaurant; instead there is 24-hour room service with snacks and drinks always available. A delicious Continental breakfast comprising freshly squeezed juice, home-made muesli and a choice of teas is served in guests' rooms each morning. The Abbey Court is just minutes away from the shops, restaurants and antique markets of Kensington and is a 10-minute taxi ride from Harrods. Heathrow is 40 minutes' drive away. Welcomes children over 12. Price guide: £110. Directions: Situated 1 minutes' walk from Notting Hill Gate tube station (central, circle and district lines).

BASIL STREET HOTEL

8 BASIL STREET, KNIGHTSBRIDGE, LONDON SW3 1AH
TEL: 071–581 3311 FAX: 071–581 3693 TELEX: 28379

The Basil feels less like an hotel and more like a home – an English country house in the heart of London, with all the atmosphere that brings: charm as well as efficiency, seclusion and privacy, and genuine care for the comfort of guests. The Basil is situated in an exclusive corner of Knightsbridge, on the threshold of both London's most exclusive residential area and its most enticing shopping district – 191 paces from Harrods and 89 paces from Harvey Nichols. The Basil is filled with valuable English and oriental antiques, carpets, tapestries, furniture, mirrors, plates,

objets d'art and paintings. It is large enough to provide all the services of a first-class hotel, yet not so large as to become impersonal. All bedrooms are individually furnished and decorated, different in shape and style but similar in comfort. There is a lovely dining room, a coffee shop, wine bar, and a lounge reserved for ladies only. Dogs by arrangement. Price guide: £94–£143. A few yards from a multi-storey car park, bus station and Knightsbridge underground.

THE BEAUFORT

33 BEAUFORT GARDENS, LONDON SW3 1PP
TEL: 071–584 5252 FAX: 071–589 2834 TELEX: 929200

Named 'one of the best hotels in the world', The Beaufort, owned by TV presenter Diana Wallis, is home to both the experienced traveller and the London first-timer. Unparalleled service and a genuine warmth and comfort are achieved through personal charm and great style. Just 100 yards from Harrods, The Beaufort is an oasis of peace and tranquillity. The ambience is truly one of a country house where guests are given their own front door key to come and go as they please. Features unique to The Beaufort show real hospitality, with all food and drinks from the 24-hour bar included in the price of a room, as is a personal laundry service. All the 28 air-conditioned bedrooms are furnished with the finest English chintzes and wallpapers. The collection of over 400 original English floral watercolours is the largest in the world. With brandy, fruit, chocolates and shortbread all in the rooms, and breakfast served there on fine Wedgwood bone china, you may be tempted to stay forever. Closed 22 December to 2 January. Price guide: £160–£220. Directions: From Harrods exit of Knightsbridge tube station, take third turning on the left.

CANNIZARO HOUSE

WEST SIDE, WIMBLEDON COMMON, LONDON SW19 4UF
TEL: 081–879 1464 FAX: 081–879 7338 TELEX: 9413837

On your next visit to London, why not indulge yourself and experience the charm of an English country house; at Cannizaro House you have the best of all worlds. This imposing house, dating from Georgian times, looks out on a spacious park and delightful gardens. It is tranquil and restful, yet is only a few miles away from the hustle and bustle of Central London. The restaurant offers the finest in classic modern cuisine; menus are changed seasonally and the wine cellar includes vintages from every respected château and, of course, Champagne from every house. Alternatively, the hotel offers a selection of private dining rooms ranging from an oak-panelled room for an intimate dinner to the magnificent Viscount Melville Suite, perfect for larger parties. Cannizaro House is also an ideal place for exclusive conferences and meetings. All bedrooms, including some with four-poster beds, and several suites are individually furnished and offer every comfort expected in a luxury hotel. By prior arrangement, children over 8 are welcome. Price guide: £95. Directions: Cannizaro House stands opposite Wimbledon Common. The nearest tube and British Rail station is Wimbledon.

HALCYON

81 HOLLAND PARK, LONDON W11 3RZ
TEL: 071–727 7288 FAX: 071–229 8516 TELEX: 266721

This de luxe establishment echoes the graciousness of the *belle époque* era with its pastel colour-scheme, specially commissioned paintings by up-and-coming artists, fresh flowers in the bedrooms and 24-hour room service. Each of the bedrooms has a truly individual style. There is an Arabian suite, which features hand-painted murals of Arabian scenes, and rooms with an oriental, chintz and floral influence. They are all air-conditioned, have satellite colour TV, in-house video, hair dryers, refrigerated room bars, and safes. Some of the en suite, Italian marble bathrooms have jacuzzis; all are stocked with complimentary Molton Brown toiletries. The Kingfisher Restaurant, hand-stencilled with pictures of foliage to create an out-of-doors atmosphere, provides imaginative cuisine complemented by a fine wine list. Situated in Holland Park, one of London's most fashionable areas, the Halcyon is well placed for visits to many historic sites and for enjoying the city's nightlife. The hotel can arrange for theatre, cinema and concert tickets for guests. Weekend breaks, which include dinner, chocolates, wine, flowers and newspapers: £310. Price guide: £250. Directions: From Holland Park tube station, turn right. Past two sets of traffic lights; hotel is on the left.

THE HOWARD

TEMPLE PLACE, STRAND, LONDON WC2R 2PR
TEL: 071–836 3555 FAX: 071–379 4547 TELEX: 268047

Situated where the City meets the West End, The Howard Hotel is ideal for business and leisure. With a decor that echoes the grace of yesteryear, the hotel's interiors are charming. Guests here experience first-class accommodation, service and cuisine. The hotel has beautifully appointed bedrooms and suites, many of which afford lovely views across the River Thames. Some of the furniture features French marquetry; the bathrooms are finished in marble. Every room is air-conditioned, has satellite television, a fridge-bar and 24-hour room service. The elegant Temple Bar provides the perfect location for a relaxing cocktail or an aperitif before enjoying the fine French cuisine in the famous Quai d'Or Restaurant with its unusual domed ceiling and renaissance decor. The hotel has a variety of suites and conference rooms which can cater for up to 120 people. Full secretarial support services are available and the rooms are equally good for private functions, dinner parties, luncheons, conferences and meetings. Price guide: £220. Directions: 20 miles from Heathrow; about 1 mile from Charing Cross (tube and BR station).

THE PORTLAND BLOOMSBURY HOTEL
7 MONTAGUE STREET, LONDON WC1B 5BP
TEL: 071-323 1717 FAX: 071-636 6498

Small can be beautiful, as this charming hotel in the fashionable area of Bloomsbury proves. The Portland Bloomsbury is a new 5 Crown hotel run under the close personal direction of manager, Ian Russell-Jarvie. Retaining many features from the original Regency building, a marble-floored entrance leads into a sitting room with a wealth of paintings and antiques. Beyond that, a petite but pretty garden backing onto the British Museum provides a relaxing sanctuary after a day in the city. The 27 en suite bedrooms combine the old and the new – Regency furnishings, antiques and all modern facilities; 24-hour room service is provided. Italian-style cuisine is served in the hotel's restaurant, open from breakfast to late evening – pastas, grilled meat and fish and sumptuous desserts. Close to Russell Square, the hotel is convenient for both the City and the West End. Covent Garden and theatreland are just a short walk away and staff will happily assist guests in the booking of tickets. Conference facilities cater for up to 12 people. Special weekend rates are also offered. Price guide: £95–£105. Directions: Russell Square tube station is on the Piccadilly Line with a direct link to Heathrow Airport.

LOWER SLAUGHTER MANOR

LOWER SLAUGHTER, NR BOURTON-ON-THE-WATER, GLOUCESTERSHIRE GL54 2HP
TEL: 0451 20456 FAX: 0451 22150 TELEX: 437287

This delightful old manor house, crafted from Cotswold stone with origins dating back a thousand years, is an ideal retreat where one can relax in pleasant surroundings in well-kept gardens. Public rooms are elegant with fine paintings and antiques, and log fires blaze in winter. Exceptionally spacious bedrooms offer all modern comforts while retaining historic charm and elegance. The restaurant serves traditional English/French cuisine using seasonal local produce; the wine cellar provides a wide selection of fine wines and service is friendly and professional. Recreational facilities include a sauna and solarium, croquet lawn and an all-weather tennis court. Trout fishing is available in the local river. The peaceful setting and location of the hotel make it an ideal base for touring the Cotswolds and surrounding areas. Conference facilities for up to 12 in a self-contained conference suite with adjoining syndicate room. Welcomes children over 8. Price guide: £114–£185. Directions: Follow signs to Lower Slaughter from A429. The manor is on the right as you enter Lower Slaughter Village.

THE FEATHERS AT LUDLOW

BULL RING, LUDLOW, SHROPSHIRE SY8 1AA
TEL: 0584 875261 FAX: 0584 876030 TELEX: 35637

This Grade I listed building has a richly decorated half-timbered front elevation and is one of the best-known timber-framed buildings in the country. An inn since 1670, Jan Morris wrote of it: 'I dare say it is the most handsome inn in the world. Everybody knows of it. It is one of the prime images of Old England, portrayed on posters and brochures wherever tourism is known'. The hotel has a wealth of antiques and old beams, and six private suites. Four magnificent new bedrooms have been added recently. The Richard III Restaurant was once the kitchen, while the Banqueting Room in the style of a baronial hall has been named the Prince Charles, in honour of the present Prince of Wales. The hotel boasts an open-air restaurant for summer dining plus a superb billiards room. The Feathers is ideally situated for touring the Marches and historic areas of England and Wales. Director: Osmond Edwards. Manager: Peter Nash. BTA Commended. AA 3 Star. Egon Ronay First Class. Price guide: £86–£120. Directions: Ludlow is on the A49 north of Hereford (access from M5 via Worcester).

PASSFORD HOUSE HOTEL

MOUNT PLEASANT LANE, LYMINGTON, HAMPSHIRE SO41 8LS
TEL: 0590 682398 FAX: 0590 683494

Passford House Hotel, the former home of Lord Arthur Cecil, is situated on the edge of the New Forest in 9 acres of delightful gardens and is a mecca for sports enthusiasts. The hotel possesses a superb leisure centre, sporting a spa pool, solarium, gym, and swimming pools, both inside and outside in a magnificent sunken garden. The bedrooms, one of which is furnished with a majestic four-poster, provide guests with every modern comfort and luxury. The elegant restaurant offers an imaginative and tempting menu complemented by a choice of fine wines. Situated just 2 miles from the Georgian town of Lymington, the hotel is an ideal base for sailing, fishing and walking. Just a short drive away are Beaulieu, the cathedral cities of Winchester and Salisbury, and the ferry to the Isle of Wight. Price guide: £95. Directions: At Lymington leave A337 at the Tollhouse Inn, then take first turning right; the hotel is found on your right.

SOUTH LAWN HOTEL

LYMINGTON ROAD, MILFORD-ON-SEA, LYMINGTON, HAMPSHIRE SO41 0RF
TEL: 0590 643911 FAX: 0590 644820

This charming country house hotel has been owned since 1971 by Ernst and Jennifer Barten, who are tireless in their endeavour to provide a high standard of accommodation. The hotel has 24 luxury en suite bedrooms, all with many modern conveniences including hair dryer and trouser press. The lounges are comfortably furnished with chintz armchairs. In the spacious dining room, which seats up to 80, guests are offered a menu featuring a wide choice of English and Continental dishes. Situated very near the coast, South Lawn is also conveniently placed for the New Forest with all that it has to offer. There are opportunities for windsurfing at Keyhaven, fishing, golf and sailing, and Beaulieu Motor Museum is also nearby. AA 3 Stars, and Egon Ronay recommended. Closed for 2 weeks at Christmas. Welcomes children over 7. Price guide: £75. Directions: Milford is on the B3058 (via A337 between Christchurch and Lymington).

THE STANWELL HOUSE HOTEL

HIGH STREET, LYMINGTON, HAMPSHIRE SO41 9AA
TEL: 0590 677123 FAX: 0590 677756 TELEX: 477463 G

General Wolfe spent his last night on English soil in this now extended and modernised Georgian house. Stanwell House, set within an acre of charming walled garden in the heart of Lymington, provides traditional comforts in the style of a small country house hotel. The 35 bedrooms and the public rooms are peaceful and elegant. The menus of the Railings Restaurant combine table d'hôte and à la carte, and are prepared from fresh fish, meats, poultry and vegetables bought directly from local markets. The wine list offers over 150 labels including vintages of the greatest vineyards. Behind the restaurant is a delightful, paved garden, opening into the Garden Suite – an ideal setting for wedding receptions or small executive meetings for up to 20 delegates. The Stanwell House Hotel lies close to the attractive quay, convenient for sailing on the Solent, investigating the seashore nature reserves or exploring Britain's oldest common forest, curiously named the New Forest. Price guide: £80. Directions: Follow signs to town centre and head towards the quay. The hotel is on the left ⅓ of the way down.

PARKHILL HOTEL

BEAULIEU ROAD, LYNDHURST, NEW FOREST, HAMPSHIRE SO43 7FZ
TEL: 0703 282944 FAX: 0703 283268

This is a graceful 18th-century manor house in the New Forest where you will wake to the sound of bird-song. Parkhill nestles in 12 acres of glorious parkland, ½ a mile from the nearest road. Situated in the grounds of a Roman fort, the hotel has a chequered and well-documented history, having been a hunting lodge, a school and a private home to different individuals, including the Duke of Clarence around 1740. It now provides its guests with peace and relaxation amid the highest standards of comfort, cuisine and service. There are 20 fully equipped bedrooms and the public rooms are spacious and tastefully furnished. As well as the Rawnsley Room with conference facilities for up to 45, the library seats eight people and may be used as an ancillary room or for private dining. There is a heated outdoor swimming pool and a lake in the grounds. Deer can be seen grazing in the grounds at eventide. You can also test your skill at croquet on the lawn. Price guide: £92–£112. Directions: From Lyndhurst take the B3056 to Beaulieu. Parkhill is 1 mile on your right.

THE LYNTON COTTAGE HOTEL

NORTH WALK, LYNTON, NORTH DEVON EX35 6ED
TEL: 0598 52342 FAX: 0598 52597

Set in magnificent unspoiled countryside, the Lynton Cottage Hotel has superlative views over Lynmouth Bay. Dating back to the 17th century, the hotel offers guests period charm and atmosphere plus every modern luxury. Blazing log fires add to the comfort of the elegantly furnished public rooms and the bedrooms are individually and tastefully furnished in traditional English style at its best. Some have special features such as four-poster beds. David Lamprell, the restaurant's award-winning chef, combines an imaginative menu with a well-chosen wine list.

Horse-riding, clay pigeon shooting, golf and salmon fishing are all available locally, and the hotel is an ideal base for visiting beauty spots like Exmoor National Park and the Valley of Rocks. Special breaks, such as mystery whodunnit and champagne weekends, are available throughout the year. Conference facilities are available for up to 18 participants. Price guide: £76–£116. Directions: Turn off the M5, take the A39 to Porlock then drive through Porlock to Lynton. The hotel is on the North Walk in Lynton.

FREDRICK'S HOTEL & RESTAURANT

SHOPPENHANGERS ROAD, MAIDENHEAD, BERKSHIRE SL6 2PZ
TEL: 0628 35934 FAX: 0628 771054 TELEX: 849966

'Putting people first' has been the guiding philosophy behind the creation of this sumptuously equipped hotel which is set in 2 acres of beautiful gardens, overlooking the greens of Maidenhead Golf Course. The idea has been to create something out-of-the-ordinary yet in the best standards of European tradition. The 37 comfortable bedrooms and suites are fully equipped with every detail, and suites have their own patio garden or balcony. The public rooms, and the light airy Wintergarden, are quiet and comfortable. Fredrick's Restaurant, which is fully air-conditioned,

has received recognition from leading guides for many years. Frequently changing menus feature imaginative dishes served in elegant surroundings. An ideal place for conferences or social functions with a capacity from 10 to 150 persons in four air-conditioned function rooms with full secretarial facilities. Closed 24–30 December. Price guide: £135–£145. Directions: Leave M4 at exit 8/9, take A423 (M) and leave at first turning signed Cox Green/White Waltham. Turn left into Shoppenhangers Road; Fredrick's is on the right.

THE OLD BELL HOTEL

ABBEY ROW, MALMESBURY, WILTSHIRE SN16 0BW
TEL: 0666 822344 FAX: 0666 825145

Established by the Abbot of Malmesbury during the reign of King John as a place for his guests to refresh themselves, this Grade I listed building could well be England's oldest hotel. It lies on the edge of the Cotswolds, at the heart of the ancient town of Malmesbury, named capital by the Saxon, Athelstan, the first King of all England. Each of the 37 centrally heated bedrooms reflects the fascinating history of the building. The wine cellar of almost 200 fine wines from around the world enhances the traditional English menu, prepared from the very best local produce and served in the Edwardian dining room; this was added in 1908. Enclosed by mellow stone walls, adjacent to the Abbey, and with a gazebo set among shrubs and roses, is the traditional English garden – an idyllic setting for a wedding reception. Price guide: £80. Directions: Once in Malmesbury, head for the Abbey. The Old Bell is located next to the Abbey, with car parking at the rear.

WHATLEY MANOR

EASTON GREY, MALMESBURY, WILTSHIRE SN16 0RB
TEL: 0666 822888 FAX: 0666 826120 TELEX: 449380

An aura of luxury surrounds this Grade II listed manor, built around a central courtyard and standing in 12 peaceful acres on the banks of the Avon. All the bedrooms are individually furnished, largely in period style. A wealth of pine and oak panelling, plus the glow of log fires in winter, create a warm, mellow atmosphere in the lounge and drawing room; the dining room affords delightful views over the gardens. Private rooms are available for receptions and there are conference facilities for up to 20 delegates. The original saddle rooms have been converted into snooker and table-tennis rooms and there are many other leisure facilities including a sauna, solarium, jacuzzi and croquet lawn. Beyond the well-tended gardens, green paddocks run down to a peaceful stretch of the River Avon for which the hotel owns the fishing rights. The Cotswolds are within easy reach and historic cities in the surrounding area include Bath, Bristol, Wells and Cirencester. Price guide: £99–£115. Directions: Whatley Manor is on the B4040 between Easton Grey and Malmesbury.

THE COTTAGE IN THE WOOD HOTEL

HOLYWELL ROAD, MALVERN WELLS, WORCESTERSHIRE WR14 4LG
TEL: 0684 573487 FAX: 0684 560662 TELEX: 339342 ATTN COTTAGE

The hotel is set in 7 acres of thickly wooded grounds high on the Malvern Hills and affords sweeping 30-mile views across the Severn Valley to the Cotswolds Hills. Owned and run by John and Sue Pattin and family, the hotel was originally a Georgian dower house, once part of the Blackmore Park seat of Sir Thomas Hornyold and now comprises three buildings. The en suite bedrooms are split between the three with some in the main part of the hotel, four cottage-style bedrooms in Beech Cottage 75 yards away and the remainder being in the Coach House 100 yards walk from the main building. These all have sun-trap balconies or patios and the finest views. The menu here is essentially English and is complemented by an adventurous wine cellar with labels from Europe, Australia, America and Chile. An adaptable conference space caters for up to 14 delegates. Dogs welcome in outer buildings. Price guide: £72–£112. Directions: 3 miles south of Great Malvern on A449, turn into Holywell Road opposite Jet petrol station. Hotel is first on right.

THE THREE SWANS HOTEL

HIGH STREET, MARKET HARBOROUGH, LEICESTERSHIRE LE16 7NJ
TEL: 0858 466644 FAX: 0858 433101 TELEX: 342375

The Three Swans has changed little since the 18th century, even the present facade forms only a layer in the building's history. The Three Swans has been a coaching inn for 500 years. Charles I took refreshment here on the day before the Battle of Naseby in 1645 and, nearly 300 years later, the Duke of Windsor was brought to the inn following a hunting accident. Inside, guests will find evidence of tasteful, gentle refurbishment. The 37 bedrooms have all been completely renovated to a high standard, and two have their own sitting area. The hotel offers a variety of public rooms in which to relax in comfort. The restaurant has gained a reputation for excellent cuisine, with imaginative menus prepared by skilled and dedicated staff under the direction of head chef, Richard Payne. Excellent bar meals are available in the conservatory and lounge bar. Attractions near Market Harborough include Rockingham Castle, Althorpe (the family home of the Princess of Wales), and the Grand Union Canal. The hotel is only 30 miles from the NEC in Birmingham, and East Midlands and Birmingham airports. Price guide: £60–£81. Directions: Leave M1 at Junction 20 and take A427 for 12 miles to Market Harborough.

THE IVY HOUSE HOTEL

HIGH STREET, MARLBOROUGH, WILTSHIRE SN8 1HJ
TEL: 0672 515333 FAX: 0672 515338 TELEX: 449703 ATTN IVY

The Ivy House Hotel is an 18th-century listed building, set in a charming cobbled courtyard leading to a walled sun terrace. It has been imaginatively and tastefully restored by owners David Ball and Josephine Scott, with public rooms in a recently developed wing; the refurbished bedrooms remain in the main building. The elegant Palladian-style restaurant offers the best of English and French cuisine. The Ivy House also provides a small purpose-built meeting room facility for senior business executives. The hotel is an ideal base for touring the attractions of Wiltshire and the Cotswolds – Avebury, Stonehenge and the Marlborough Downs – with the cities of Bath and Salisbury only a short drive away. For the sports enthusiast fishing, golf and sailing are nearby and shooting can be arranged locally. Children over 12 welcome. Dogs by arrangement. Price guide: £71. Directions: The hotel is in Marlborough High Street, just off the A4 from Bath.

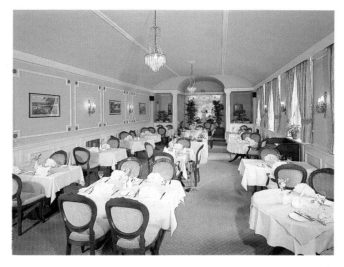

DANESFIELD HOUSE

MEDMENHAM, MARLOW, BUCKINGHAMSHIRE SL7 3ES
TEL: 0628 891010 FAX: 0628 890408

Opening in March 1991 is Danesfield House, a stunning Victorian Gothic property, which rests between Marlow and Henley, in 65 acres of idyllic grounds overlooking the River Thames. The 90 exquisitely furnished en suite bedrooms have two telephone lines each, in-house films and satellite TV channels plus a video. Service, though attentive, is not intrusive. The cuisine here is exceptional and there are four individually designed restaurants to choose from: Swedish, French, Brasserie and Loggia. The hotel's numerous facilities include a range of business services – personal computers, audio-visual aids, two conference rooms, a grand banqueting hall and a helipad – plus a boutique, baby-sitting service, complimentary minibus, archery, and temporary membership of local golf clubs. Shooting, riding, polo and gliding are also available nearby. The hotel arranges special events ranging from pub crawls to hot-air ballooning. Just a short drive from the hotel are the Chilterns and many pretty villages including Pangbourne, Goring-on-Thames and Hambleden. Price guide: £165–£215. Directions: Between M4 and M40 on the A4155 between Marlow and Henley-on-Thames.

JERVAULX HALL

NR MASHAM, RIPON, NORTH YORKSHIRE HG4 4PH
TEL: 0677 60235

Originally built as the manor house for the Earl of Ailesbury during the mid-1800s, the hotel is set in 8 acres of landscaped gardens and woodland and is adjacent to the ruined, 12th-century Jervaulx Abbey. Personally run by John and Margaret Sharp, the warmth of your welcome is guaranteed as is the high standard of cuisine. Fresh vegetables and soft fruits, local lamb and seasonally available game are included on the menu. To complement the food, there is a well-chosen wine list. The hotel's two reception rooms are comfortably furnished with antiques. Both have open fires which are lit in cooler weather. Situated at the edge of the Yorkshire Dales National Park, Jervaulx Hall is an ideal base for exploring the beautiful countryside. Middleham Castle, Bramham Park, Castle Howard and the cities of Harrogate (six times winner of the Britain in Bloom Award), Ripon and York are nearby. Open mid-March to mid-November. Price guide: £110–£120 (includes dinner). Directions: Between Masham and Middleham on A6108, adjacent to Jervaulx Abbey.

10 rms

RIBER HALL

MATLOCK, DERBYSHIRE DE4 5JU
TEL: 0629 582795 FAX: 0629 580475

A listed historical building, starred in its class, dating from the 1400s. On the borders of the Peak National Park in the peaceful backwater of Riber village, this luxurious Elizabethan manor house is set in its own grounds with a delightful walled garden and orchard. The finely furnished bedrooms with antique beds, mostly four-posters, are located around an attractive courtyard. Five have whirlpool baths. Acknowledged as an outstanding restaurant, Riber Hall offers an extensive wine list, game when in season and personal service in a relaxed and intimate atmosphere enhanced by fine Wedgwood china and cut glass. Conferences, wedding receptions and small dinner parties can be catered for in a beamed private room. Riber Hall enjoys peace, quiet and seclusion in the foothills of the Pennines. Five stately homes, including Chatsworth House and the Peak National Park, are nearby. Golf and riding are available, and the all-weather tennis court has a tennis-trainer ball machine. Price guide: £78–£120. Directions: 20 minutes from Junction 28 of M1, off A615 at Tansley to Riber.

FIFEHEAD MANOR

MIDDLE WALLOP, STOCKBRIDGE, HAMPSHIRE SO20 8EG
TEL: 0264 781565 FAX: 0264 781400

Some parts of Fifehead Manor are mediaeval while the foundations date back to the 11th century. It was originally part of the estates of the Saxon, Earl Godwin and, in its time, has been both a nunnery and family home. Nowadays, it is a comfortable hotel with 15 attractive bedrooms, some of which have been adapted for guests with disabilities. The cuisine is the responsibility of the capable and imaginative chef, Hans De Gier, and meals are served in the dining room (candle-lit in the evenings) which has two large, stone fireplaces. The hotel is ideally placed for visiting Salisbury and Winchester Cathedrals, Wilton House and Stonehenge. RAC and BTA Commended. Two-night breaks for two people sharing are available from November until Good Friday at £200. This price includes dinner. Dogs by arrangement. Closed 2 weeks at Christmas. Price guide: £75–£95. Directions: The manor is at the west end of the village on the A343.

PERITON PARK HOTEL

MIDDLECOMBE, NR MINEHEAD, SOMERSET TA24 8SW
TEL: 0643 706885 FAX: 0643 702698 TELEX: 42513 REF PP

A handsome country residence built in 1875, Periton Park is set in 32 acres of woodland, pastures and gardens in the heart of rural West Somerset. Spacious, elegantly decorated bedrooms give panoramic views over the parkland and countryside. Comfortable and welcoming, the public rooms are ideal for a quiet drink, or to relax with a good book or a game of cards. The menu is imaginative and varied, and there is always a vegetarian choice. Croquet and boules can be played in the hotel's grounds, and horses are available for experienced riders. Hunting, fishing and shooting – including clay pigeon – can be arranged during the season. Located at the edge of the Exmoor National Park, the hotel is near to the Quantock Hills and the beautiful Somerset and North Devon coast. The area is rich in historic buildings, craft centres and picturesque villages. Special breaks are available. Price guide: £75. Directions: Periton Park is situated on the left off the A39 just after Minehead, in the direction of Lynmouth and Porlock.

THE MILLER'S HOUSE HOTEL

MARKET PLACE, MIDDLEHAM, NORTH YORKSHIRE DL8 4NR
TEL: 0969 22630

Crossley and Judith Sunderland's hotel is an elegant Georgian house, just off the cobbled market square in the quiet village of Middleham, the heart of the Yorkshire Dales. Recently refurbished, the Miller's House commands splendid views from its elevated position. Middleham is a major racehorse training centre and has been home to three Grand National winners. Superb picnic hampers are provided for race meetings or trips out around the Dales and Herriot country. After a day out, guests can enjoy a candle-lit dinner in the restaurant, which offers French and English cuisine, complemented by an excellent wine list. Special gourmet wine-tasting weekends are regularly organised. York and Harrogate, plus racing, fishing and golf facilities, are within easy reach. Middleham Castle in the village was once the northern seat of Richard III. Also nearby are Bolton and Richmond Castles, Jervaulx Abbey and Castle Howard. Closed in January. Children over 10 welcome. Price guide: £60–£70. Directions: Take A684 to Bedale and Leyburn; the left turning immediately before Leyburn takes you to Middleham.

AYTON HALL

LOW GREEN, GREAT AYTON, NORTH YORKSHIRE TS9 6BW
TEL: 0642 723595 FAX: 0642 722149

Ayton Hall, the home of Melvin and Marian Rhodes, is a Grade II listed building of special architectural and historic interest. Built on foundations dating back to 1281, the Hall can claim strong connections with the famous Captain James Cook FRS. Ayton Hall is situated in 6 acres of landscaped gardens with archery, tennis, croquet and trapshooting within the grounds for the sports enthusiast. The bedrooms, all tastefully decorated and with splendid views over the unspoiled countryside, offer visitors every modern comfort. The elegant restaurant provides superb traditional English and international cuisine, with an emphasis on fresh produce from the kitchen gardens, combined with an extensive and imaginative wine list. The Captain's Table, a private dining room overlooking the floodlit lily pond, provides a perfect setting for dinner parties of up to 14, while the James Cook Room is available for small business meetings and conferences. The hotel is open all year. Special weekend breaks available. Price guide: £95–£125. Directions: Great Ayton is on the A173 south west of Guisborough, and is reached from Middlesbrough via the A172.

THE SPREAD EAGLE HOTEL

SOUTH STREET, MIDHURST, WEST SUSSEX GU29 9NH
TEL: 0730 816911 FAX: 0730 815668 TELEX: 86853 SPREAG G

Five hundred and fifty years of history surround the hotel – one of England's oldest. It was a tavern in 1430, later a famous coaching house, and the atmospheric influence of the mediaeval, Jacobean, Tudor and Georgian periods are beautifully preserved inside and out, with added luxury and 20th-century conveniences. The candle-lit dining room, with its huge inglenook fireplace and dark oak beams hung with traditional Sussex Christmas puddings, is a perfect setting for the classic and innovative cuisine. In all the airy bedrooms, many panelled and furnished with antiques, much thought has gone into the use of fabrics and furnishings. The garden has a secluded walled courtyard full of roses and clematis. The Spread Eagle is an ideal base for exploring the delights of Sussex, including Chichester Cathedral, Fishbourne Roman Palace and Downland Museum. Dogs welcome by arrangement. Price guide: £80–£170. Directions: Midhurst is on the A286 between Chichester and Milford.

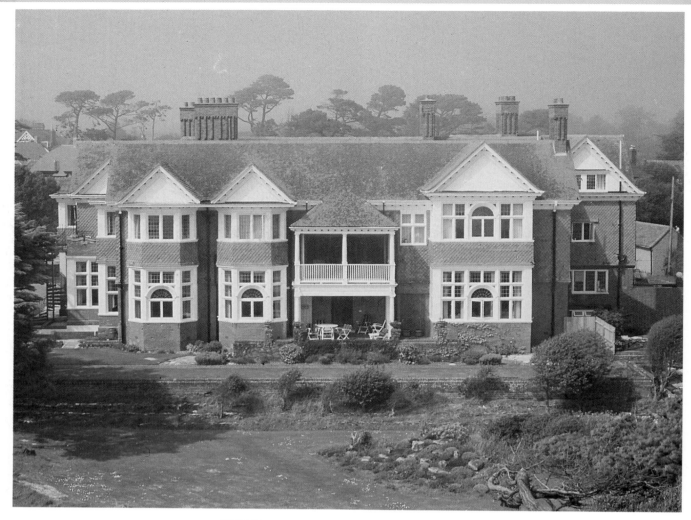

WESTOVER HALL

PARK LANE, MILFORD-ON-SEA, LYMINGTON, HAMPSHIRE SO41 0PT
TEL: 0590 643044 FAX: 0590 644490

This attractive country house hotel is situated in a beautiful location at the edge of the New Forest, overlooking the Solent and the Isle of Wight. At Westover Hall, which stands in its own gardens and has direct access to the beach, a peaceful and tranquil atmosphere has been cultivated. Most of the bedrooms, each individually decorated and furnished to meet the highest standard of comfort, have panoramic views over the open sea. Oak-panelled public rooms give an air of warmth and intimacy, as does the cosy lounge overlooking the sea. Chef, Phillippe Barthelemy, awarded a Michelin Star in France, prepares fine traditional French and English food for the exclusive restaurant. The elegant bar provides a comfortable setting in which guests may enjoy a drink. The hotel has conference facilities for up to 25 people. It is an ideal base for touring the New Forest and Hampshire and is convenient for the ferry to the Isle of Wight. Tennis court: 5 minutes' walk. Golf courses within 15 minutes' drive. Price guide: £75–£120. Directions: From Exit 1 (Cadham) of the M27, take the A337 towards Lymington. About 3 miles outside Lymington in the Bournemouth direction, take the B3058 to Milford-on-Sea. The hotel is at the end of the village overlooking the sea.

MOORE PLACE

THE SQUARE, ASPLEY GUISE, NR WOBURN, BEDFORDSHIRE MK17 8DW
TEL: 0908 282000 FAX: 0908 281888

This elegant Georgian mansion was built by Francis Moore in the tranquil Bedfordshire village of Aspley Guise in 1786. To the original house in the village square has been added a Victorian-style conservatory restaurant, and a collection of new bedrooms, creating a courtyard featuring a rock garden, lily pool and waterfall. In the locally acclaimed restaurant, the cooking is modern English, and there is a good wine selection. Vegetarian meals are always on the menu. The 54 en suite bedrooms have direct-dial telephones, colour television, tea/coffee making facilities and hair dryers. There are three private function rooms in the Georgian house catering for banquets and conferences. The rooms are traditionally decorated, and equipped with full audio-visual facilities. Moore Place is close to Woburn Abbey, Dunstable Downs, Whipsnade Zoo and the city of Milton Keynes. Price guide: £90–£140. Directions: Only 2 minutes' drive from Junction 13 of the M1 motorway, Moore Place is superbly located for both business and leisure.

THE BEACON COUNTRY HOUSE HOTEL

BEACON RD, MINEHEAD, SOMERSET TA24 5SD
TEL: 0643 703476 FAX: 0643 702050

The Beacon Country House Hotel, set in 20 acres and enjoying panoramic views, is an elegant Edwardian building which has undergone extensive refurbishment whilst retaining its original character and charm. The public rooms are tastefully furnished in relaxing shades of pink and green and boast open fires in less clement weather. Master chef Penny Fulcher-Smith offers an imaginative menu with great emphasis placed on the best of fresh local produce complemented by an extensive wine list. During the summer months, diners can also enjoy the unusual sight of badgers being fed on the lawns. The individually styled bedrooms are truly luxurious and combine every modern facility with the elegance of a bygone age. For the sports enthusiast, there is an open-air swimming pool in the grounds and adjacent to the hotel is a livery service. Beacon Country House .is an ideal base for touring the West Country and the unspoilt beauty of Exmoor. Shooting and riding breaks are also available by arrangement. Price guide: £60–£70. Directions: Leave the M5 at Junction 25, and drive to Minehead on A358. Continue along Townsend Road and Friday Street; right at T-junction, then second left at Blenheim Road, first left Martlett Road. At war memorial, straight over into Burgundy Road; round hairpin bend, hotel is at end of Beacon Road on right.

MONK FRYSTON HALL

MONK FRYSTON, LEEDS, NORTH YORKSHIRE LS25 5DU
TEL: 0977 682369 FAX: 0977 683544 TELEX: 556634

This mellow old manor house with its origins dating back to the Middle Ages, is of great architectural interest. The mullioned and transomed windows and the family coat of arms above the doorway are reminiscent of a more gracious age. From the Hall the terrace leads to the Italian gardens which overlook an ornamental lake. Purchased by the Duke of Rutland in 1954, the Hall has been transformed into a luxury hotel offering a combination of period elegance and the best in modern facilities. The bedrooms are spacious and extremely well appointed. Whilst savouring the traditional cuisine of the restaurant, guests can enjoy wonderful views of the terrace and park. Wedding receptions and dinner/dances are catered for in the oak-panelled Haddon Room with its splendid fireplace. The Rutland Room is available for conferences. An ideal venue for businessmen, tourists and those just wanting to relax. Within easy distance of York (16 miles), Leeds (14 miles) and Harrogate (18 miles). Price guide: £86–£100. Directions: 3 miles off the A1 on the A63 towards Selby in the centre of Monk Fryston.

THE KINGS ARMS INN

MONTACUTE, SOMERSET TA16 6UU
TEL: 0935 822513

This handsome, Elizabethan coaching inn, situated in one of Somerset's most unspoiled villages, is built, like many local houses, of Ham Stone, which has mellowed beautifully over the centuries. The atmosphere inside is very relaxed; the bedrooms are decorated in pretty pastel shades and the reception rooms are comfortable and inviting. The restaurant in the elegant Abbey Room has a very good reputation for its traditional English food, although some unusual dishes do crop up. Montacute House, one of the most important houses in the West Country, is nearby. It is a shining example of Tudor domestic architecture and has many tapestries, traditional English furniture, heraldic glass, plasterwork and panelling. Brympton d'Evercy, Sherborne Castle, Yeovilton Air Museum, Cricket St Thomas Wildlife Park and a butterfly park are all in the vicinity – and the sea is just a ½ hour's drive away. Price guide: £58–£75. Directions: The Kings Arms is 3½ miles from Yeovil on the A3088.

MANOR HOUSE HOTEL

MORETON-IN-MARSH, GLOUCESTERSHIRE GL56 0LJ
TEL: 0608 50501 FAX: 0608 51481 TELEX: 837151

This 16th-century manor house with beautiful gardens has been tastefully extended and restored to retain many of its historic features, such as a priest's hole and secret passages. The 38 well-appointed bedrooms have been individually decorated and furnished. The restaurant offers traditional English cuisine using only the freshest ingredients, and offers an excellent wine list. For the guest wishing to relax, leisure facilities include an indoor heated swimming pool, spa bath and sauna. For the sports enthusiast, tennis, golf, horse-riding and squash are all within easy reach. The spacious conference facilities of the hotel have been designed not to intrude upon the services offered to other hotel guests, while giving a pleasant setting combined with peace and modern facilities. The Manor House is the ideal base for touring, with an array of sights from the fabulous towns of Stratford-upon-Avon and Warwick to the historic centres of Cheltenham, Oxford and Bath. Price guide: £65–£122 including dinner. Directions: The hotel is located on the A429 Fosse Way near the junction of the A44 and A429 north of Stow-on-the-Wold.

LINDEN HALL HOTEL

LONGHORSLEY, MORPETH, NORTHUMBERLAND NE65 8XF
TEL: 0670 516611 FAX: 0670 88544 TELEX: 538224

This impressive Georgian mansion is approached via a private, mile-long drive, and seclusion is assured within its 300 acres of park and woodland. There is a dignified air about the gracious public rooms with their fine marble fireplaces, antiques and period features; the atmosphere, however, is always relaxed. The 45 bedrooms are individually and harmoniously furnished with tasteful fabrics and drapes. All have en suite bathrooms, in-house video and a host of thoughtful extras. In the elegant setting of the Dobson Restaurant, which affords views of the rugged coastline on one side and formal gardens on the other, meals are presented with style and are complemented by an outstanding wine list. A full range of audio-visual equipment is available for conferences, seminars and exhibitions. Other amenities at Linden Hall include sauna, solarium, hairdresser, beautician, shooting and a croquet lawn. Price guide: £105–£170. Directions: The hotel is on the A697 just north of Longhorsley.

POLURRIAN HOTEL

POLURRIAN COVE, MULLION, HELSTON, CORNWALL TR12 7EN
TEL: 0326 240421 FAX: 0326 240083

In a magnificent cliff-top position 300 feet above a secluded surfing beach, the Polurrian Hotel is situated in 12 acres of landscaped gardens. The views across to St Michael's Mount and Land's End are stunning. Owned and operated by the Francis family for 45 years, Polurrian offers an unrivalled range of leisure activities for all the family including the Leisure Club with its marbled, heated indoor swimming pool, solarium, sauna, gymnasium, health salon and children's playroom. There is also a heated outdoor swimming pool, plus tennis, snooker, croquet, squash and minigolf facilities. Also, the 18-hole Mullion Golf Course is only 2 miles away. The bedrooms are well-appointed and offer guests every modern luxury including baby-listening; accommodation is also available in self-catering apartments. In the restaurant you can enjoy fresh fish caught from the hotel's own boat. Kynance Cove, Lizard Point and Goonhilly Earth Station are some of the many places of interest to visit. ETB 4 Crowns. Open March to mid-December. Price guide: £103–£158 including dinner. Directions: From Helston, follow the signs A3083 to the Lizard, after 6 miles turn right onto the B3296 to Mullion.

ROOKERY HALL

WORLESTON, NR NANTWICH, CHESHIRE CW5 6DQ
TEL: 0270 626866 FAX: 0270 626027 TELEX: 367169 ROOKHALL

Built 200 years ago, and subsequently restyled into a small palatial château, this Grade II listed building is poised on a hill overlooking the Cheshire Plain, and is acknowledged as one of the finest country houses in the area. In the grounds there are sweeping lawns, an immense kitchen garden, a lily pond, a large fountain and riverside meadows. The polished mahogany and walnut panelling of the dining room with its fine plaster ceiling, combines with the rich styling to create a feeling of spaciousness and dignity. The menu is modern English, of excellent quality, and to accompany this an outstanding list of 250 wines is offered.

All the bedrooms are luxuriously decorated. Tennis, putting and croquet, clay pigeon shooting, coarse fishing on the River Weaver, a helipad and conference facilities for up to 60 people are all available. Children over 10 welcome. 3 AA Stars and RAC Blue Ribbon for 1990. Price guide: £110–£240. Directions: The Hall is a good stopping place to, or from, the North, being 165 miles from London and 205 miles from Edinburgh. From M6 Junction 16 take the A500 to Nantwich, then the B5074 to Worleston.

RELAIS &
CHATEAUX

CHEWTON GLEN HOTEL

NEW MILTON, HAMPSHIRE BH25 6QS
TEL: 0425 275341 FAX: 0425 272310 TELEX: 41456

Chewton Glen offers the best of all worlds. Situated in parkland between the New Forest and the sea, peace and quiet is guaranteed here. From the luxurious bedrooms and suites to the internationally acclaimed Marryat Restaurant, where gourmet cuisine and premier wines are served, the hotel's interiors calm the spirit while its leisure facilities foster relaxation. With two indoor tennis courts, an indoor swimming pool, a gymnasium with fully computerised equipment, sauna, steam bath, spa pool and hairdressing salon, guests can tone up, unwind and forget the hustle and bustle of everyday life. For anyone who is feeling below par on arrival, there is a team of highly trained therapists available to pamper you and ease any discomfort. Therapies include reflexology, shiatsu, aromatherapy, massage and hydrotherapy. More serious sports injuries can be dealt with here, too. The hotel has a croquet lawn and a 9-hole, par-3 golf course in the grounds. There are facilities for most other sports nearby. Acclaimed by major guides, Chewton Glen is the only hotel outside London to have BTA 5 Gold Crowns. Children over the age of 7 are welcome. Price guide: £165 excluding breakfast; including service and VAT. Directions: Please ask for details when booking.

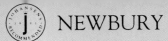

FOLEY LODGE HOTEL

STOCKCROSS, NEWBURY, BERKSHIRE RG16 8JU
TEL: 0635 528770 FAX: 0635 528398

Set in the heart of beautiful Berkshire countryside, this former Victorian hunting lodge has been developed into a luxury country house hotel. The individually designed and furnished bedrooms look out over trees, garden and open countryside, while the elegant lounge and cocktail bar are perfect venues for an aperitif, or in which to relax and soak up the atmosphere of the house. The beauty of the rich Victorian decor in the à la carte restaurant is complemented by the superb quality of the hotel's fine French and traditional English cuisine. The internationally renowned chef, François Reverchon, uses fresh local produce to prepare his imaginative dishes; the menus are changed daily. There is an octagonal pagoda leisure complex constructed in the style of a grand Victorian conservatory. Lush greenery, a mezzanine restaurant and a snooker table surround the circular pool. For conferences and business meetings, the hotel has a comprehensive selection of facilities. Oxford, Newbury Racecourse and Highclere Castle are nearby. Price guide: £110. Directions: Foley Lodge is in the village of Stockcross on the B4000, 1½ miles west of Newbury and close to the M4, A4, and A34.

SWYNFORD PADDOCKS HOTEL

SIX MILE BOTTOM, NR NEWMARKET CB8 0UE
TEL: 0638 70234 FAX: 0638 70283

Known formerly as The Lodge, Lord Byron would retreat here during his incestuous love affair with the occupant of the house, his half-sister, Augusta. Many of the poet's works were penned while he sat in the grounds. Today, as Swynford Paddocks, the house still gives the impression of a large private residence and it certainly retains some charming personal touches. Each bedroom is very different; all are styled tastefully by a local interior designer and guests will find iced water and shortbread awaiting them in their rooms. Game is a speciality of the chef, Philip Bennison, as is baked avocado, filet Medora in truffle sauce and that fast disappearing accoutrement, the sweet trolley. Afternoon tea is taken very seriously – scones and pastries are baked daily. In the grounds there is a croquet lawn, putting course, giant chessboard and an all-weather tennis court. For equine enthusiasts, arrangements can be made to view some famous thoroughbreds and their foals at a neighbouring stud. There is a traditional Christmas party every year and a Boxing Day trip out. Conference facilities are available for up to 20 people. The hotel is an ideal base from which to explore East Anglia – Cambridge, Newmarket, Ely and Bury St Edmunds are all close by. Price guide: £90–£150. Directions: Beside the A1304, a few miles south west of Newmarket.

HOTEL BRISTOL
NARROWCLIFF, NEWQUAY, CORNWALL TR7 2PQ
TEL: 0637 875181 FAX: 0637 879347

The Hotel Bristol, built in 1934, overlooks the superb golden sands of Tolcarne beach and the Atlantic Ocean. The hotel has been lovingly restored, combining the grand proportions of the 30s with every modern comfort; the bedrooms, most with sea views, offer guests luxury and spaciousness. The restaurant boasts an extensive seasonal menu, relying on fresh local produce. For sports enthusiasts there is an indoor swimming pool, table tennis and a full-sized billiard table; a sauna, solarium and hairdressing service are also available. Golf and bowling are close at hand and, in addition, riding, sailing and fishing can be arranged locally. The hotel is an ideal base for touring the rugged and unspoiled beauty of the Cornish countryside, a Mecca for keen walkers, and the attractions of Newquay such as the zoo and Trenance Leisure Park are but a short walk away. A new conference hall has been added providing facilities for up to 100. Price guide: £70–£85. Directions: The hotel is on the Tolcarne cliffs at the entrance to Newquay.

PASSAGE HOUSE HOTEL
KINGSTEIGNTON, NEWTON ABBOT, DEVON TQ12 3QH
TEL: 0626 55515 FAX: 0626 63336

Overlooking the Teign estuary, this new purpose-built hotel provides a peaceful and luxurious stay. The interior decor, with its muted colours, reflects the surrounding countryside. In the bedrooms, every comfort is offered including 24-hour satellite TV. The relaxing theme is continued in the public rooms with their fine furniture, river views and mirrored bar. Large picture windows and a pretty colour scheme make this a delightful place. The five-course table d'hôte and à la carte menus offer imaginative use of Devon recipes, using the freshest local fare including Teign salmon, oysters and game. Throughout the hotel the service is remarkably friendly and efficient. For the active guest, the hotel has a fully equipped leisure club. Besides the indoor pool, there is a hydro spa, steam room, sauna, solarium and gymnasium. A helipad is available. Nearby facilities include sailing, water-skiing, golf and more. Price guide: £85–£95 (special breaks available). Directions: Turn off the A380 on to the A381, follow the signs for the racecourse, turn left at the mini-roundabout and the hotel is first left.

REDWORTH HALL HOTEL

REDWORTH, NR NEWTON AYCLIFFE, COUNTY DURHAM DL5 6NL
TEL: 0388 772442 FAX: 0388 775112 TELEX: 587485

Redworth Hall Hotel is a 17th-century, tastefully converted, manor house with 100 bedrooms some of which are suitable for guests with disabilities and/or incorporate loop systems for the hard of hearing. The furnishings throughout range from antique to fine reproduction. Reputedly haunted, a £5,000 bounty, comprising accommodation and meals, is available to guests who help to prove its ghostly pedigree. The hotel's health club includes a heated indoor swimming pool, which has a hoist for guests with disabilities, a spa bath, sunbeds, steam bath, two squash courts, a sauna, snooker tables, a fully equipped gymnasium and a children's room. Conferences and day meetings can be held in the Surtees Suite (capacity 250), the Baronial Hall (150) and eight syndicate rooms (20 each). In the Baronial Hall 'The Land of the Prince Bishops' mediaeval banquets are held throughout the year. Parking is available for up to 200 cars. The hotel is situated in 25 acres of parkland and woods, which contain many varieties of mature and rare trees. The Crozier Cocktail Bar Restaurant has three dining areas which provide everything from a breakfast buffet to an à la carte dinner; the cocktail bar overlooks the walled garden. Half-price, 3-night stays are available at certain times of the year. Price guide: £76–£85. Directions: Beside A1M, 8 miles north of Scotch Corner.

BROOKDALE HOUSE

NORTH HUISH, SOUTH BRENT, DEVON TQ10 9NR
TEL: 0548 82402

Sympathetic restoration by owners Carol and Charles Trevor-Roper has turned this listed Tudor Gothic rectory into a mellow and welcoming country house hotel of the highest calibre. The setting is tranquil, well away from the bustle of the popular holiday resorts nearby. Yet the whole of the beautiful South Hams, with its superb coastline, is only a 20-minute drive away. The atmosphere here is relaxed. Bedrooms are spacious and kitted out with everything you could need – right down to a trouser press. The hotel is filled with the fragrance of fresh flowers and through the graceful Gothic windows, you can look out onto 4 acres of Victorian wooded, walled gardens complete with stream and waterfall. However, the heart of the hotel is its restaurant. The menu changes daily and, as far as possible, comprises organically grown vegetables and free-range produce. A typical menu might include pan-fried scallops with chervil sauce or braised lambs tongues to start. Main courses range from roast fillet of monkfish to lightly roasted breast of duck. Welcomes children over 10. Price guide: £75–£100. Directions: Turn off B3210 in Avonwick opposite the Avon Inn. Turn left by telephone box and follow the signs to the hotel atop the hill.

KIRKBY FLEETHAM HALL

KIRKBY FLEETHAM, NORTHALLERTON, NORTH YORKSHIRE DL7 0SU
TEL: 0609 748711 FAX: 0609 748747

This luxurious Georgian Hall is situated in the heart of James Herriot country between the Yorkshire Moors and Dales. It stands in its own 30-acre estate, complete with lake, adjoining a 12th-century church. Kirkby Fleetham Hall offers guests sumptuous antique-filled interiors; each of the 22 period bedrooms is individually designed, has a private bathroom and a host of extras with which guests can pamper themselves. Some suites have whirlpool baths; a few ground floor rooms have patios which guarantee guests complete privacy. The owners, Roderick and Janine Richman, will give you a warm welcome. The Hall has its own Victorian walled garden which produces herbs, fruit and vegetables for use in its kitchen. The elegant dining room, with its polished mahogany tables set with fine bone china, sparkling crystal glasses and gleaming silver cutlery, affords views across the grounds. Price guide: £100–£175. Directions: Hotel is halfway between London and Edinburgh. Leave A1 at Kirkby Fleetham sign just south of Catterick Airfield; take first left then turn left again. The Hall is ½ mile further on.

PARK FARM HOTEL

HETHERSETT, NORWICH, NORFOLK NR9 3DL
TEL: 0603 810264 FAX: 0603 812104

Park Farm occupies a tranquil and secluded location in beautifully landscaped surroundings, yet is only a few minutes from the centre of Norwich. There are luxurious bedrooms, many with four-poster beds and jacuzzi baths. The hotel also has other fine facilities for guests wishing to relax and feel healthy and be at ease, including an indoor heated swimming pool, a sauna, a solarium and a games room. A very high standard of cuisine and the owners' close involvement with the day-to-day running of Park Farm ensure its popularity. There is a landing strip for light aircraft and a helipad in the grounds. Putting, tennis and croquet are all available at the hotel. Nearby Norwich is a historic and interesting city with a bustling market centre, castle museum and lovely cathedral. Closed for a few days at Christmas. Price guide: £65–£105. Directions: Park Farm is south of Hethersett on the B1172.

LANGAR HALL

LANGAR, NOTTINGHAMSHIRE NG13 9HG
TEL: 0949 60559 FAX: 0949 61045

The family home of Imogen Skirving, built in 1830, combines the standards of good hotel-keeping with the hospitality and style of country-house living. The 11 bedrooms are individually designed, and have all been completely refurbished. The public rooms retain their original antique furnishings and an interesting collection of paintings. All rooms have beautiful views of the garden, park and moat. Dinner is served in the pillared dining hall where a collection of 19th- and 20th-century paintings is exhibited for sale. Imogen and her chef work together to produce an excellent, varied menu of French influenced cuisine. An ideal venue for small conferences. Dogs by arrangement. Closed first 2 weeks of January. Price guide: £60–£95. Directions: Langar is accessible via Bingham on the A52, or Cropwell Bishop from the A46 (both signposted). The house adjoins the church and is hidden behind it.

WALTON'S

NORTH LODGE, 2 NORTH ROAD, THE PARK, NOTTINGHAM NG7 1AG
TEL: 0602 475215 FAX: 0602 475053

Built in the 1800s as a hunting lodge to the Castle Deer Park, Walton's has been transformed into a lively hotel. The Harry Brown Trio, playing in the style of Oscar Peterson, the elegant restaurant, the half-tester beds and antique furniture all combine to give the impression of a country house of the Thirties. The restaurant serves mainly French cuisine and seafood is a speciality: smoked salmon Fabergé, Madeira herrings, scallops poached in Pernod, lobsters, and venison from the nearby estate are regulars on the menu. Blues Bistro, a new restaurant, serves meals priced from £10, and is very popular. Walton's is only ¾ of a mile from the city centre. Price guide: £65–£75. Directions: From Junction 25 of the M1, take the A52 towards Nottingham; follow city centre signs from the University, and Walton's is 1½ miles at the top of Derby Road hill.

CHEVIN LODGE

YORKGATE, OTLEY, WEST YORKSHIRE LS21 3NU
TEL: 0943 467818 FAX: 0943 850335 TELEX: 51538

A really unusual place – you would probably have to travel to Scandinavia to find a similar set-up to Chevin Lodge. The hotel is built entirely of Finnish logs, and is set in 50 acres of birch wood with lakes, in the beauty spot known as Chevin Forest Park. The hotel bedrooms are spacious and carefully designed; some have patio doors with access to the lakeside gardens. There are also luxury lodges tucked away in the woods which provide alternative accommodation to the hotel bedrooms. There are

jogging and cycling trails in the woods and a sauna or jacuzzi in the private leisure suite. Imaginative and appetising meals are served in the beautiful balconied restaurant which overlooks the lake. Chevin Lodge has conference facilities for up to 120 and is an ideal centre from which to visit Leeds, Bradford and Harrogate; all are within 20 minutes' drive. Price guide: £85–£98. Directions: From A658 between Bradford and Harrogate, take the Chevin Forest Park road, then left into Yorkgate for Chevin Lodge.

LE MANOIR AUX QUAT' SAISONS

GREAT MILTON, OXFORD OX9 7PD
TEL: 0844 278881 FAX: 0844 278847 TELEX: 837552

Set in 27 acres of enchanting gardens and woodland, this is one of Britain's most outstanding hotels. The history of the manor can be traced back 750 years, and has welcomed many famous visitors including Oliver Cromwell. The restaurant, overlooking the beautiful, landscaped gardens, offers a diverse and varied menu which includes seasonal specialities. The cuisine is largely the creation of internationally renowned chef/patron, Raymond Blanc, whose dishes are as close to perfection as one can hope to find in terms of taste, composition and presentation. The wine list is in keeping with the food – imaginative, extensive and exciting. Oxford, Woodstock and Blenheim Palace are just a short drive away; golf and other sports facilities are available nearby. Dogs accommodated by arrangement. Closed 24 December–17 January. Price guide: £168. Directions: From London, travel on M40, exit at Junction 7 (A329 to Wallingford). After approximately 1½ miles, take the second turning on the right, which is signposted Great Milton Manor.

STUDLEY PRIORY

HORTON-CUM-STUDLEY, OXFORD OX9 1AZ
TEL: (086735) 203/254 FAX: 086735 613 TELEX: 262433

Studley Priory, with an exterior little changed from Elizabethan days, nestles peacefully in 13 acres of secluded and wooded gardens, situated on a site giving unparalleled views over the Cotswolds, Chilterns and the Vale of Aylesbury. The bedrooms, tastefully and imaginatively furnished, reflect the high standard consistent throughout the hotel; cots are available for young children. The restaurant, boasting the best of both English and French cuisine, provides a seasonally varying menu relying on fresh local produce, complemented by an extensive and well-balanced wine list. The Priory offers excellent conference facilities and is ideally placed for Oxford, Ascot, Newbury and Cheltenham. Blenheim Palace, the Manors of Waddesdon and Milton, Broughton Castle and the Great Western Museum of Railways are but some of the notable places of interest to visit. Golf and riding are available nearby. The hotel has a grass tennis court and facilities for croquet. Price guide: £88–£135. Directions: The hotel is situated at the top of the hill of the village of Horton-cum-Studley.

WESTON MANOR

WESTON-ON-THE-GREEN, OXFORDSHIRE OX6 8QL
TEL: 0869 50621 FAX: 0869 50901 TELEX: 83409

Weston Manor, home to four earls and subsequently the property of King Henry VIII, has been imaginatively restored offering guests every modern luxury while retaining the architectural features and charm of bygone days. It is set in 13 acres of formal and semi-formal gardens, over which the bedrooms have superb views. The elegant restaurant with its magnificent vaulted ceiling boasts the best of modern English cuisine. Facilities include squash court, heated swimming pool and croquet. The ancient city of Oxford, Blenheim Palace and Woodstock are but a short drive away. Price guide: £95–£120. Directions: 8 miles north of Oxford on the A43.

THE SUNHILL HOTEL

ALTA VISTA RD, GOODRINGTON SANDS, PAIGNTON, DEVON TQ4 6DA
TEL: 0803 557532 FAX: 0803 663850

Spectacular views, a warm welcome and value for money bring guests back time and again to Sunhill Hotel. The bedrooms, the dining room, the bar and terrace all overlook the sea and Goodrington Sands. Owned by Bob and Barbara Bewick, Sunhill was extensively refurbished in 1989. Families with children over the age of 4 can be accommodated but the clientele is mainly adults who appreciate peace and quiet. Special features include bridge weekends and racing breaks of two and four days. Transport to, and undercover seating at, local racecourses is provided, along with packed lunches. All guests have to do is pick the winners! Other local attractions include Kent's Cavern, Buckfast Abbey and the Dart Valley Steam Railway. Torquay, Brixham and Dartmouth are easily accessible and Torbay Leisure Centre is a 4 minute walk across the local park. A snooker table and a sauna are on the premises. Price guide: £50–£72. Directions: Exeter A38, take Torbay exit to Paignton, along seafront, up Roundham Road which leads into Alta Vista Road.

PENHAVEN COUNTRY HOUSE
PARKHAM, NR BIDEFORD, NORTH DEVON, EX39 5PL
TEL: 02375 711/388 FAX: 02375 878

Set in 11 acres of mature gardens and woodland, this former rectory represents a haven of peace and tranquillity to its visitors. Proprietors, Maxine and Alan Wade, take great pride in their hotel's reputation for soothing away the stresses of modern-day living, while offering visitors every comfort. The way to unwind 'Penhaven style' is to take a walk along its nature trail; its flowers and wildlife make it irresistible to birdwatchers, naturalists and walkers. Or visit the National Trust properties nearby and the Glassworks and Rosemoor Gardens at Torrington. At the end of the day, relax in front of a log fire in one of the hotel's lounges and dine in its Victorian Orangery which has views across the Yeo Valley to Exmoor. Penhaven's food provides the real high spot. Fresh, home-grown vegetables and lobster, crab and other seafood from nearby Clovelly are available every evening. Local Devon cheeses and freshly produced sweets complement the dinner. Price guide: £87–£110 including dinner.. Directions: From Bideford, take A39 towards Bude. At Horns Cross, turn left opposite Coach and Horses and follow signs to Parkham.

TEMPLE SOWERBY HOUSE HOTEL
TEMPLE SOWERBY, PENRITH, CUMBRIA CA10 1RZ
TEL: 07683 61578 FAX: 07683 61578

Temple Sowerby House stands in 2 acres overlooking Cross Fell, the highest peak in the Pennines and noted for its spectacular ridge walk. This old Cumbrian farmhouse, with Georgian additions, features a conservatory overlooking a lovely walled garden, and provides guests with a haven of peace and tranquillity. The cuisine is simply superb; beautifully presented with care and attention and served in the cosy atmosphere of the panelled dining room or the Rose Room overlooking the garden. The whole house exudes warmth and comfort with beams, antiques and log fires; the bedrooms are individually furnished. You will be accorded a very warm welcome by the resident owner Rosemary Edwards. Price guide: £54–£62. Directions: Temple Sowerby lies on the A66, 5 miles from Exit 40 of the M6 motorway, between Penrith and Appleby.

HIGHER FAUGAN COUNTRY HOUSE HOTEL
NEWLYN, PENZANCE, CORNWALL TR18 5NS
TEL: 0736 62076 FAX: 0736 51648

In this most westerly, mild resort area of England, stands Higher Faugan. It was built by artist Alexander Stanhope Forbes RA in 1904, and is situated in 10 acres of lawns, gardens and woodlands. The grounds are also furnished with a putting green, swimming pool and tennis court. Indoors can be found a full-sized snooker table and exercise room. The menu in the restaurant changes daily and features local fish and home-grown produce. Michael and Christine Churchman are especially proud of their home-made sweets which use plenty of fresh cream. You can laze with a bar lunch by the pool or explore 50 miles of spectacular coastline – Land's End, The Lizard, Helford River and St Mawes. Price guide: £60–£90. Directions: The hotel can be found off the B3315 in Newlyn, 2 miles along Mount's Bay from Penzance.

MILLAND PLACE

MILLAND, LIPHOOK, NR PETERSFIELD, HAMPSHIRE GU30 7JW
TEL: 042876 633 FAX: 042876 643

Built on the slopes of a natural amphitheatre, with spectacular views stretching across the South Downs, this restored country house hotel is only ½ mile from the A3. Accessed by its own private bridge, and set in 7 acres of landscaped gardens with waterfalls, fountains and streams leading down to a lake, the history of the house is as colourful as the magnificent display of rhododendrons. The 18 en suite bedrooms, many with balconies overlooking the gardens, are rich in luxurious furnishings and surprisingly spacious, retaining the elegance and charm of a bygone era. One of the hotel's greatest assets is its English chef de cuisine, Sean Denny, who trained with Anton Mosimann at the Dorchester. A *Daily Telegraph* food writer wrote, after an evening at Milland Place, 'We could detect the influence of a great master . . . it is serious eating'. Mr Denny makes his own bread, brioches and preserves, fresh produce arriving daily from France. A more relaxed and intimate atmosphere would be hard to find whether spending a weekend shooting, riding, playing golf or hosting an executive conference in this exclusive setting. The cities of Guildford, Winchester and Chichester are within easy reach. Price guide: £80–£130. Directions: Follow the signs to Milland from the A3 (London to Portsmouth road) 2 miles south of Liphook.

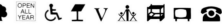

ELFORDLEIGH

COLEBROOK, PLYMPTON, DEVON PL7 5EB
TEL: 0752 336428 FAX: 0752 344581

The Elfordleigh Estate, originally a major west country seat, is set in 65 acres of grounds overlooking the beautiful Plym valley and has been sympathetically refurbished to create a luxury hotel, golf and country club. It guarantees its guests peace and tranquillity. Guests may dine in either the Country Pantry Restaurant or the silver-serviced Churchill's Restaurant, which has oak-panelled walls and an elegant conservatory overlooking the hotel's magnificent gardens, where table d'hôte and à la carte menus are available. Elfordleigh offers many sporting and recreational facilities – it has a fully equipped gymnasium, two heated swimming pools, a squash court, a purpose-built track for jogging plus a Roman-style jacuzzi, two solaria, sauna and steam room. There are three all-weather tennis courts, a golf course (par 68) and a croquet lawn. A beauty therapist is on hand to provide top-to-toe beauty treatments. Set within easy reach of the Devon coast and Dartmoor, Elfordleigh is only 7 miles from Plymouth City. There are conference facilities for up to 100 delegates. Price guide: £79–£84. Directions: Take A374 Plympton Road from Marsh Mills roundabout. Turn left into Larkham Lane, continue into Crossway. Turn left at Boringdon Hill. The hotel is 1 mile further on.

POLHAWN FORT
RAME, TORPOINT, CORNWALL PL10 1LL
TEL: 0752 822864 FAX: 0752 822341

Polhawn Fort is a grand and unspoiled Napoleonic sea fortress which has long been a unique, Cornish family home. The Fort provides an idyllic retreat in a stunning setting, with lawns and gardens which afford endless sights, scents and sounds of the sea, and cuisine which is renowned. All bedrooms face the sea and have magnificent views, flagstoned floors and king-size beds. The main lounge is some 80 feet long, shaped by massive brickwork vaulted arches, with granite pillars and window surrounds. The large sofas and welcoming armchairs ensure this is a comfortable place to relax. At certain times of the year the whole Fort is available for private group bookings, for events such as weddings, anniversaries, banquets, business seminars, or simply for family holidays. There is a tennis court set into the cliffside, excellent fishing from the rocks below, and a private beach. Golf is available at the nearby links or the championship course at St Mellion, and first-class clay pigeon and skeet shooting, riding, sea angling and shark fishing are easily arranged. Although the setting is wild and remote, Plymouth is only 30 minutes' drive away. Price guide: £60–£120. Directions: On the Rame Head Peninsula, the Fort is 1 mile outside Cawsand on the Whitsand Bay coast road.

HAMLYNS

BLACKLANDS, SPARKWELL, NR PLYMOUTH, SOUTH DEVON PL7 5DF
TEL: 075537 219

Isambard Kingdom Brunel designed Hamlyns and stayed here while building the Great Western Railway. In 1854 the manor was bought by the Conran family and exactly 100 years later it was sold to the Hamlyn family who now reside here. It is perhaps the fact that Hamlyns is privately owned that gives it an individual atmosphere. The bedrooms are delightfully furnished in Victorian style and all have panoramic country views. The public rooms are spacious and elegant with oak panelling, large open fires and splendid views over the sloping lawns to the parkland. The restaurant specialises in French and country cuisine, with Devon snails or mousseline of salmon in champagne sauce to whet the appetite – truly mouthwatering menus. Hamlyns is ideally suited to all occasions: weddings, garden parties, private dinner parties and conferences. Experienced and talented staff ensure professional service in a relaxed atmosphere. Dartmoor, Plymouth, South Hams and all the delights of Devon are on your doorstep. Price guide: £55–£100. Directions: Situated east of Plymouth, just north of the A38 between Plympton and Ivybridge.

POOL COURT RESTAURANT WITH ROOMS

POOL BANK, POOL-IN-WHARFEDALE, OTLEY, WEST YORKSHIRE LS21 1EH
TEL: 0532 842288 FAX: 0532 843115

Michael and Hanni Gill have built their reputation on the excellence of their cuisine and hence prefer their establishment to be regarded as a restaurant with rooms rather than a hotel. For over 20 years, Pool Court has won top ratings from most major guides. The brigade of chefs produce a balance of French, classic and innovative dishes while the service from the front-of-house staff, many of whom have been with the owners for several years, is courteous, enthusiastic and friendly. The wine list of nearly 200 bins is professionally chosen with interesting bottles available right across the price scale. This fine, Georgian mansion has six distinctive, en suite bedrooms complete with every conceivable luxury. The restaurant can be made available for exclusive parties of up to 85 guests for a four-course meal, or for buffets of up to 75 people. Wedding parties are a special feature. Pool Court's Georgian cellar rooms, with their vaulted ceilings and original stonework, also provide an intimate and atmospheric area for business or family parties of up to 30. Harrogate, Leeds and Bradford are all within 10 miles. Price guide: £95–£120. Directions: Pool-in-Wharfedale lies at the junction of the A659 and A658, 3 miles from Leeds/Bradford Airport.

THE MANSION HOUSE

THAMES STREET, POOLE, DORSET BH15 1JN
TEL: 0202 685666 FAX: 0202 665709 TELEX: 41495

The Mansion House, a superb Georgian building, is situated in a quiet street in the heart of the well-preserved, ancient town of Poole. The hotel has been lovingly restored, offering guests every modern luxury whilst retaining the charm of bygone days. The bedrooms are individually and tastefully furnished, most with fine antiques, and all demonstrate the personal touch. Excellent traditional English and French cuisine, using choice local produce, is served in the hotel restaurant, complemented by a fine selection of wines. For the sports enthusiast fishing, golf and sailing are readily available. Local places of interest to visit during your stay include the Isle of Purbeck, Corfe Castle and a maritime museum. Two conference rooms provide meeting facilities for 14 and 31 people respectively. Price guide: £91–£105. Directions: Thames Street runs between The Quay and West Street by Poole Bridge.

THE ANCHOR HOTEL

EXMOOR NATIONAL PARK, PORLOCK HARBOUR, EXMOOR, SOMERSET TA24 8PB
TEL: 0643 862636 FAX: 0643 862843

Superbly situated by a small picturesque harbour with splendid views across the Bristol Channel, and set amid Exmoor's magnificent scenery and dramatic coastline, the Anchor is well-known for its comfort and good cuisine. The resident proprietors, Pandy Sechiari and Donald Wade, together with their staff, are anxious to help their guests in any way possible. A visit to Exmoor National Park is to return to that fast vanishing, old rural England where time seems to pass slowly and the atmosphere and charm seems unchanged for generations. There are deep wooded valleys which cradle sparkling rivers, moody stretches of wild heather moorland, sweeping fields and, along the dramatic coastline, some of the highest cliffs in England. Wildlife abounds in the countryside and there are many wonderful walks and drives to be had. Or you can go pony trekking, riding, sailing, surfing or swimming, or take a picnic to a secluded spot and while away the hours just looking at the views and relaxing. Price guide: £60–£99. Directions: Leave the A39 at Porlock; 1¾ miles to Porlock Harbour.

PORT GAVERNE HOTEL

NR PORT ISAAC, NORTH CORNWALL PL29 3SQ
TEL: 0208 880244 FAX: 0208 880151

This early 17th-century inn full of charm and character, situated in a sheltered cove ½ mile from Port Isaac, is fringed by National Trust land. All 19 bedrooms are cosy and well appointed with private baths. Guests also have the choice of seven special 18th-century beamed cottages, each fully equipped. A unique collection of old photographs of the area, watercolours and oils adorns this highly individual hotel. The dining room, also open to non-residents, serves superb food using the best local produce. An à la carte menu, supplemented by chef Ian Brodey's dishes of the day, offers an enviable choice. From Easter until 1 November there is a hot or cold buffet with local specialities at midday in the dining room, and bar snacks in the evening in the lounge bar. There is a sheltered swimming cove right in front of the hotel, and miles of beautiful coastal paths. Golf, fishing, pony trekking, surfing and sailing are within easy reach. A member of the Hospitality Hotels of Cornwall group. Closed 5 January–15 February. Price guide: £64–£82. Directions: Port Gaverne is signposted from the B3314 south of Delabole and is reached via the B3267; follow signs *only* for Port Gaverne and *not* Port Isaac.

THE LUGGER HOTEL
PORTLOE, NR TRURO, CORNWALL TR2 5RD
TEL: 0872 501322 FAX: 0872 501691

Welcome westward – that is the warm invitation from the Powell family at the Lugger Hotel, which affords every comfort and fabulous views seaward. Built in the 17th century, and originally a smugglers' inn, the Lugger Hotel is situated at the very water's edge of a picturesque Cornish cove on the beautiful Roseland Peninsula. The menu features English and Continental dishes including delicious local seafood, with a wide choice of wines. Facilities include a solarium and sauna. All rooms have en suite shower or bathroom plus toilet. The perfect place to escape from the hustle and bustle of everyday life, the hotel has been awarded 4 Crowns by the English Tourist Board and has received a 'Commendation' from the British Tourist Authority every year since 1974. Open from mid-February to early December. Children over 12 welcome. Price guide: £88–£100 including dinner. Directions: A390 from Plymouth, B3287 from St Austell to Tregony, and A3078 to Portloe.

BREAMISH COUNTRY HOUSE HOTEL

POWBURN, ALNWICK, NORTHUMBERLAND NE66 4LL
TEL: 066578 266/544 FAX: 066578 500

Set in 5 acres of peaceful grounds at the foot of the Cheviot Hills, Breamish House is undoubtedly one of the finest small country house hotels in this part of England. This elegant Georgian building was originally a 17th-century farmhouse which was converted in the 1800s to a hunting lodge, and is ideally placed in the heart of unspoiled countryside with many historic places of interest to visit. The hotel's restaurant has won an enviable reputation for fine food, its cordon bleu chefs producing menus with both flair and imagination. Available locally are horse-riding, golf and fishing facilities. Business travellers will find Breamish House a pleasant alternative to 'group' hotels. The hotel is listed AA 2 Star, RAC 3 Red Stars. Closed January. Children over 12 welcome. Dogs by arrangement. Price guide: £98–£135 (includes dinner). Directions: Powburn is on the A697 south of Berwick-upon-Tweed.

THE BRIDGE HOTEL

PRESTBURY, CHESHIRE SK10 4DQ
TEL: 0625 829326 FAX: 0625 827557

The original inn dates from 1626 and was converted from a number of small cottages. Now there are three public rooms which have retained much of the inn's original appearance: old beams, antique furniture, wattle and daub walls and even a secret tunnel below. The bedrooms – many of which overlook the River Bollin – are light and well-equipped. Six rooms are in the old building, 17 in a recently added wing which also houses conference facilities for up to 70 delegates. The restaurant is an adapted, 17th-century hammer-beamed room and can cater for all occasions – 'the newly married . . . or the newly motivated'. You can choose from a fixed price or à la carte menu and the cuisine is traditional English. The choice of wines on offer is very extensive. Sightseers can explore the nearby Peak National Park, Chatsworth House, Tatton Park, and, in Liverpool, the Albert Docks. All are worth more than a casual glance. Price guide: £93–£103. Directions: In the centre of the village next to the church. Prestbury is on the A538 from Wilmslow to Macclesfield.

BARTLE HALL HOTEL

LEA LANE, BARTLE, NR PRESTON, LANCASHIRE PR4 0HA
TEL: 0772 690506 FAX: 0772 690841

This luxury country house hotel set in 16½ acres of gardens and woodland has been recently refurbished, with the addition of the fine Leonardo's restaurant and Peacock Rooms making a congenial setting for functions of all kinds. The reception lounge and the bar area have an informal and relaxed atmosphere. They afford fine views of the gardens, where the resident peacocks strut. The elegant dining room, with its crisp pink napery, is an inviting setting in which to sample the tasty menu. Starters such as escargots, galantine of duckling and oysters Kilpatrick catch the eye, and Italian-style main courses might include *piccata florentine, pollo Alessandra* or *filetto stroganoff*. The four-poster bed in the bridal suite sets the tone for the rest of the comfortably furnished bedrooms, with all modern amenities in a period setting. Bartle Hall has conference facilities for between 12 and 30 people, and a function room seating 250. Price guide: £65–£80. Directions: Leave M6 at Junction 32, towards Preston. Follow signs for Ingol. At large roundabout follow sign to Woodplumpton then signs to Kirkham, and after 2–3 miles Bartle Hall is on the right.

GIBBON BRIDGE COUNTRY HOUSE AND RESTAURANT

CHIPPING, NR PRESTON, LANCASHIRE PR3 2TQ
TEL: 0995 61456 FAX: 0995 61277

Set on the banks of the beautiful River Loud, this country house hotel is run by a mother and daughter team – Margaret and Janet Simpson – and offers the modern traveller comfort, consideration plus a cosy family atmosphere. Outside, the landscaped gardens are a tribute to the love of the country; inside, there is an air of warmth and tranquillity. The spacious bedrooms are furnished in pretty, light-coloured chintz fabrics, and many have their own lounge or gallery complete with comfortable chairs and deep sofas. The superb restaurant offers traditional English fare with an imaginative and tempting menu making excellent use of local produce. The hotel also has its own health and beauty parlour where you can relax and let skilful hands soothe away your worries or, if you are feeling energetic, work off any extra pounds and tone up in the gym. There are excellent conference facilities for up to 120 people. Chauffeur-driven cars and tours available. Helicopter landing facilities in the grounds. BTA Commended; Britain in Bloom award. Price guide: £60–£70. Directions: From Junction 32 of M6 take A6 to Broughton, then B5269 to Longridge. Follow signs as far as Chipping, turn right at the T-junction; Gibbon Bridge is just under a mile further on.

CHEQUERS HOTEL

CHURCH PLACE, PULBOROUGH, WEST SUSSEX RH20 1AD
TEL: 07982 2486 FAX: 07982 2715 TELEX: 67596

This historic Grade II listed building, standing on a sandstone ridge overlooking the South Downs and the Arun Valley, dates from the time of Queen Anne. In the garden, there is a new conservatory. The open log fire in the comfortable lounge is lit in the winter months and the restaurant offers substantial portions of traditional English fare. The table d'hôte menu, making use of fresh market produce, is changed daily. Of the 11 bedrooms, 3 are family rooms and 4 are on the ground floor. Situated inland, ½ an hour from Brighton and 15 minutes from Worthing, the hotel is conveniently placed for visiting the old Roman city of Chichester, Arundel Castle and other stately homes, as well as the coast. Goodwood and Fontwell race courses are to hand and opportunities for horse-riding, clay pigeon shooting, fishing and golf are nearby. There are 5 golf courses within 30 minutes' drive. Packed lunches and maps can be provided for guests who wish to walk the South Downs. Price guide: £56–£66. ETB 4 Crowns. RAC Merit Awards. Directions: At the top of the hill, at the northern end of the village, you will see the hotel opposite the church.

THE PEAR TREE AT PURTON

CHURCH END, PURTON, SWINDON, WILTSHIRE SN5 9ED
TEL: 0793 772100 FAX: 0793 772369

Set in 7½ acres of grounds, this former vicarage for the parish church of St Mary's overlooks traditional Victorian gardens, and affords views beyond of the rolling Cotswold Hills and the source of the River Thames. Proprietor Anne Young picks herbs and fresh flowers from the gardens, which she tends herself, while co-proprietor Francis Young applies his international hotel management experience to the hotel's award-winning restaurant. The extensive wine list features many lesser known wines as well as traditional favourites. The 18 elegant rooms and suites are each named after notable characters associated with the village of Purton, such as Anne Hyde – the mother of Queen Mary and Queen Anne. Nestled in the famous Vale of the White Horse, at the southern edge of the Cotswolds, The Pear Tree is ideally situated for exploring the surrounding English countryside. Price guide: £85–£120. Directions: At Junction 16 of the M4 follow the signs to Purton. Go through the village until you reach a triangle with Lloyds Bank opposite, turn right up the hill, follow the road and go past the tithe barn. The hotel is 50 yards further on.

NUTFIELD PRIORY

NUTFIELD, REDHILL, SURREY RH1 4EN
TEL: 0737 822072 FAX: 0737 823321

Nutfield Priory, one of the Hidden Hotels group, is an architectural extravagance built by a Bradford MP. Towers, elaborate carvings, cloisters and stained glass combine to create a very unusual building. Fresh flowers are a thoughtful extra provided in the spacious and beautifully furnished bedrooms. The unique cloistered restaurant, the elegant lounges and library furnished with antiques, all help to make this hotel special. Conferences and seminars of all sizes can be professionally managed in the hotel's six conference rooms. Nutfield Priory is set in 40 acres of gardens and parkland, with views across the Surrey and Sussex countryside. Within the grounds of the hotel, Fredericks Leisure Club is available for guests' use. Its facilities include a sauna, spa, solarium, gymnasium, steam room, and – a welcome attraction – a crèche. Squash, badminton and snooker are also available. Closed 27–30 December. Price guide: £105–£220. Directions: Nutfield is on the A25 between Redhill and Godstone, and can easily be reached from Junctions 6 and 8 of the M25. Travelling from Godstone, the Priory is on the left just after the village of Nutfield.

PENGETHLEY MANOR

NR ROSS-ON-WYE, HEREFORDSHIRE HR9 6LL
TEL: 0989 87211 FAX: 0989 87238 TELEX: 35332 Attn. P.H.

Set in 15 acres of well-tended grounds in an area of outstanding natural beauty, Pengethley provides genuine country house hospitality. All 22 bedrooms reflect the character of this former country squire's house, including four-poster and canopied beds. The oak panelling in the entrance hall survived the fire which destroyed the Tudor house in the early 1800s; the house was rebuilt, remaining in the Symonds family over 400 years. Guests at Pengethley enjoy excellent cuisine in style; fresh Wye salmon, prime Hereford beef, tender Welsh lamb, with herbs and vegetables from the garden. The service is very special too; attentive but never intrusive. For smaller meetings, training programmes and executive conferences, the recently refurbished Chandos Suite offers privacy and security, one hour's drive from Birmingham, Cardiff, Newport and Bristol. Helipad on site. Price guide: £110–£160. Directions: 5 miles from Ross-on-Wye, 10 miles from Hereford on the A49.

WHARTON LODGE

WESTON-UNDER-PENYARD, NR ROSS-ON-WYE, HEREFORDSHIRE HR9 7JX
TEL: 0989 81795 FAX: 0989 81700

This gracious Georgian house, situated in 15 acres of parkland, has been home to Mary Gough's family for four generations. Guests here are treated as personal friends and a friendly, family atmosphere ensures that you will experience something very special. All the bedrooms are exquisitely furnished and decorated; each has an individual character. Attention to detail is very much in evidence, with bathrobes and lovely toiletries adding a personal touch to the luxurious surroundings. The views from the bedrooms of the Herefordshire countryside are delightful. A relaxing drink before dinner can be enjoyed in the intimate yet elegant surroundings of the drawing room. From the perfectly set tables to the superb choice offered on the menu, dining here makes you feel that nothing is too much trouble. The lovely market town of Ross-on-Wye is nearby and the Herefordshire countryside gives you plenty to explore. Children over 12 are welcome. Phone toll free from USA (reservations only), 1–800–235–0714. Price guide: £90–£120. Directions: Take the A40 to Ross-on-Wye. Situated between Weston-under-Penyard and The Lea.

SYKESIDE COUNTRY HOUSE HOTEL

RAWTENSTALL ROAD END, HASLINGDEN, ROSSENDALE, LANCASHIRE BB4 6QE
TEL: 0706 831163 FAX: 0706 830090

Sykeside, the former home of Lancashire composer Alan Raws-thorne, is a Grade II listed mansion built in 1883, set in almost 3 acres of beautiful gardens. The building has been sensitively restored and retains its fine architectural features, yet offers guests every modern luxury. The most recent addition, a Victorian conservatory, provides a relaxing pre-dinner area where the resident pianist entertains on most evenings each week. All the bedrooms have been individually decorated and lavishly appointed, each with its own en suite luxury bathroom, with the executive en suites providing jacuzzi or sauna facilities. One of the bedrooms has been specially designed and equipped with the disabled guest in mind. The lounge, with extensive views over the front lawns, has a splendid marble and brass fireplace with an open fire. Exquisite English cooking, relying on fresh local produce, combined with a well-chosen wine list and is served in the elegant and relaxing atmosphere of the restaurant. Conference facilities available for up to 40 participants. The local golf course is only 10 minutes' walk away. Guide dogs only are accommodated. Price guide: £60–£100. Directions: Turn off M65 or the end of M66 onto A56 link. The hotel is off A56 on the A680 when approaching from M66, and the A681 when approaching from M65.

TYLNEY HALL

ROTHERWICK, NR HOOK, HAMPSHIRE RG7 9AJ
TEL: 0256 764881 FAX: 0256 768141 TELEX: 895864

Arriving at this hotel in the evening, with its floodlit exterior and forecourt fountain, you can imagine yourself arriving for a party in a private stately home. Grade II listed and set in 66 acres, Tylney Hall typifies the great houses of the past. Aperitifs are taken in the wood-panelled library bar; *haute cuisine* delights in the glass-domed restaurant complemented by old-style courteous service. The hotel is rated by the *Daily Mail* as one of the top 12 hotels in the country for leisure facilities. Outdoors, there is a swimming pool, tennis court and croquet lawn, while golf, archery, horse-riding and clay pigeon shooting can be arranged locally. Indoors, there is a swimming pool with a whirlpool facility, multi-gym, sauna and snooker table. Surrounding the hotel are wooded trails ideal for rambling enthusiasts. Functions for up to 100 are catered for in the large baronial hall, while smaller, intimate gatherings are held in one of eight meeting rooms. Basingstoke, Alton and Farnborough are all nearby. Price guide: £99. Directions: A33 to Basingstoke, left at end of dual carriageway. Take B3349 towards Hook, turn right to Rotherwick. Turn left to Newnham just after pond. Hotel 1 mile further on right.

EAST LODGE COUNTRY HOUSE HOTEL

ROWSLEY, MATLOCK, DERBYSHIRE DE4 2EF
TEL: 0629 734474

East Lodge Country House Hotel was originally built as the East Lodge to Haddon Hall. Expanded to its present size in Victorian times, it was sold as a private home by the Duke of Rutland in the 1920s. Now it is the home and business of John and Angela Beecroft. The interiors are decorated in traditional English country house style. Each room has a different colour-scheme and furniture styles range from practical pine to solid oak; from mellow mahogany to pure white. The four course menus are changed daily 'to avoid boring the residents', says John. Set in 10 acres of grounds, the house is 4 miles from Matlock with its spa baths and 3 miles from Bakewell, where exceedingly good tarts are baked. It is a good base for touring Derbyshire and the Peak District being 1½ miles from Chatsworth House and just a short drive from Crich and its tramway museum. Buxton with its theatre, roman baths and modern shops is 12 miles away and, for walkers, nearby Dovedale is a must. Price guide: £60–£75. Directions: By the junction of the A6 and Beeley Road.

THE GROSVENOR HOTEL

CLIFTON ROAD, RUGBY, WARWICKSHIRE CV21 3QQ
TEL: 0788 535686 FAX: 0788 541297

A warm welcome awaits you at the Grosvenor which has recently been extensively renovated. You can relax on the patio or in the lawned garden before moving into the elegant Regency dining room to sample the excellent menu and comprehensive wine list. Each of the en suite bedrooms has been individually furnished: some have brass bedsteads and some have a jacuzzi. For romantics and honeymooners, the sumptuous bridal suite has a double jacuzzi. The hotel also has a swimming pool and leisure centre with a sauna, solarium and fitness equipment. There are conference facilities for up to 20 delegates. The hotel is within easy reach of the National Exhibition Centre, Birmingham International Airport, Rugby School and Stratford-upon-Avon. Price guide: £65–£85. Directions: On the corner of Clifton Road and Grosvenor Road, 5 minutes' walk from the town centre.

BARNSDALE LODGE

THE AVENUE, RUTLAND WATER, NR OAKHAM, RUTLAND LE15 8AH
TEL: 0572 724678 FAX: 0572 724961

Your hosts, Robert Reid and the Hon Thomas Noel, invite you to enjoy the hospitality of their recently restored, 17th-century country farmhouse hotel. Set in the heart of the ancient county of Rutland amid unspoiled countryside overlooking Rutland Water, Barnsdale Lodge combines the gracious living of yesteryear with those, almost forgotten, high standards of English service. The 17 bedrooms, each furnished in Edwardian style and with private facilities, express a mood of quiet and relaxing comfort. Honeymoon suites are a speciality at Barnsdale. Traditional English cuisine and fine wines are served in our Edwardian style dining rooms. A Silver trolley of prime roast beef is always available. Elevenses, Buttery lunches, afternoon teas and suppers may be taken in the bar, drawing rooms or on the patio. Barnsdale has three fully equipped conference rooms and facilities for wedding receptions and parties. For guests' children, a safe play area is provided. Within easy reach of the hotel are such historic attractions as Burghley House, Belvoir and Rockingham Castles; also cathedrals at Ely and Peterborough. Rutland Water offers much of interest to the sports enthusiast and to nature lovers. Price guide: £55–£65. Directions: Barnsdale Lodge is situated on the A606 Oakham to Stamford road.

NORMANTON PARK HOTEL

NORMANTON PARK, RUTLAND WATER SOUTH SHORE, RUTLAND, LEICESTERSHIRE LE15 8RP
TEL: 0780 720315 FAX: 0780 721086

Normanton Park Hotel is on the South Shore of Rutland Water, a leading leisure and sports centre where canoeing, water-skiing, wind-surfing and yachting are available. The hotel is a Grade II listed, award-winning restored Georgian coach house which offers visitors every luxury while retaining original architectural features. The elegant Peacock Room Restaurant affords magnificent views over the Water, just 50 yards away, and offers traditional English menus – fresh local produce is always used. Good cuisine is complemented by the hotel's extensive and well-chosen wine list. Snack meals, cream teas and speciality ice creams are available anytime in the galleried coffee lounge. The hotel stands in 4 acres of grounds originally designed as pleasure gardens in the 18th century which has one of the oldest Cedar of Lebanon trees in the country. Set in the heart of the Midlands, the hotel is a good base from which to explore the many market towns of East Anglia, Cambridge, Calke Abbey, and National Trust properties such as Belton House and Canons Ashby. Cycling, horse-riding and birdwatching are also available locally. Price guide: £61–£70. Directions: Take A606 Stamford towards Oakham, turn along South Shore to Edith Weston.

BOLT HEAD HOTEL

SOUTH SANDS, SALCOMBE, SOUTH DEVON TQ8 8LL
TEL: 054884 3751 FAX: 054884 3060

In a quite spectacular setting 140 feet above sea-level, this attractive hotel has one of the finest coastal positions imaginable. The air-conditioned restaurant is arranged on two levels and commands dramatic views of the Salcombe Estuary. The bedrooms are furnished in pine with Laura Ashley decor and are equipped with good en suite bathrooms complete with hair dryers. Each room also has remote-control TV, direct-dial telephone, radio, listening/intercom, etc. There is an attractive bar, heated outdoor swimming pool, private moorings and plenty of car parking. The hotel is also directly adjacent to miles of magnificent National Trust cliff land at Bolt Head. Closed from 13 November to 16 March. Dogs by arrangement. Price guide: £96–£138 (includes dinner). Directions: Please contact the hotel for directions.

SOAR MILL COVE HOTEL

SOAR MILL COVE, SOUTH DEVON TQ7 3DS
TEL: 0548 561566 FAX: 0548 561223

Soar Mill Cove Hotel is owned and loved by the Makepeace family who, with their dedicated staff, provide that special kind of caring service. The magnificent setting is a flower-filled coombe, which faces its own sheltered sandy bay and is entirely surrounded by hundreds of acres of National Trust coastlands. It is probably the last truly unspoiled area of South Devon. Yet the distance from the motorway system (A38) is only 15 miles. Entirely on ground level, each bedroom has a private patio opening onto the gardens. In winter the log fires and efficient double glazing ensure warmth throughout the hotel. There are indoor and outdoor pools, both spring-water fed, the former being maintained all year at a constant 88°F. Imaginative and innovative cuisine reflects the very best of the West of England; fresh crabs and lobster caught in the bay are a speciality. Soar Mill Cove is situated midway between Plymouth and Torquay and close to the old ports of Salcombe and Dartmouth. Closed 29 December to early February. Children and dogs by arrangement. Price guide: £98–£130. Directions: A384 to Totnes, then A381 to Soar Mill Cove.

NUNSMERE HALL

TARPORLEY ROAD, SANDIWAY, CHESHIRE CW8 2ES
TEL: 0606 889100 FAX: 0606 889055

Set in the peace and quiet of the Cheshire countryside, Nunsmere Hall is owned and run by Malcolm and Julie McHardy and offers all the atmosphere and hospitality of a country house. The 10 acres of wooded gardens, surrounded on three sides by a 60-acre lake, provide a tranquil, relaxed setting. Local leisure facilities include two notable golf courses and the Cheshire Polo Club which is next door. Clay pigeon shooting, archery and a helipad are all available by arrangement in the grounds. The bedrooms and suites are all light, spacious and have private bathrooms, luxury toiletries and a trouser press. Each affords spectacular views of the lake or over the terrace to the sunken gardens and croquet lawn. The old library provides facilities for senior executive meetings and special celebrations. The creative cuisine uses only the freshest, seasonal produce. Although secluded, Nunsmere is convenient for major towns and motorway networks. Price guide: £95. Directions: Leave M6 at Junction 18 northbound, or 19 southbound, then take A556 to Sandiway. At the second set of traffic lights turn left onto the A49. The hotel is 1 mile further on the left.

HOLBECK HALL HOTEL

SEACLIFF ROAD, SOUTH CLIFF, SCARBOROUGH, NORTH YORKSHIRE YO11 2XX
TEL: 0723 374374 FAX: 0723 351114

Holbeck Hall is a late Victorian mansion, situated on Scarborough's South Cliff with magnificent views over the sea, and set in 3 acres of superbly tended grounds, including a rose garden and natural woodland. The Hall has been sensitively restored, while retaining fine period features such as the imposing baronial hall complete with minstrels' gallery. The bedrooms are tastefully and imaginatively decorated. The restaurant boasts the best of English and French cuisine, providing a menu which relies on seasonal fresh local produce – a speciality being locally caught fish – complemented by a fine selection of wines. The Hall is an ideal base for conferences and senior-level management meetings for up to 45. Fishing, golf, sailing and squash are within easy reach and Castle Howard, the mediaeval city of York and the artists' havens at Runswick and Robin Hood's Bay are but some of the notable places of interest to visit. Price guide: £94–£114. Directions: Seacliff Road lies on the seaward side of the A165 Filey Road in Scarborough.

WREA HEAD COUNTRY HOTEL

SCALBY, NR SCARBOROUGH, NORTH YORKSHIRE YO13 0PB
TEL: 0723 378211 FAX: 0723 363457

Wrea Head Country Hotel is a Victorian country house built in 1881 and situated in 14 acres of wooded and landscaped grounds on the edge of the North York Moors National Park, yet only 3 miles from Scarborough. Scenic drives can take in the quaint coastal villages of Robin Hood's Bay, Runswick and Staithes, as well as historic Whitby. A little further afield are Castle Howard and the city of York with its famous Minster and city walls both steeped in history. The house is furnished with many antiques and paintings, and the interesting panelled main hall and inglenook fireplace, with blazing log fires in winter, add a cheerful welcome.

All the bedrooms are individually decorated to the highest standard, most having delightful views of the garden. The elegant Russell Flint Restaurant serves the best traditional English fare using fresh local produce and the finest ingredients, complemented by an interesting wine list. The hotel is open all year and offers weekend breaks throughout. Price guide: £80–£100. Directions: Follow the A171 north from Scarborough, past the Scalby Village sign until hotel is signposted. Follow the road over the ford and then turn first left up the drive to the hotel.

CHARNWOOD HOTEL
SHARROW LANE, SHEFFIELD S11 8AA
TEL: 0742 589411 FAX: 0742 555107

This Georgian mansion, a listed building dating from 1780, was once owned by William Wilson of the world-famous Sharrow Snuff Mill. Recently extended, this beautiful 'country house in town' has two new restaurants – Henfrey's and Brasserie Leo – a Georgian-style, 70 seater banqueting hall, a library and five new suites, one of which is designed with the needs of disabled guests in mind. Other rooms have a theme. There is the Pavlova room for the romantic, the Pavarotti – large and grand – the intimate Piaf room and the stately Woodford Room. Award-winning chef, Wayne Bosworth, has created a menu of traditional French fare for the brasserie and has enhanced Henfrey's reputation for the delicacy of its cuisine. The hotel is less than a mile from Sheffield city centre with its hectic nightlife, and the stunning Peak National Park is a 10-minute drive away. The spa town of Buxton with its opera house and Abbeydale Industrial Hamlet are also nearby. Price guide: £91–£94. Directions: The hotel is in Sharrow Lane near the junction with London Road and Abbeydale Road.

CHARLTON HOUSE HOTEL

CHARLTON ROAD, SHEPTON MALLET, SOMERSET BA4 4PR
TEL: 0749 342008 FAX: 0749 346362

This country manor house dates from the 17th century and stands in 6 acres of landscaped grounds which feature a trout lake. The grounds run alongside the River Sheppey and afford lovely walks. Each bedroom varies in style from pretty pastel shades to quaint and beamed. In the coach house annexe, there is a spacious suite and a family room. The imaginative menu is modern English and is based on top-quality produce, locally grown when possible. Illuminated by candles and warmed by a log fire on chilly evenings, the restaurant's atmosphere is relaxed and the chandelier-hung conservatory extension gives the impression that you are dining outside. The hotel boasts a Swedish-style swimming pool and sauna, a hard tennis court and helicopter landing facilities. Golf is available at Mendip, 2 miles away. Charlton House is a good base from which to explore the Mendips, Bath, Wells, Glastonbury, Longleat House and Safari Park, Wookey Hole and the Cheddar Gorge. Price guide: £75–£95. Directions: Charlton House is ½ mile from Shepton Mallet centre on the A361 to Frome.

THE EASTBURY HOTEL

LONG STREET, SHERBORNE, DORSET DT9 3BY
TEL: 0935 813131 FAX: 0935 817296 TELEX: 46644 EASTBY

Built in 1740, during the reign of George II, this elegant town house has been transformed into a small, but gracious, hotel. The Eastbury is set in an acre of walled garden, close to the centre of Sherborne and near to its Abbey and castles. The bedrooms are named after English garden flowers and are beautifully decorated and furnished in keeping with the Georgian origins of the house. The restaurant offers English cuisine, including vegetarian meals, using the finest fresh local produce, and has an extensive wine cellar. Pre-eminence is given to personal service, whether guests are busy company executives or leisurely holiday makers exploring Thomas Hardy's Dorset. The Eastbury provides a romantic setting for wedding receptions. Conference facilities for up to 80 delegates are available. Price guide: £80. Directions: On the A30, ½ mile from Sherborne station.

ROWTON CASTLE
SHREWSBURY, SHROPSHIRE SY5 9EP
TEL: 0743 884044 FAX: 0743 884949

Standing on the site of a Roman Fort, the original Rowton Castle suffered destruction by Llewellyn, Prince of Wales, in 1282. With a large tower reputedly dating back to this time, this Grade II* listed, 17th-century building with additions by George Wyatt, has been lovingly restored to create one of the most beautiful hotels in the area. Ranging from singles to suites, all the bedrooms are spacious and tastefully furnished. The public rooms are elegant and include a range of private suites to cater for conferences and banquets of all sizes. Also open to non-residents, the 17th-century, oak-panelled restaurant has a rich, warm character. Table d'hôte and à la carte menus are offered, featuring a wide selection of freshly prepared and vegetarian dishes. For relaxation, guests can play croquet or stroll in the formal gardens, which have views of the Welsh mountains beyond. Rowton Castle is well situated for exploring the rolling countryside of Shropshire, yet is only 10 minutes' drive from the historic market town of Shrewsbury. Price guide: £65–£85. Directions: Rowton Castle is beside the A458 Welshpool to Shrewsbury road.

ALBRIGHT HUSSEY HOTEL AND RESTAURANT

ELLESMERE ROAD, SHREWSBURY, SHROPSHIRE SY4 3AF
TEL: 0939 290523/71 FAX: 0939 291143

A 16th-century moated manor house, this Grade II* listed building has been fully restored and refurbished to its former glory over a 2 year period by the present owners, Vera and Franco Subbiani, and their son Paul. A wealth of antique furnishings enhance the hotel's atmosphere of luxury and one of the de luxe bedrooms contains a four-poster spa bath as well as a four-poster bed: most unusual indeed! The high standard of accommodation is supported by the excellence of the imaginative cuisine. This historic building stands in 4 acres of grounds and exquisitely landscaped gardens fronted by a moat with resident Australian black swans and a variety of ducks. Local landmarks include the former Roman city of Viroconium, Attingham Park, a stately home owned by the National Trust, Ironbridge Gorge, the birthplace of the Industrial Revolution and, of course, the mediaeval town of Shrewsbury. Under the personal supervision of the owners, the Albright Hussey provides quality, comfort and luxury. Price guide: £80–£110. Directions: The hotel is 2½ miles from Shrewsbury town centre on the A528 Ellesmere road.

HOTEL RIVIERA

THE ESPLANADE, SIDMOUTH, DEVON EX10 8AY
TEL: 0395 515201 FAX: 0395 577775 TELEX: 42551

This grand Regency building (c.1820) welcomes all those with a taste for gracious living in this dignified seaside resort. The hotel overlooks Lyme Bay and has an unrivalled position at the centre of the Esplanade. Family owned and managed, the Hotel Riviera has a reputation for courteous, traditional service. No effort is spared in maintaining and improving the standards of this fine hotel, which has been totally refurbished for 1991. To dine at the Hotel Riviera is a delightful experience, for the extensive à la carte and table d'hôte menus offer fare to excite the most discerning palate. Seafood is a speciality and a fine selection of wines are available to complement your meal. The attractive Cavalier conference and ballroom has its own bar and is a popular venue for private functions as well as for business meetings. The hotel offers a reduced tariff for luxury holiday breaks taken during the autumn, winter, or spring, and at weekends. Arrangements can be made for golf, tennis and game shooting. Price guide: £94–£126 including dinner. Directions: The hotel is situated at the centre of the Esplanade.

THE LYNCH COUNTRY HOUSE HOTEL

SOMERTON, SOMERSET TA11 7PD
TEL: 0458 72316 FAX: 0458 74370

The Lynch is a delightful Georgian Grade II listed country house in beautiful grounds, lovingly restored and refurnished with antiques to provide a charming small hotel. The bedrooms, all with en suite bathrooms, are attractively presented with thoughtful touches such as bathrobes and magazines. Two have Georgian four-poster beds while others have Victorian bedsteads. The hotel's elegant dining room serves many mouthwatering dishes, and overlooks the lawns and lake. It is decorated in a theme of soft apricot and cream. Hot air ballooning can be arranged from the hotel grounds. In the heart of rural Somerset, this is an excellent centre from which to visit numerous stately homes and gardens, such as Barrington Court, Sherborne Castle or Stourhead. This is also a good base from which to visit the annual Bath and West Show or for walking, touring, hunting, racing or fishing. Price guide: £50–£95. Directions: Somerton is on the B3151 between Yeovil and Street.

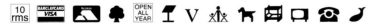

COLLAVEN MANOR HOTEL

SOURTON, NR OKEHAMPTON, DEVON EX20 4HH
TEL: 083786 522 FAX: 083786 570

Set on the north-western edge of Dartmoor, this lovely 15th-century manor house, built of fine mellow stone, lies in 5 acres of delightful gardens and paddocks and affords glorious views over ragged tors and the magnificent countryside round about. Only the finest quality food is served. The menus here range from country house cooking to gourmet. A selection of fine wines from France and Italy is available to complement your meal. The bedrooms, all with gorgeous views, are sumptuously furnished to meet every requirement and are decked with fresh flowers. In the grounds, facilities include clay pigeon shooting, a croquet lawn and a small pitch-and-putt green. Children over 12 are welcome. Conference facilities for up to 20 delegates are available. RAC 3 Stars. Price guide: £77–£95. Directions: The hotel is 8 miles south of Okehampton on the A386, 2 miles from A30 trunk road.

GLAZEBROOK HOUSE HOTEL

SOUTH BRENT, DEVON TQ10 9JE
TEL: 0364 73322 FAX: 0364 72350

Glazebrook House is a spacious and elegant mid-Victorian country house set on an elevated, 4 acre site within the Dartmoor National Park. The gardens are stocked with sequentially flowering plants and shrubs to provide colour throughout the seasons. As well as providing a retreat for guests who want nothing but peace and quiet, the house is the perfect setting for business meetings, conferences and wedding receptions. Excellent food is provided by the chef, David, who trained at the Savoy and has worked with Raymond Blanc. Sue and Laurence Cowley have owned the hotel since 1987. Sue is responsible for the Sanderson and Laura Ashley style decor set with swags and tails. Laurence, formerly a company director, is also a trained and accomplished chef. Together they have created a wonderfully well-run hotel where excellence is the goal. The house is an ideal base from which to explore the South Hams coast and the surrounding moors. It is also within easy reach of the business centres of Plymouth and Exeter. There is a leisure complex nearby and the hotel can arrange shooting parties. Price guide: £65–£125. Directions: From M5 Exeter, take the A38 Plymouth to South Brent exit. The hotel is signposted from then on.

THE SWAN HOTEL

MARKET PLACE, SOUTHWOLD, SUFFOLK IP18 6EG
TEL: 0502 722186 FAX: 0502 724800 TELEX: 97223 ADNAMS G

Rebuilt after a fire in 1659, the Swan was remodelled in the 1820s; with further additions in 1938. The hotel provides all modern services while retaining its classic dignity and tranquil elegance. Many of the individually decorated bedrooms in the main hotel offer a glimpse of the sea, while the garden rooms are clustered around a former bowling green. The drawing room has the traditional character of an English country house and the reading room upstairs is ideal for quiet relaxation or a private party. The menu, based on the best fresh ingredients, changes daily in the elegant dining room, and is complemented by a renowned wine list. Southwold is built around a series of delightful greens and has a fine church, a lighthouse and a brewery, as well as the shingle beach and a golf course. Music lovers come to nearby Snape Maltings for the Aldeburgh Festival and other concerts. The Swan makes an ideal base for touring the coast and countryside of Suffolk and Norfolk. Dogs by arrangement only. Price guide: £74–£96. Directions: The hotel is on the Market Place at the centre of Southwold.

SOPWELL HOUSE

COTTONMILL LANE, SOPWELL, ST ALBANS, HERTFORDSHIRE AL1 2HQ
TEL: 0727 864477 FAX: 0727 44741 TELEX: 927823

Sopwell House, an elegant Georgian manor, for centuries the home of the Earls of Verulam and latterly the Mountbattens, is set in 12 acres of tranquil grounds overlooking the unspoiled Hertfordshire countryside. The hotel, refurbished in 1990, has been tastefully restored and the bedrooms, while offering guests luxury and comfort, retain the atmosphere of days gone by. The delightful conservatory restaurant, with views over the gardens, offers the best in modern English cuisine and provides an imaginative, seasonal menu. Sopwell House has extensive business facilities, including 14 boardrooms available for meetings, as well as a large ballroom for functions such as weddings and dances. For sports enthusiasts, croquet, golf and squash are available nearby, as are the stately homes of Woburn Abbey and Hatfield House. A leisure club and a further 20 luxury bedroom suites will be opening late summer 1991. Dogs by prior arrangement. Price guide: £102. Special weekend rates available. Directions: Take A1081 from the A414 Hatfield to St Alban's road.

ST MICHAEL'S MANOR HOTEL
FISHPOOL STREET, ST ALBANS, HERTFORDSHIRE AL3 4RY
TEL: 0727 864444 FAX: 0727 48909 TELEX: 917647

This fascinating manor house, dating from the 16th century, is set in 5 acres of beautiful grounds at the heart of Roman Verulamium. The Oak Lounge, part of the original Tudor structure, has a wonderful Elizabethan plastered ceiling with *fleur-de-lys* and stylised floral bosses. The Manor has undergone many structural changes over the centuries producing a happy blend of different architectural styles. In 1987, a delightful Victorian-style conservatory was added as an extension to the restaurant overlooking the award-winning gardens. These elegant surroundings, together with extensive menus, which always offer a vegetarian selection, and the cellars of many fine wines, make dining at St Michael's Manor a pleasant experience. Closed 3 days between Christmas and New Year. Children over 10 welcome. Dogs by arrangement. Price guide: £90. Directions: Fishpool Street runs from the Abbey at the junction of the A5 and A6. The hotel has a central position in the town, close to the A5183.

THE GARRACK HOTEL

BURTHALLAN LANE, ST IVES, CORNWALL TR26 3AA
TEL: 0736 796199 FAX: 0736 798955

This small, intimate family owned and managed hotel, secluded and full of character, is set in 2 acres of gardens and affords views over Porthmeor Beach and beyond to St Ives Bay. Most of the bedrooms in the original house are in keeping with the style of the building. The additional rooms, including the honeymoon suites, are modern in design and afford lovely sea views. Most rooms have a private bathroom; all have baby-listening facilities. Guests return time and again to enjoy the informal yet professional service where the emphasis is on good food and hospitality. The attractive restaurant, which overlooks the bay, specialises in seafood; fresh lobsters are available from a storage tank. The wine list includes over 70 labels from ten different regions. Relaxation is assured here: there are open log fires, an indoor swim/spa pool, a sauna and solarium. There is also ample car parking. Dogs by prior arrangement. Price guide: £62–£88. Directions: A30–A3074–B3311–B3306. Go ½ mile, turn left at mini-roundabout, hotel 300 yards further on.

HOTEL TRESANTON

ST MAWES, CORNWALL TR2 5DR
TEL: 0326 270544 FAX: 0326 270002

Tucked away in 1½ acres at the edge of the sleepy fishing village of St Mawes, where time seems to move at quite a different pace from the rest of the world, Hotel Tresanton is an ideal place to forget for a while the pressures of modern life. All bedrooms give fine views of this impressive sweep of the Cornish coastline, as do the terraces, decked with many varieties of tropical plants. Local seafood dishes, as one might expect, are a speciality of the hotel. Attractions of the village include the harbour, St Mawes Castle, nearby National Trust gardens, golf, fishing and sailing.

Bathing is available near the hotel, and escorted horse rides can be arranged. Transport can be arranged to the hotel from St Austell or Truro railway stations and St Mawgan Airport (25 miles). Closed November/March but open for Christmas and New Year. Welcomes children over 10. Price guide: £118–£150 (including dinner and afternoon tea). Directions: From St Austell on the A390 turn left on the B3287 via Tregony to St Mawes. Hotel is situated 200 yards from St Mawes Castle.

THE GEORGE OF STAMFORD

ST MARTINS, STAMFORD, LINCOLNSHIRE PE9 2LB
TEL: 0780 55171 FAX: 0780 57070 TELEX: 32578

The George, a beautiful 16th-century inn, offers a lounge with open log fire (sometimes used to toast muffins for tea), a garden lounge with exotic plants (orchids, orange trees, coconut palms) where you can choose from hot dishes or an extensive cold buffet, and an oak-panelled restaurant much frequented by the appreciative local community. Chris Pitman's menu is traditional in basis, enhanced by his experience in Swiss and Italian kitchens. Outside there is a courtyard for eating *al fresco*, a walled garden, the Monastery Garden and a croquet lawn. The separate Business Centre (formerly the livery stables) offers exceptional facilities: five fully equipped executive offices; two boardrooms; a conference room for 50 people with built-in cine-screen, multiple lighting system and complete range of audio-visual equipment; a receptionist and full secretarial service. AA 3 Stars. Price guide: £100–£150. Directions: Travelling north or south on the A1 take the B1081 into Stamford, follow through to the town centre where you will see the hanging gallows traversing the road with the name of The George of Stamford upon it. The car park is just to the side of this road, behind the hotel.

WHITEHALL

CHURCH END, BROXTED, ESSEX CM6 2BZ
TEL: 0279 850603 FAX: 0279 850385

Full of the charm and atmosphere of days gone by, coupled with the comforts and conveniences of the 20th century, sums up this quite delightful small manor whose origins can be traced back to 1151. Beams, great open fireplaces in which log fires burn in inclement weather, comfortable chairs and sofas, and a warm welcome typify this little gem. The beautiful dining room with its great vaulted timbered ceiling is the setting for delicious food and fine wines, while the charming bedrooms are individual in character and furnished in delicate pastel shades. Situated within its own lovely walled garden, Whitehall is a tranquil rural retreat, yet it is a mere 1 hour's drive from London, and Stansted Airport is only minutes away. Cambridge is nearby and there are many small Tudor villages to visit in the surrounding area. Welcomes children over 5. AA Best Newcomer 1988. Closed 23–30 December. Price guide: £95–£120. Directions: Take Junction 8 off the M11, towards Stansted Mount Fitchet, then take the B1051 for 8 miles; the hotel is on the right.

STAPLEFORD PARK

NR MELTON MOWBRAY, LEICESTERSHIRE LE14 2EF
TEL: 057284 522 FAX: 057284 651 TELEX: 342319

The most important privately owned stately home in the UK to be converted into a hotel, Stapleford Park has already won many awards for its American restaurateur Bob Payton and his wife Wendy. Their aim is to combine the relaxed, unpretentious American style of hospitality with the more traditional atmosphere of an English country house. The house, which once belonged to the six Earls of Harborough, stands in 500 acres of gardens, woods and parkland. Outdoor pursuits are plentiful: equestrian sports, clay pigeon shooting, fishing, tennis, croquet, basketball and walking; game shooting, trout fishing and golf are available nearby. Leading contemporary designers have created 35 highly individual bedrooms and suites, each equipped to luxurious standards: major expansion is planned for 1991/92 to bring the number of bedrooms to about 55. The intricate art of Grinling Gibbons, England's greatest wood carver, adorns the fine dining room where diners may enjoy first-class American cuisine. Opportunities for sightseeing abound in the area, which is becoming known as 'the Cotswolds without the tourists'. Price guide: £115–£300. Directions: Stapleford is signposted from the B676 between Melton Mowbray and Saxby, and from the A606 between Melton Mowbray and Oakham.

HANCHURCH MANOR

HANCHURCH, STOKE-ON-TRENT, STAFFORDSHIRE ST4 8JD
TEL: 0782 643030 FAX: 0782 643035

Hanchurch Manor is a Grade II listed building dating from the early part of the 19th century. This elegant, Tudor-style house, with its stone mullioned windows and projecting gables is convenient for the M6 but commands lovely views of open countryside, and guests at the Manor will enjoy the relaxed and gracious atmosphere of a traditional country house. The public rooms are comfortable and beautifully decorated, the bedrooms spacious and luxurious. All have direct-dial telephones plus a radio and colour satellite television with telextext. Dinner is served in one of the three delightful dining rooms; the food is prepared with great imagination and a consideration for healthy eating. Only the best fresh produce is used, organically grown whenever possible. A typical menu might include a succulent fillet of lamb with tarragon sauce, or delicately flavoured fillets of pink trout meunière. The à la carte menu is excellent, the wine list first-class. Shooting, fishing and golf are all available nearby, and there are conference facilities for up to 16 people. Price guide: £105–£125. Directions: M6 Exit 15; A519 to Eccleshall; 1 mile on right-hand side.

ABINGWORTH HALL

THAKEHAM ROAD, STORRINGTON, WEST SUSSEX RH20 3EF
TEL: 0798 813636 FAX: 07983 3914 TELEX: 877835

Abingworth Hall stands in 8 acres of charming and mature gardens which includes an ornamental lake with two islands and a variety of interesting trees and shrubs. The health-conscious are catered for with an outdoor heated swimming pool, a croquet lawn, pitch and putt and a hard tennis court within the grounds. There are magnificent views over the rolling South Downs. The restaurant boasts the best of English and French cuisine. It relies on fresh local produce and thus offers seasonal variety, combined with an interesting and extensive wine list. Boardroom meetings for up to 24 delegates are possible. For the sports enthusiast, golf, sailing, riding and clay pigeon shooting are all close at hand. Parham House, Goodwood House and Racecourse, Petworth House, Arundel Castle and Chichester Festival Theatre are some of the nearby places of interest to visit. The hotel welcomes children over 10. Price guide: £80. Directions: The hotel is on the B2139, 2 miles from Storrington and 4 miles from Coolham.

GRAPEVINE HOTEL

SHEEP STREET, STOW-ON-THE-WOLD, GLOUCESTERSHIRE GL54 1AU
TEL: 0451 30344 FAX: 0451 32278 TELEX: 43423

In Stow-on-the-Wold, regarded by some as the jewel of the Cotswolds, the Grapevine has an atmosphere that instantly makes you feel welcome and at ease. The bedrooms, all with en suite bathrooms, are beautifully furnished and have many exposed Cotswold stone walls. Be pampered at this award-winning hotel in the centre of the Cotswolds. Enjoy the relaxed and informal atmosphere in the romantic vine-clad conservatory restaurant, with its imaginative cuisine and caring staff for whom nothing is too much trouble. This is an exceptional small hotel where you will enjoy the best of personal service. Whether on business or touring, you will want to repeat the Grapevine experience! Price guide: £78–£106. Directions: Sheep Street is part of the A436 in the centre of Stow-on-the-Wold.

WYCK HILL HOUSE

STOW-ON-THE-WOLD, GLOUCESTERSHIRE GL54 1HY
TEL: 0451 31936 FAX: 0451 32243

Wyck Hill House is a magnificent Cotswold mansion constructed in the early 1700s, reputedly on the site of an early Roman settlement. It is set in wooded and landscaped gardens of 100 acres, overlooking the magnificent Windrush Valley. The hotel has been tastefully restored and the bedrooms have been individually furnished to combine superb antiques with modern facilities. There is a suite with a large, antique four-poster bed, which is ideal for honeymoons and special occasions. The cedar-panelled library is an ideal room in which to read, if you wish, and to relax with morning coffee or afternoon tea. The award-winning restaurant provides the highest standards of modern British cuisine, from the freshest of seasonally available local produce. The menus are complemented by a superb wine list. Wyck Hill House hosts several special events, including opera, travel talks, cultural weekends and a variety of special themes. The hotel is an ideal base from which to tour the university city of Oxford and the ancient city of Bath. Cheltenham, Blenheim Palace, Bladon and Stratford-upon-Avon are just a short drive away. Special price, 2-night breaks are available. Price guide: £90–£165. Directions: Stow-on-the-Wold is at the junction of the A426, A429 and A424.

SALFORD HALL HOTEL

ABBOT'S SALFORD, NR EVESHAM, WORCESTERSHIRE WR11 5UT
TEL: 0386 871300 FAX: 0386 871301 TELEX: 336682

Steeped in history, this romantic Tudor manor house stands in the picturesque village of Abbot's Salford, amid rolling country-side. The atmospheric charm and character of times past become doubly appealing when combined with modern comfort in the form of gracious furnishings, outstanding food and a selection of fine wines. Full of character, the bedrooms – each named after a historical personage – are individually decorated with period furniture and luxurious fitments. The old chapel, complete with priest hole, is now a quiet lounge. Guests can also relax in the conservatory lounge or on the sunny terrace within the walled flower garden. The hotel's facilities include snooker, outdoor tennis court, a sauna and solarium. In the heart of Old England, Salford Hall is surrounded by the historic and the picturesque: Stratford and Shakespeare country, the magical Cotswolds, and many ancient castles. The Regency spa of Cheltenham, an excellent shopping centre, is nearby. Price guide: £95–£140. Directions: Abbot's Salford lies about 8 miles west of Stratford-upon-Avon on the A439 towards the Vale of Evesham.

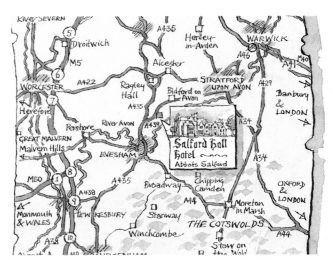

ETTINGTON PARK HOTEL

ALDERMINSTER, NR STRATFORD-UPON-AVON, WARWICKSHIRE CV37 8BS
TEL: 0789 740740 FAX: 0789 450472 TELEX: 311825

A Gothic mansion is nothing if not grand, albeit neo! And positively exuding grandeur, Ettington Park rises majestically over 40 acres of Warwickshire parkland, surrounded by terraced gardens and carefully tended lawns, where guests can wander at will to admire the pastoral views and specimen trees. The interior is breathtaking, amazingly opulent, decorated with flowers, beautiful antiques and original paintings, where guests are pampered with every luxury. On an appropriately grand scale, the 48 bedrooms and the superb leisure complex, which includes a heated swimming pool, spa bath, solarium and sauna, make this not only a perfect choice for the Sybarite but also an incomparable conference centre with excellent facilities. The menu is in fine English style, served with panache in a dining room with carved wooden friezes and the *bon viveur* will enjoy a leisurely perusal of the wine list. Riding, tennis, clay pigeon shooting, archery, croquet, fishing are all available. Suitable for children over 7. Special weekend breaks available. Price guide: £135–£150. Directions: From the M1 take the M5 at Junction 17. Turn south on to the A34. Ettington Park is 6 miles south of Stratford.

THE SWAN DIPLOMAT

STREATLEY-ON-THAMES, BERKSHIRE RG8 9HR
TEL: 0491 873737 FAX: 0491 872554 TELEX: 848259

In a beautiful setting on the banks of the historic River Thames this hotel offers today's traveller extremely comfortable accommodation. All the 46 bedrooms, many of which have balconies overlooking the river, are appointed to very high standards with individual decor and furnishings. The Riverside Restaurant, with its idyllic views and elegant decor, serves food and wines of an exceptional standard and diners can look out at the attractive Oxford College Barge moored alongside, which is a stylish venue for meetings and cocktail parties. Business guests are well catered for – the hotel has six elegant conference suites, the largest of which can accommodate up to 90 guests. Reflexions Leisure Club is superbly equipped for fitness programmes and beauty treatments; rowing boats and bicycles may be hired. Tennis, squash, horse-riding, fishing and clay pigeon shooting can all be arranged by the hotel for its guests. Dogs are welcome. Oxford, Windsor, London and Heathrow Airport are all within an hour's drive of the hotel. Price guide: £90–£200. Directions: The hotel lies just off the A329 in Streatley Village.

STONEHOUSE COURT HOTEL

BRISTOL ROAD, STONEHOUSE, NR STROUD, GLOUCESTERSHIRE GL10 3RA
TEL: 0453 825155 FAX: 0453 824611

This distinguished Grade II listed country house, set in 6 secluded acres of lovely gardens and parkland, was built in the 17th century. Within the handsome stone exterior, the hotel – with its oak panelling, soft lighting, open stone fireplaces and comfortable furnishings – radiates a mellow warmth, while staff provide a service which complements the relaxed atmosphere without sacrificing a high degree of personal attention. The cocktail bar and restaurant provide elegant surroundings in which guests may enjoy a cuisine utilising the best of fresh local produce, accompanied by a comprehensive wine list. For wedding receptions the Stonehouse Court Hotel provides an idyllic setting. The purpose-built conference centre, facilities for helicopter landings and proximity to Staverton airport and the M5, make this hotel ideal for busy company executives, as well as holidaymakers exploring the lovely Cotswolds or the historic centres of Bath and Stratford-upon-Avon. Coarse fishing and golf are available nearby. Price guide: £80. Directions: 1½ miles from Junction 13 on the M5 motorway. Stonehouse station is ½ mile away.

PLUMBER MANOR

STURMINSTER NEWTON, DORSET DT10 2AF
TEL: 0258 72507 FAX: 0258 73370

Plumber Manor is a tastefully restored Jacobean building in local stone, set in extensive, tranquil gardens in the heart of Hardy's Dorset, and has been in the owner's family since the early 17th century. Leading off a charming gallery hung with family portraits are six very comfortable bedrooms, and the conversion of a natural stone barn lying within the grounds has added a further ten very large bedrooms some of which have window seats overlooking the stream and garden. The elegant restaurant has three connecting dining rooms, and is well known for its original and varied menu. A boardroom seating 14 people is available.

Only 30 miles from the coast, the Manor is perfect for exploring the Dorset countryside and places such as Milton Abbas, Cerne Abbas and Lyme Regis. Golf, clay pigeon shooting, fishing and riding are available nearby. For guests wishing to take their own horse so that they can hunt with local packs, the hotel provides free stabling. Closed during February. Children over 12 are welcome. Price guide: £70–£100. Directions: Plumber Manor is 2 miles south-west of Sturminster Newton on the Hazelbury Bryan road, off the A357.

New Hall

WALMLEY ROAD, ROYAL SUTTON COLDFIELD, WEST MIDLANDS B76 8QX
TEL: 021–378 2442 FAX: 021–378 4637 TELEX: 333580

Reputedly the oldest fully moated manor house in England, New Hall is set in 26 acres and dates back to the 12th century. This magnificent manor house is a feast both for the eyes and the palate. The grounds and gardens are extensively shrubbed and wooded with terraced walks, orchards, croquet lawns, shady groves and open fields. The cocktail bar overlooks the enclosed moated garden with its spectacular yew topiary. Guests dine sumptuously in the oak-panelled restaurant where chef Glenn Purcell creates award-winning cuisine. New Hall won the *Good Food Guide's* County Restaurant of the Year Award 1990 and an AA Rosette for good food and service. The bedrooms and suites are individually and thoughtfully furnished and contain every modern comfort. All the rooms afford lovely views through their latticed windows. New Hall is ideal for business, providing a memorable venue for important meetings and conferences. Close to Birmingham's exhibition centre, Warwick, Kenilworth and Stratford, with fishing and golf nearby. Price guide: £92–£150. Directions: From Exit 9 on M42, take A4097 to Sutton Coldfield. Follow signs to Walmley, turn right on to B4148 to Sutton Coldfield. New Hall 1 mile further on left.

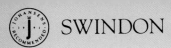

SALTHROP HOUSE

SALTHROP, NR SWINDON, WILTSHIRE SN4 9QP
TEL: 0793 812990 FAX: 0793 814380

Once the home of the Duke of Wellington, this lovely Georgian house stands in 16 acres of grounds which enclose woodlands rich in wildlife. Guests here are made to feel like welcome visitors to a private country house; the service is relaxed with the emphasis on personal attention. All bedrooms are exceptionally well-decorated and fully complement the hotel's handsome exterior. Each bathroom is a model of design with classic Victorian fittings. The resident owners, Michael and Jane Gould, do everything they can to make their guests comfortable. Chef Rozanne MacLean ensures that dining at the Salthrop is a similarly personal experience. Her carefully prepared meals are complemented by fine wines stored in the original cellar. There are conference facilities for up to 25 delegates, including three meeting rooms and boardroom-style accommodation. Leisure pursuits include croquet and clay pigeon shooting. Children over 14 welcome. Price guide: £105–£130. Directions: From Junction 16 on the M4, 2 miles south towards Broadhinton and Marlborough.

THE CASTLE AT TAUNTON

CASTLE GREEN, TAUNTON, SOMERSET TA1 1NF
TEL: 0823 272671 FAX: 0823 336066 TELEX: 46488

The Castle has been welcoming travellers to Taunton since the 12th century. Rich in drama and romance, it has been the scene of many historical events: it was in the Great Hall that Judge Jeffreys held his infamous Bloody Assizes and where the perpetrators of the Duke of Monmouth's rebellion were summarily dealt with. Monmouth had been declared King by his followers, on taking the Castle in June 1685. Some 200 years earlier, the same fate befell Perkin Warbeck, who had arrived at the Castle claiming to be Richard, Duke of York, and had declared himself King. Today The Castle lives at peace. Overlooking the quiet of Castle Green, it preserves the atmosphere of its ancient tradition yet ranks as one of René Lecler's '300 Best Hotels in the World'. The Castle cares about food and the way it is presented, and cares about wine and the way it is stored. The same care is evident in the individuality and elegance of the bedrooms and the warmth and friendliness of the welcome you receive. Golf, tennis and riding facilities plus Cedar Falls Health Farm are nearby; clay pigeon shooting and ballooning are also available. Price guide: £95. Directions: The Castle is signposted in the centre of Taunton.

Seen in all the best places

BUCKDEN
COLLECTION OF SUITCASES

PAPWORTH
Finest Leather Luggage
CAMBRIDGE
ENGLAND

Papworth Travel Goods, Papworth Everard, Cambridge CB3 8RG, England
Tel 0480 830345 Fax 0480 830781 Telex 94012570 PAPIG Answerphone 0480 830186

MADELEY COURT HOTEL

TELFORD, SHROPSHIRE TF7 5DW
TEL: 0952 680068 FAX: 0952 684275

Madeley Court, a 16th century manor, has recently been restored with real understanding and affection for its history and character, and now provides a superb, peaceful venue for guests engaged on either business or pleasure. A luxury hotel, it retains many original features including stone and half-timbered walls, a huge oak spiral staircase and panelled rooms. The unique appeal of the hotel is emphasised by the use of beautiful period fabrics and handsome antique furniture throughout. Some of the suites have whirlpool baths and all afford views over either the lake or courtyard. The restaurant has been created from the original 13th-century hall, and the cuisine is of the highest standard. The extensive wine list includes many fine French labels. There is also a brasserie, with a daily blackboard menu, which offers a selection of beers. Private dining rooms are ideal for business meetings and other parties. There are several conference rooms available, together with full secretarial back-up. There is no shortage of interesting places to visit: the Ironbridge Gorge – a World Heritage Site – Attingham, Powys Castle, Weston Park, Boscobel House and Shrewsbury are all on the doorstep. Price guide: £90–£110. Directions: By car; leave M54 at Exit 4. By train; hotel is 4 miles from Telford station (2½ hours from London).

CALCOT MANOR

NR TETBURY, GLOUCESTERSHIRE GL8 8YJ
TEL: 0666 890391 FAX: 0666 890394

Calcot Manor is set peacefully amid acres of rolling countryside close to the historic market town of Tetbury. The Cotswold manor house dates back to the 15th century and was, until 1983, a farmhouse. Its beautiful stone barns and stables include a 12th-century tithe barn. The rooms are all individually designed with co-ordinating bathrooms, some with whirlpool baths. The drawing room offers peaceful relaxation overlooking the terrace and lawns. In autumn and winter log fires crackle and glow all day. The restaurant, decorated in soft greens and apricot, has won the highest accolades, and is a perfect setting for Ramon Farthing's consistently delightful menus. Nearby: beautiful Cotswolds villages, Peter Scott's Wildfowl Trust and the many delights of Bath. There is always a welcome at Calcot; the Ball family run the establishment to the highest standards and enjoy sharing their home and pampering their guests. Price guide: £95–£140. USA toll free reservations 1-800-544 4970. Directions: Calcot is located 4 miles outside Tetbury on the A4135 and is best approached from Junction 18 of the M4 or Junction 13 of the M5.

TEWKESBURY HALL HOTEL

PUCKRUP, NR TEWKESBURY, GLOUCESTERSHIRE GL20 6EL
TEL: 0684 296200 FAX: 0684 850788

Set between the Cotswold and Malvern Hills, 114 acres of idyllic parkland surround this imposing country house hotel. Quietly luxurious, the bedrooms have been imaginatively decorated and furnished to reflect the seasons of the year, with pretty florals in the Spring Room and sunny yellows in the Summer Suite. Opulent easy chairs in the magnificent drawing room encourage relaxation, while the attractive bar and the airy Orangery are available for a wide variety of drinks. Unusual and elegant, the restaurant's decor enhances enjoyment of the cuisine, with fresh local produce from the famed Vale of Evesham. The tasteful Garden Suite, with its chandeliered ballroom, caters for conferences of up to 200 people. To the north is Worcester and Great Malvern, while to the east the Vale of Evesham leads to Shakespeare Country. Just west of the hotel, the River Severn meanders south towards Tewkesbury with its magnificent Abbey. An 18-hole golf course will be available by early 1992. Dogs are accommodated by arrangement. Price guide: £95–£125. Directions: The hotel is just 2 miles north of Tewkesbury on the A38, and only a few minutes from Junction 8 of the M5, via Junction 1 of the M50.

THORNBURY CASTLE

THORNBURY, NR BRISTOL, AVON BS12 1HH
TEL: 0454 418511 FAX: 0454 416188 TELEX: 449986

Begun in 1510, Thornbury Castle was once owned by Henry VIII, who stayed here with Anne Boleyn. Today, it is the only Tudor castle in England operated as a hotel. The handsome proportions of the internal architecture, including ornate oriel windows, panelled walls and large open fires, as well as the quality of its furnishings and decor, all help to re-create a sense of living in the grand style. The luxuriously equipped bedchambers abound with period details; the devotion to excellence can also be appreciated in the award-winning restaurant with its renowned cuisine. In addition to personally guided tours to such attractions as the Cotswolds, Bath, Avebury, Wells and Glastonbury, there is the Thornbury Castle Shooting Club, specialising in clay pigeon shoots, and golf may be played at several fine clubs nearby. In 1990, the hotel was named 'International Country House Hotel of the Year' (Andrew Harper's *Hideaway Report*) and 'The Most Civilised Restaurant in Britain' (Domecq La Ina). It was also named as having the 'Wine List of the Year' (over 40 covers), by Decanter/Martell Cognac. Closed 10 days in January. Price guide: £85–£180. Directions: The Castle lies by the parish church at the north end of Thornbury.

HOMERS HOTEL

WARREN ROAD, TORQUAY, SOUTH DEVON TQ2 5TN
TEL: 0803 213456 FAX: 0803 213458

Built in the days of gracious living, the hotel maintains an atmosphere of peace. The service is unobtrusive but faultless. The main bedrooms, lounges and dining room provide magnificent views of Torbay. Some bedrooms open onto the gardens; all are individually decorated and benefit from en suite facilities. The hotel's restaurant, Les Ambassadeurs, is Egon Ronay recommended and renowned for its superb international cuisine, and extensive stock of château-bottled wines. The menu is changed daily to take advantage of the fresh local produce. The Oatley family, together with master chef, Graham Bedford, have created speciality gourmet evenings and weekends, which are held throughout the year and have proved very popular, as are the Christmas and New Year programmes. Homers is an ideal venue for small conferences and functions, catering for up to 45 persons. Recreational facilities are available and the family will be pleased to make any arrangements. AA 3 Star HBL Award. Closed January. Price guide: £72–£130 including dinner. Directions: At the sea-front in Torquay, turn left and, driving up the hill, take the first turn right into Warren Road.

THE OSBORNE

MEADFOOT BEACH, TORQUAY, DEVON TQ1 2LL
TEL: 0803 213311 FAX: 0803 296788

The mixture of Mediterranean chic and much-loved Devon landscape has a special appeal which is reflected at The Osborne. Here the friendly atmosphere of a country house is combined with the superior standards of service and comfort expected of a hotel on the English Riviera. The Osborne has become known as the 'country house by the sea'; most of the 23 bedrooms have breathtaking views and The Langtry's Restaurant, which provides the finest English cuisine and tempting regional specialities, overlooks the sea. The Continental-style Raffles Brasserie has a wide-ranging menu available throughout the day. There are 5 acres of attractive gardens, and a health club, indoor and outdoor heated pools plus a tennis court in the grounds. Sailing, fishing, ballooning, archery, clay pigeon shooting and golf can be easily arranged. Devon is a county of infinite variety with a landscape which ranges from majestic cliffs to tranquil lanes and villages; from bustling harbours to the wilds of Dartmoor. All these attractions, and the stylish resort of Torquay, are within easy reach of the hotel. Price guide: £108. Directions: The Osborne is in Meadfoot, a quiet location to the east of Torquay.

ORESTONE MANOR HOUSE

ROCKHOUSE LANE, MAIDENCOMBE, NR TORQUAY, DEVON TQ1 4SX
TEL: 0803 328099 FAX: 0803 328336

Built circa 1809 as a Georgian country lodge, Orestone Manor is now a secluded country house hotel set in private sub-tropical gardens, surrounded by an area of outstanding natural beauty, overlooking the sea. The spacious grounds contain a putting course and, for the summer, there is an outdoor heated swimming pool. Golf, sailing, boating, riding, and tennis are all available nearby. Also close by are Dartmouth and Powderham Castles, the Dart Valley, Buckfast Abbey and several National Trust properties. Beyond these lies the splendour of Dartmoor National Park. However, Orestone Manor is just a few minutes' drive away from the beaches, nightlife and other attractions of Torquay. All in all, it is a perfect holiday base. The hotel has 20 comfortable en suite bedrooms, a large restaurant with renowned cuisine, a friendly atmosphere, dedicated staff and offers generous hospitality. There are conference facilities for up to 20 people. BTA Commended. AA 3 Stars. Special Christmas and New Year breaks available. Price guide: £60–£90, including dinner. Directions: The hotel is signposted 3 miles east of Torquay on the A379 coast road.

ALEXANDER HOUSE
TURNERS HILL, WEST SUSSEX RH10 4QD
TEL: 0342 714914 FAX: 0342 717328 TELEX: 95611 ALEX G

Alexander House, a magnificent mansion in its own secluded park, is one of the most luxurious hotels in England, providing an informal atmosphere where each person is regarded as an individual guest in an English country house. Delicious classic English and French cuisine, rare wines and vintage liqueurs are to be enjoyed among myriad other pleasures. Stunning interiors and original works of art add to the general *joie de vivre*. The discreetly decorated suites enjoy lovely views of the Sussex countryside. Outside, guests can play tennis, croquet, clock golf or simply enjoy the extensive grounds. Nearby are golf courses, trout fishing and horse riding. Glyndbourne, Brighton, many historic properties and numerous famous gardens lie within 25 miles. A chauffeur-driven Daimler limousine provides transport for guests when required, taking only a few minutes to reach Gatwick Airport. Children over 7 are welcome. Price guide: £173. Directions: Alexander House is situated on the B2110, 1 mile east of Turners Hill crossroads, towards East Grinstead.

SHARROW BAY

HOWTOWN, LAKE ULLSWATER, PENRITH, CUMBRIA CA10 2LZ
TEL: 07684 86301/86483 FAX: 07684 86349

Now in its 43rd year, Sharrow Bay is known to many discerning people the world over, who return again and again. But it wasn't always so. In 1948 Francis Coulson arrived with £500, a bicycle, two saucepans and a dog. He was joined by Brian Sack in 1952 and the partnership flourished to make Sharrow Bay what it is today. In a magnificent lakeside situation, bedrooms are luxuriously furnished with antiques, many pictures and pieces of porcelain plus a host of thoughtful extras. All public rooms are delightful in their decor with furnishings which are both elegant and restful. Fresh flowers and *objets d'art* abound. But perhaps if one had to single out one aspect alone for which Sharrow Bay is renowned, it would be for its food. Each meal is an event, a mouth-watering adventure! Breakfasts and afternoon teas are equally superb. In the Bank House, a 17th-century farmhouse 1 mile away, similar standards apply. Closed 1 December–beginning March. Welcomes children over 13. Price guide: £250 including dinner. Directions: M6 Junction 40; A592 to Lake, onto Pooley Bridge; then take the Howtown road for 2 miles.

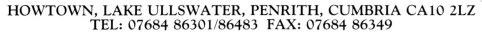

LORDS OF THE MANOR HOTEL

UPPER SLAUGHTER, NR BOURTON-ON-THE-WATER, CHELTENHAM, GLOUCESTERSHIRE
GL54 2JD TEL: 0451 20243 FAX: 0451 20696 TELEX: 83147 VIA OR G

Situated in the heart of the Cotswolds on the outskirts of one of England's most unspoiled and picturesque villages stands the Lords. Built in the 17th century of honeyed Cotswold stone, the house enjoys magnificent views over the surrounding meadows, stream and parkland. For generations the house was the home of the Witts family, who historically had been Rectors of the Parish. It is from these origins that the hotel derives its unusual name. Charming, walled gardens provide a secluded retreat at the rear of the house. Each bedroom bears maiden names of ladies who married in to the Witts family; each room is individually and imaginatively decorated with traditional chintz and period furniture. Reception rooms are magnificently furnished with fine antiques, paintings, traditional fabrics and masses of fresh flowers. Log fires blaze in inclement weather. The heart of this English country house is its dining room where truly memorable dishes are created from local produce. Nearby are Blenheim Palace, Warwick Castle, the Roman antiquities at Bath, and, of course, Shakespeare country. Price guide: £100. Directions: Upper Slaughter is 2 miles west of the A429 between Stow-on-the-Wold and Bourton-on-the-Water.

THE LAKE ISLE

16 HIGH STREET EAST, UPPINGHAM, RUTLAND, LEICESTERSHIRE LE15 9PZ
TEL: 0572 822951 FAX: 0572 822951

This small, personally run restaurant and town house hotel is situated in the centre of the pretty market town of Uppingham, dominated by the famous Uppingham Public School and close to Rutland Water. The entrance to the hotel is reached from a quiet yard hung with flowering baskets, and there is a small, informal, walled garden. In their bedrooms, all named after wine regions of France, guests will find fresh fruit, mineral water and a decanter of sherry. The restaurant provides small, weekly-changing menus using fresh ingredients from as far afield as Paris and Scotland. The extensive wine list of over 300 wines ranges from regional wines to clarets from the '50s and '60s, about 100 of which are half bottles. Special 'wine evenings' are held four times a year to enable guests fully to appreciate this unique cellar. Burghley House and the castles of Rockingham and Belvoir are but a short drive away. Price guide: £56–£60. Directions: The hotel is in the High Street and is reached via Reeves Yard.

HATTON COURT HOTEL

UPTON HILL, UPTON ST LEONARDS, GLOUCESTERSHIRE GL4 8DE
TEL: 0452 617412 FAX: 0452 612945 TELEX: 437334 HATCRT G

Hatton Court is a picturesque, ivy-clad manor house, perched 600 feet above sea level on an escarpment, with superb views over the magnificent and unspoiled scenery of the Severn Valley and Malvern Hills. The hotel, set in 37 acres of beautifully maintained gardens and green pastures, has been lovingly refurbished. Its bedrooms, while offering visitors every modern comfort and providing considerate extras, retain the charm and atmosphere of a bygone age. The award-winning restaurant features the best of traditional English and classic cuisine. As it relies on fresh local produce, it varies seasonally but is always combined with an extensive and well-chosen wine list. For the sports enthusiast, fishing, golf, squash, pony trekking and clay pigeon shooting are available nearby as are the elegant spa towns of Bath and Cheltenham, Slimbridge Wildfowl Trust, Prinknash Abbey, Berkeley Castle and Stratford-upon-Avon. Price guide: £92–£110. Special 2-night breaks are offered for £210–£240. Directions: Hatton Court is located 3 miles south of Gloucester on the B4073, Gloucester–Painswick road, off A46.

THE MANOR HOUSE

NORTHLANDS, WALKINGTON, NORTH HUMBERSIDE HU17 8RT
TEL: 0482 881645 FAX: 0482 866501

Set in 3 acres of tree-lined grounds, overlooking parkland, The Manor House is on the fringe of the great rolling Yorkshire Wolds. This late 19th-century retreat is perfect for those seeking relaxation and sybaritic pleasure. The bedrooms, with their attractive views, are individually furnished and decorated to the highest standard; guests are pampered with unexpected and useful personal comforts. The chef/patron, Derek Baugh, formerly of the Dorchester Hotel, has evolved a distinctive, creative style of cuisine and the connoisseur will find Mrs Baugh's confections an irresistible temptation. Summer evenings may be spent wining and dining in the conservatory overlooking the south terrace and lawns. Riding, clay pigeon shooting, racing and golf are all nearby, and the hotel has its own croquet lawn. Welcomes children over 12 and dogs by arrangement. Price guide: £80–110. Directions: From Walkington on B1230 towards Beverley, turn left at traffic lights, then left and left again for the hotel.

THE SPRINGS HOTEL

NORTH STOKE, WALLINGFORD, OXFORDSHIRE OX10 6BE
TEL: 0491 36687 FAX: 0491 36877

In the heart of the beautiful and historic Thames Valley, the Springs Hotel – one of the first mock-Tudor houses to be built in England – lies in 30 acres of gardens overlooking the spring-fed lake from which it gets its name. In the panelled reception lounge traditional furnishings and a glowing log fire reinforce a friendly, relaxed atmosphere. The bedrooms are complete with every luxury down to ice cubes and bathrobes, and the two suites have jacuzzi spas. The candle-lit restaurant looks out onto the floodlit lake, the home of swans, wild ducks and kingfishers, while the tastefully furnished, oak-panelled cocktail bar overlooks the grounds to the lake. The menu offers the finest quality international cuisine, and guests may eat outdoors in the summer. Facilities at the Springs include a swimming pool, tennis court, putting green, croquet lawn, sauna bath and touring bicycles. Oxford and Windsor are nearby and there is access to many major sporting events such as horseracing at Newbury and Cheltenham, and the Royal Henley Regatta. Price guide: £110–£140. Directions: From the M40, take Exit 6 onto B4009, through Wallingford to Benson, turn left onto A423, straight on for A4074 to Reading at roundabout. After ½ mile, go right back onto B4009. Springs ½ mile further, on right.

FAIRLAWNS HOTEL AND RESTAURANT

LITTLE ASTON ROAD, ALDRIDGE, WALSALL, WEST MIDLANDS WS9 ONU
TEL: 0922 55122 FAX: 0922 743210 TELEX: 339873

Marquee weddings, theme parties – anything from a casino evening to a barn dance – and conferences comprising up to 60 delegates can all be catered for at Fairlawns. So, of course, can families – and their dogs. Hotel manager Nigel Needham says Fairlawns restaurant is the 'jewel in our crown' and chef, Stefan Wilkinson, changes the bill of fare weekly to take advantage of the best seasonal produce. Menus can be tailored to suit the needs of everyone from young children and anyone on a special diet to the high-powered executive who wants to impress a client. Ideally placed for exploring local beauty spots – Cannock Chase and the Derbyshire Dales are only a short drive away – and for shopping in nearby Birmingham, Derby and Wolverhampton; the hotel is also within easy reach of leisure facilities such as swimming pools and golf courses. With the NEC only 25 minutes away, your needs, whether business or pleasure, can be catered for. Price guide: £47.50–£87.50. Directions: 800 yards from the crossroads of the A454 (Walsall-Sutton Coldfield) and A452 (Chester Road).

THE HAYCOCK HOTEL

WANSFORD-IN-ENGLAND, NR PETERBOROUGH, CAMBRIDGESHIRE PE8 6JA
TEL: 0780 782223 FAX: 0780 783031 TELEX: 32710 HAYCOK G

An historically interesting building, The Haycock, a celebrated early 17th-century coaching inn, still has an 18th-century sign depicting drunken Barnaby in his haycock. It has been recently extensively refurbished, while retaining its period character. It is set in a beautiful unspoiled village, and has picturesque grounds reaching down to the river. The hotel has its own cricket pitch and guests can enjoy a leisurely game of boules on the lawn. All the bedrooms are individually and delightfully furnished, and the public rooms are welcoming and atmospheric.

The restaurant is renowned for its traditional English cooking: prime Scotch sirloin from the trolley, steak and kidney pie or pudding, and game in season, are served with fresh Fenland vegetables. There is an extensive wine list, and an unusual range of first-class wines are available by the glass. The Haycock also has an excellent new business centre, a ballroom overlooking the gardens, and its own cricket pitch. Price guide: £80–£100. Directions: The hotel is clearly signed from the A1 a few miles south of Stamford.

HANBURY MANOR

THUNDRIDGE, NR WARE, HERTFORDSHIRE SG12 0SD
TEL: 0920 487722 FAX: 0920 487692 TELEX: 817515

Hanbury Manor combines impressive original features – beamed ceilings, oak panelling and superb tapestries – with a host of up-to-the-minute leisure facilities. The hotel's fitness centre includes an indoor swimming pool, squash courts, gym, plus sauna and steam baths. Resident beauty therapists soothe away guests' cares with the aid of herbal wraps, mineral baths and massage. Fitness assessment therapists can advise on a personal keep-fit programme. The hotel has 2 snooker tables, tennis courts and a jogging trail. An 18-hole championship golf course designed by Jack Nicklaus II has been created in the grounds. Shooting, archery, horse-riding, and hot air ballooning are available by arrangement. There are four restaurants varying in style from the formal dining of the Zodiac Restaurant to the casual Vardon Grill. All cuisine is under the guidance of the eminent Albert Roux of Le Gavroche fame. For the business community, there are ten well-appointed conference rooms which can cater for up to 100 delegates. Fax, photocopying and secretarial services are available, and there is a helipad in the grounds. The hotel is an ideal base from which to explore the heartland of England. Price guide: £130–£300. Directions: 28 miles north of London on A10, north of Ware.

98 rms

THE PRIORY HOTEL

CHURCH GREEN, WAREHAM, DORSET BH20 4ND
TEL: 0929 551666 FAX: 0929 554519 TELEX: 41143 PRIORY G

Dating from the early 16th century, the former Lady St Mary Priory has offered sanctuary to travellers for centuries. Now, under the ownership of Stuart and John Turner, it offers a retreat from the hustle and bustle of city life. The Priory stands in 4 acres of landscaped gardens on the banks of the River Frome surrounded by the idyllic Dorset countryside. The bedrooms are all different and most offer outstanding views of the Purbeck Hills. A former boathouse has been transformed into two spacious luxury suites at the river's edge. Furnished with antiques, the drawing room, residents' lounge and intimate bar together create a convivial atmosphere. An imaginative menu using fresh, seasonal produce is available in both the traditional dining room and the unusual Abbots Cellar. Nearby there are facilities for sailing, fishing, golf and rambling; other local attractions include Corfe Castle, Lulworth Cove, Poole and Swanage. Price guide: £85–£160. Directions: Wareham is on the A351 to the west of Bournemouth and Poole. The hotel is beside the River Frome to the east of Wareham.

BISHOPSTROW HOUSE

BISHOPSTROW, WARMINSTER, WILTSHIRE BA12 9HH
TEL: 0985 212312 FAX: 0985 216769 TELEX: 444829

Bishopstrow House was built by John Pinch of Bath in 1817 and today guests can enjoy the grace of a Georgian mansion together with the benefits of modern facilities, like heated swimming pools. The finely proportioned public rooms are home to English and French antiques, 19th-century oil paintings and Persian carpets. The bedrooms are grandly furnished with canopied beds, festoon draperies and, in some cases, private safes. Some bathrooms have large, circular baths fitted with jacuzzi whirlpools.

The emphasis is on imaginative cooking in the modern style, with English and French dishes prepared by Chris Suter, winner of the Young Chef of the Year Award 1990. Longleat House, the beautiful gardens and arboretum of Stourhead, Bath and Shaftesbury are close at hand and the West Wiltshire Golf Course is about ½ a mile away. Children over 3 are welcome. Price guide: £110–£272. Directions: Bishopstrow House is just south-east of Warminster on the B3414.

THE GLEBE AT BARFORD

CHURCH STREET, BARFORD, WARWICKSHIRE CV35 8BS
TEL: 0926 624218 FAX: 0926 624625

The Glebe is an elegant Georgian house dating from 1820; formerly a rectory, it stands in an acre of lawned garden alongside the village church. The bedrooms are all individually furnished, and the restaurant provides the best of traditional English and Continental cuisine. All rooms and public areas have recently been upgraded and refurbished, and new leisure facilities have been added. Guests can now relax and get fit in the new leisure complex which includes an indoor pool, steam room, sauna, sun-terrace and fitness centre. The hotel is an ideal base for touring the historic towns of Stratford-upon-Avon and Leamington Spa, and the nearby Cotswolds. Birmingham International Airport and the National Exhibition Centre are only 18 miles away. A fine golf course is within easy reach. Price guide: £89.50–£110. Directions: Barford lies on the A429 south of Warwick.

WOOD HALL

LINTON, NR WETHERBY, WEST YORKSHIRE LS22 4JA
TEL: 0937 67271 FAX: 0937 64353

Wood Hall is an elegant, Georgian house with a Jacobean wing, overlooking the River Wharfe. Its grounds, of over 100 acres, are approached via a private drive through farmland. The bedrooms are of a very high standard, and some have their own drawing rooms. Memorable cuisine, complemented by a wide choice of wines, is served in three dining rooms. The hotel has excellent facilities for small conferences in private rooms, with business aids, fax and secretarial services. Other enviable facilities include ample car parking, a helipad, private trout and barbel fishing in a mile-long stretch of the Wharfe, plus billiards, croquet, and miles of jogging paths. Ballooning, golf, clay pigeon shooting and archery are available by arrangement. Nearby are stately homes and adventure parks, art galleries and the magnificent Yorkshire Dales. Harrogate, Leeds and York are within 15 minutes' drive. Price guide: £105–£135. Directions: From Wetherby take A661 towards Harrogate, take turning for Sicklinghall and Linton, then left turn for Linton and Wood Hall. Turn right opposite the Windmill Public House, and the hotel is 1¼ miles further on.

WOODHAYES COUNTRY HOUSE HOTEL

WHIMPLE, NR EXETER, DEVON EX5 2TD
TEL: 0404 822237

A small and luxurious Georgian country house hotel with the atmosphere of a private house. The beautifully proportioned and exquisite rooms will satisfy even the most discerning. The dining room has French doors leading onto a suntrap, paved terrace; the food is a balance of French and English, with an explanatory wine list. The snug bar leading from the green lounge – a lovely, sunny, flowery room – provides a traditional atmosphere in which to enjoy your pre-dinner drink. This charming house is situated in delightful gardens where you can enjoy a gentle game of croquet or a more vigorous game of tennis. Welcomes children over 12. Price guide: £75. Directions: Whimple lies just off the A30 between Exeter and Honiton.

WILLINGTON HALL HOTEL
WILLINGTON, NR TARPORLEY, CHESHIRE CW6 0NB
TEL: 0829 52321 FAX: 0829 52596

Built by a Cheshire landowner and converted into a hotel by one of his descendants 12 years ago, Willington Hall is set in parkland with wonderful views across to the Welsh mountains. The beautiful gardens complement the building's secluded warmth and comfort. The hotel, very popular with local people, is under the personal supervision of Ross Pigot who, along with the friendly and attentive staff, will make you very welcome. An ideal spot for those who want to explore the historic city of Chester, and who prefer the tranquillity of a country house hotel. Nearby are Tatton Park, Beeston Castle and Oulton Park racetrack. Closed Christmas Day. Price guide: £70. Directions: Take the A51 from Tarporley to Chester and turn right at the Bulls Head public house at Clotton. The Willington Hall Hotel is 1 mile ahead on the left.

THE STANNEYLANDS HOTEL

STANNEYLANDS ROAD, WILMSLOW, CHESHIRE SK9 4EY
TEL: 0625 525225 FAX: 0625 537282

Privately owned and managed by Gordon Beech, Stanneylands is a handsome country house set in several acres of impressive gardens which feature a unique collection of trees and shrubs. The tastefully furnished bedrooms offer delightful views over the extensive gardens or the rolling Cheshire countryside. Classically furnished public rooms give a relaxing atmosphere of quiet luxury. In the restaurant, renowned as one of the best in the Manchester area, attentive staff serve the finest of English contemporary cuisine, and live occasional music enhances the enjoyment. In addition, a private oak-panelled dining room can accommodate up to 50 people; there is also a larger suite for conferences or personal celebrations. Conveniently located for tours of the gentle Cheshire Plain or the more rugged Peak District, and with its bustling market towns and important industrial heritage, Cheshire has something for everyone. Children over 14 are welcome. Price guide: £102–£120. Directions: Only 3 miles from Manchester International Airport, Stanneylands is located on a minor road which runs from the B5166 at Styal to the A34 between Wilmslow and Handforth. Bear right on this road and you will find the hotel just after crossing the River Dean.

BEECHLEAS

17 POOLE ROAD, WIMBORNE MINSTER, DORSET BH21 1QA
TEL: 0202 841684

Beechleas is a beautifully restored Georgian Grade II listed building with all en suite accommodation. It is situated 5 minutes walk from the centre of Wimborne Minster town with its ancient Minster and is within easy reach of such National Trust properties as Corfe Castle, Badbury Rings and the Kingston Lacy Estate. From here, you can relax with a ramble through the rolling Dorset countryside, browse in the country antique shops or enjoy the sophisticated facilities of Bournemouth and Poole, just 20 minutes drive away. All the food is carefully prepared in Beechleas' own kitchen where only the very best, fresh and natural produce is used. Most of the produce is bought from nearby Hockey's farm. Price guide: £60–£80. Directions: From London take the M3, then A349 to Poole Road. From Salisbury take the A338. From Devon follow the A35/A31.

LAINSTON HOUSE HOTEL
SPARSHOLT, WINCHESTER, HAMPSHIRE SO21 2LT
TEL: 0962 63588 FAX: 0962 72672 TELEX: 477375

Standing in 63 acres of superb downland countryside, this graceful William and Mary country house has been lovingly converted into an excellent hotel which retains all the elegance and warmth of the original manor. Stylish, individually designed bedrooms invite relaxation, and the main reception rooms are elegantly and comfortably furnished. Freshly prepared food, excellent service and superb views over the lawns combine to make the restaurant one of the most popular in Hampshire. The hotel has facilities for small informal meetings, or larger gatherings in the superbly restored 17th-century barn. The charming grounds hold many surprises – a 12th-century chapel, reputedly haunted, an 18th-century herb garden, a dovecote and a croquet lawn. Historic Winchester and the Royal Winchester Golf Course are a short distance away, while Romsey Abbey, Salisbury and the New Forest are within easy reach. The hotel has its own stretch of the River Test which is available to guests and provides excellent trout fishing. Other facilities available locally include riding and shooting. Price guide: £120–£250. Directions: Lainston House is well signposted off the A272 Winchester/Stockbridge road, at Sparsholt 2½ miles from Winchester.

GILPIN LODGE

CROOK ROAD, WINDERMERE, CUMBRIA LA23 3NE
TEL: 09662 88818 FAX: 09662 88058

Gilpin Lodge is a delightful small Lakeland country house hotel and restaurant situated in 20 tranquil acres of woodland and gardens. The idyllic surrounding countryside, with Lake Windermere only 2 miles away, must be explored to appreciate its true beauty. Windermere Golf Club is ½ mile away, and guests also have free use of the Parklands Country Club nearby. The hotel also has a croquet lawn. Inside, John and Christine Cunliffe have created a pastoral ambience, with their beautifully decorated and elegantly furnished public rooms. The superb and imaginatively cooked five-course dinners are created by Christine. Bedrooms have big bathrooms and every facility one would expect from this special hotel offering the highest standards of comfort. The new wing, comprising drawing room and three large bedrooms with four-poster beds, evokes the Gilpin Lodge tradition of spaciousness, comfort and elegance. ETB Highly Commended (4 Crowns). Price guide: £60–£110. Directions: Gilpin Lodge is on the B5284 west of Crook.

LANGDALE CHASE
WINDERMERE, CUMBRIA LA23 1LW
TEL: 05394 32201 FAX: 05394 32604

The shore of Lake Windermere is the glorious setting where Langdale Chase nestles in its own immaculate 5-acre grounds, offering a unique opportunity to rest and feast the eyes on picturesque views of this famous lake and the Langdale Pikes beyond. Here, guests are pampered with gracious hospitality enhanced by the decorous warmth of oak panelling, the welcoming crackle of a log fire in autumn and spring, and an excellent menu. From the hall, a magnificent staircase leads to individually furnished bedrooms, and in a tranquil bedroom over the lakeside boathouse the weary traveller can indulge in the luxury of being lulled to sleep by the gentle lap of the waters. Fishing, golf, sailing and water-skiing are within easy reach. Nearby: the homes of Ruskin and Wordsworth, Beatrix Potter's farms, and England's oldest narrow-gauge railway. Open all year. Price guide: £90–£130. Directions: Situated on the A591 3 miles north of Windermere, 2 miles south of Ambleside.

OAKLEY COURT

WINDSOR ROAD, WATER OAKLEY, NR WINDSOR, BERKSHIRE SL4 5UR
TEL: 0628 74141 FAX: 0628 37011 TELEX: 849958

Built in 1859, the grandeur of this Victorian hotel, situated in 35 acres of lush gardens sloping down to the River Thames, is quite awe-inspiring. The drawing room, library and sitting room have been lovingly restored in the traditional country house style. The luxury here is refined and understated, assuring you that this hotel is one of distinction. The Oak Leaf Restaurant is renowned for its modern French cuisine, prepared for you by one of England's master chefs. It is hard to believe as you relax in these superb surroundings, attended to by impeccable staff, that you are only minutes away from Heathrow and the M4. The modern world seems a million miles away as you enjoy the hotel's excellent facilities, including its historic billiard room and exclusive fishing rights on the Thames. Should you wish to venture outside this haven, Windsor, Eton and Ascot are within easy reach. Price guide: £140–£340. Directions: Situated just off the A308, between Windsor and Maidenhead.

THE OLD VICARAGE COUNTRY HOUSE HOTEL

CHURCH ROAD, WITHERSLACK, NR GRANGE-OVER-SANDS, CUMBRIA LA11 6RS
TEL: 044852 381 FAX: 044852 373

The Old Vicarage, a delightful Georgian period house, where the co-owners, Roger and Jill Burrington-Brown and Stan and Irene Reeve, go out of their way to ensure guests' wellbeing, is a must for lovers of peace and good food. Many of the rooms have a Victorian feel. The bedrooms are en suite and are furnished with antiques, bric-à-brac, and Victorian wine and medicine bottles discovered during gardening work. Five luxurious new rooms are in The Orchard House which opens onto woodland. One has a four-poster bed; the others have private terraces. In the res-

taurant, managed by David Moses, chef Stuart Harrison ensures that high quality cuisine is available daily and the good food is complemented by a wine list of over 150 labels. The Old Vicarage is AA Red Star and BTA Commended. Closed for Christmas week. Welcomes children over 12 years and dogs by arrangement. Price guide: £70–£120. Directions: Leave the M6 at Junction 36, follow sign for Barrow A590. Witherslack is about 10 minutes' drive, on the right.

SECKFORD HALL
WOODBRIDGE, SUFFOLK IP13 6NU
TEL: 0394 385678 FAX: 0394 380610 TELEX: 987446

Seckford Hall, built in 1530, is set in 34 acres of tranquil parkland containing a lake, where guests may fish for trout. Furnished throughout as a private house with many fine period pieces, the panelled rooms, beamed ceilings, carved doors and great stone fireplaces are displayed against the splendour of English oak. The bedrooms have been individually and tastefully furnished. Traditional and international cuisine is served in the restaurant, while light snacks can be taken in the Buttery, which overlooks the pool in the new Courtyard development. Formerly a Tudor tithe barn, the Courtyard at Seckford Hall opened recently with a complex of ten cottage-style suites, one of which has been designed with the disabled guest in mind, and leisure facilities including an indoor swimming pool, spa and gym. The Hall is an ideal base for touring Suffolk and visiting the beauty spots of Constable country. For the sports enthusiast, six golf courses are within easy reach, and facilities for squash, fishing and sailing are a short drive away. The hotel is closed on Christmas Day. Price guide: £80–£120. Directions: Remain on the A12 Woodbridge bypass until you see the blue and white hotel sign.

THE FEATHERS HOTEL

MARKET STREET, WOODSTOCK, OXFORDSHIRE OX7 1SX
TEL: 0993 812291 FAX: 0993 813158 TELEX: 83147 VIA OR G

This comfortable hotel dates from the 17th century and stands in the centre of Woodstock, a few minutes' stroll from the entrance to Blenheim Palace, home of the 11th Duke of Marlborough and birthplace of Sir Winston Churchill. The Feathers, furnished throughout with antiques, is privately owned and run. Log fires burn in the public rooms in cooler weather and the restaurant is renowned. In the summer, lunch may be taken in the courtyard garden off the Garden Bar which is a popular local meeting place. Full secretarial facilities are available for guests who are on business. Woodstock is one of England's loveliest and best-known country towns. It dates from the 12th century, is built largely of Cotswold stone and has a wealth of attractive shops and museums. It is only 8 miles from Oxford and ideally placed for touring some of the most beautiful and historic places in England. Price guide: £90–£125. Directions: From the south, take A34 to Woodstock; take 2nd left after Blenheim Palace gates. The hotel is on the corner of Market Street.

WOOLACOMBE BAY HOTEL

SOUTH STREET, WOOLACOMBE, DEVON EX34 7BN
TEL: 0271 870388 FAX: 0271 870388 Ext 437 TELEX: 46761

Woolacombe Bay Hotel stands in 6 acres of grounds leading to 3 miles of golden sand. Built in the days of gracious living, the hotel exudes a feeling of luxury and style. The superbly equipped bedrooms offer such additional facilities as satellite TV and baby-listening, and the urivalled recreation on hand includes unlimited free access to tennis, squash, indoor and outdoor pools, billiards, bowls, sauna, solarium, croquet, dancing and films. The hotel can also arrange chartered power-boating, massage, horse-riding, pheasant and clay pigeon shooting, etc. But being energetic is not a requirement for enjoying the qualities of Woolacombe Bay. Many of its regulars choose simply to relax in its grand public rooms and in the grounds which extend to the rolling surf of an impressive bay. Some of the finest coastal scenery in England is to be found within 10 minutes' drive. An hour's motoring and you are in the Doone Valley, arguably the most beautiful part of Exmoor. Preferential rates are offered for golf at the renowned Saunton Golf Club. The restaurant offers traditional English and French cooking. Theme weekends and midweek breaks include golf, horse-riding and clay pigeon shooting. AA and RAC 3 Stars; WCTB 5 Crowns. Price guide: £92–£172.50 including dinner and VAT. Weekend breaks available. Directions: Centre of village off main Barnstaple to Ilfracombe road.

WATERSMEET HOTEL
MORTEHOE, WOOLACOMBE, DEVON EX34 7EB
TEL: 0271 870333 FAX: 0271 870890

Watersmeet Hotel, poised in a superb setting along National Trust coastline, has gardens leading directly to the beach below. The resident owners, Brian and Pat Wheeldon, ensure that Watersmeet distils the stylistic and luxurious atmosphere of a country house. The main bedrooms overlook the sea, and there are panoramic coastal views from all the lounges. The beautiful Pavilion Restaurant, where both English and Continental cuisine is served, together with an excellent choice of wines, affords especially lovely views. The decor throughout is fresh and good use is made of co-ordinated designer fabrics. The hotel has been awarded all three merit awards by the RAC – for excellent hospitality, restaurant and comfort – a triple distinction which very few hotels achieve. Croquet in the gardens is one of the sports facilities on offer; clay pigeon shooting and horse-riding are available too, and concessionary rates are provided for golf on the nearby championship course at Saunton. Closed in January. Price guide: £80–£150 including dinner. Directions: From Barnstaple follow A361 signed Ilfracombe, after 8 miles turn left at roundabout and follow signs to Mortehoe.

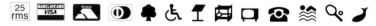

WROXTON HOUSE HOTEL

WROXTON ST MARY, NR BANBURY, OXFORDSHIRE OX15 6QB
TEL: 0295 730777 FAX: 0295 730800

Built of honeyed local stone, Wroxton House has undergone a sensitive restoration to link three village houses, dating from the 17th century, with a delightful clocktower wing and conservatory lounge. The relaxing character of the hotel is created by a carefully chosen staff who combine attentive service with friendliness and informality. Guests' privacy is assured in the spacious lounges which are bright and airy and feature thoughtfully chosen furnishings and comfortable armchairs. The 32 en suite bedrooms have been individually decorated and the original timbers preserved in many of the older rooms. The classic English styles complement the deeply polished woods of the furniture. Dine by candle light in the intimate restaurant created from three adjoining rooms in which the Cotswold atmosphere is enhanced by original beams, inglenooks, carved oak recesses, horse brasses and pewter. The expertly prepared menus proffer chef Didier Bienaime's personal interpretation of classic British dishes which make imaginative use of the freshest local produce. Golf can be arranged. Price guide: £65–£95. Directions: Wroxton is 2 miles outside Banbury on the A422 Stratford road.

BILBROUGH MANOR COUNTRY HOUSE HOTEL

BILBROUGH, YORK YO2 3PH
TEL: 0937 834002 FAX: 0937 834724

Colin and Susan Bell's decision to install a butler at Bilbrough Manor is a reflection of the skill and wit with which they run their hotel. This warm and friendly country house hotel offers all the gracious elements of the 'Upstairs Downstairs' portrayal of service, comfort and fine food. The tremendous character of the place hits you straightaway – finely proportioned rooms with oak panelling, beautiful fireplaces with open fires in winter and gorgeous, comfortable furnishings. The cuisine served in the oak-panelled dining room, managed by Antonio Esteve, is prepared by an enthusiastic team of young chefs led by David Deacon who specialises in classic French fare. The hotel is on the edge of the conservation village of Bilbrough, just 5 miles from the centre of York. Over 100 acres of farm and woodland surround the gardens where you can relax or play croquet on the lawn – out of the way of the helicopter landing pad. From the gardens you can see to the Vale of York and beyond to Ilkley Moor. The hotel can arrange fishing and shooting for guests and there are horse-riding facilities nearby. Children over 12 welcome. Price guide: £85–£140. Directions: From A64 at Bilbrough (west of York), turn opposite Happy Eater, then first left to the manor.

THE GRANGE HOTEL

CLIFTON, YORK YO3 6AA
TEL: 0904 644744   FAX: 0904 612453   TELEX: 57210

Set close to the ancient city walls of York, this classic Regency town house has been carefully restored and its beautifully proportioned rooms richly and sympathetically decorated. The flower-filled morning room is especially warm and welcoming, with deep sofas and a blazing log fire in cooler months. The luxurious bedrooms, all en suite, are individually designed and decorated with antique furniture and English chintz. Attention to detail and efficient room service ensure guests every comfort. For The Ivy Restaurant, the very best in French and traditional country house cooking is prepared by Cara Baird, who comes to The Grange from London's renowned *Le Gavroche* Restaurant. The menu is complemented by an excellent wine list. Light gourmet dishes are served in The Brasserie with interesting wines at reasonable prices. Full conference facilities are available in the library and drawing room. A syndicate room is also available. Price guide: £95–£120. Directions: The Grange Hotel lies on the A19 York–Thirsk road.

MIDDLETHORPE HALL

BISHOPTHORPE ROAD, YORK YO2 1QB
TEL: 0904 641241 FAX: 0904 620176 TELEX: 57802

Middlethorpe Hall, built in 1699, was the home, during the 18th century, of Lady Mary Wortley, the celebrated diarist. Set in 26 acres of parkland to the south of the ancient city of York, the hotel grounds include a walled garden, ha-has, a white garden, a small lake, a dovecote and some unusual specimen trees. The bedrooms have been individually and tastefully decorated, in keeping with the architecture of the building. In addition, some incorporate special features such as a four-poster and a *trompe l'œil* window. The restaurant offers the best of contemporary English cookery providing an imaginative menu combined with a carefully chosen wine list. The hotel overlooks the racecourse, and central York, with its fascinating restored buildings, streets and museums, is nearby. The keen walker can explore the beauty of the Dales and the magnificent scenery of the Yorkshire Moors, while Fountains and Rievaulx Abbeys and the country houses of Castle Howard and Beningborough are a short drive away. Children over 9 are welcome. Price guide: £133–£151. Directions: Take the A64 off A1 near Tadcaster, follow the signs to York West, then smaller signs to Bishopthorpe.

MOUNT ROYALE HOTEL

THE MOUNT, YORK YO2 2DA
TEL: 0904 628856 FAX: 0904 611171 TELEX: 57414

The Mount Royale is a tasteful blending of two elegant and lovingly restored William IV houses. It is personally run by proprietors Richard and Christine Oxtoby. With its acre of Old English garden, which features a heated swimming pool, this is a peaceful haven near the centre of York. The bedrooms are imaginatively and comfortably furnished, many with beautiful, antique beds. The restaurant, overlooking the gardens, offers the best of traditional English cuisine. Other amenities include a snooker room with a full-sized table, steam room, sauna, solarium and trimnasium. The historic and well-preserved city of York is minutes away, with its Minster and mediaeval streets. Its equally famous race course, where guests can enjoy the flat racing from May to October, is within walking distance of the hotel and for country lovers, the Yorkshire Dales are nearby. Dogs by arrangement. Price guide: £80–£95. Directions: From the A64 follow signs to York west. Hotel is on the right past the racecourse.

The following establishments can be found in *Johansens Recommended Country Inns and Restaurants in Great Britain 1991:*

The Bell Hotel
Market Hill
Clare
Suffolk CO10 8NN
Tel: 0787 277741
Price guide: £60–£95

The Acorn Inn Hotel
28 Fore Street
Evershot
Dorset DT2 0JW
Tel: 0935 83228
Price guide: £44–£80

The Bell Hotel
Church Street
Charlbury
Nr Oxford
Oxfordshire OX7 3AP
Tel: 0608 810278
Price guide: £69–£73

The Anchor Inn
Exebridge
Nr Dulverton
Somerset TA22 9AZ
Tel: 0398 23433
Price guide: £53

The Bell Inn
High Road
Horndon-on-the-Hill
Essex SS17 8LD
Tel: 0375 642463
Price guide: £60–£75

The Angel at Ludlow
Broad Street
Ludlow
Shropshire SY8 1NG
Tel: 0584 872581
Price guide: £62–£87

The Bell Inn
Great North Road
Stilton
Peterborough PE7 3RA
Tel: 0733 241066
Price guide: £75

Bank House Hotel
Church Street
Uttoxeter
Staffordshire ST14 8AG
Tel: 0889 566922
Price guide: £50–£70

The Black Horse Inn
Grimsthorpe
Bourne
Lincolnshire PE10 0LY
Tel: 077832 247
Price guide: £55–£65

Bankes Arms Hotel
Manor Road
Studland
Dorset BH19 3AU
Tel: 092944 225
Price guide: £50–£60

The Black Rabbit
Mill Road
Offham
Arundel
West Sussex BN18 9PB
Tel: 0903 882828
Restaurant only

The Barn Owl Inn
Aller Mills
Kingskerwell
Newton Abbot
Devon TQ12 5AN
Tel: 0803 872130/968
Price guide: £60–£75

The Blue Boar Inn
North Heath
Chieveley
Newbury
Berkshire RG16 8UE
Tel: 0635 248236
Price guide: £75

**The Barton Angler
Country Inn**
Irstead Road
Neatishead
Nr Wroxham
Norfolk NR12 8XP
Tel: 0692 630740
Price guide: £42–£77

**The Brickhouse Hotel and
Restaurant**
Chipping
Nr Preston
Lancashire PR3 2QH
Tel: 0995 61316
Price guide: £46

The Chequers Inn
Kiln Lane
Wooburn Common
Buckinghamshire HP10 0JQ
Tel: 06285 29575
Price guide: £75–£90

The Cholmondeley Arms
Cholmondeley
Cheshire SY14 8BT
Tel: 0829 720300ʻ
Price guide: £45

The Colesbourne Inn
Colesbourne
Nr Cheltenham
Gloucestershire GL53 9NP
Tel: 024287 376
Price guide: £48

The Compass Inn
Tormarton
Nr Badminton
Avon GL9 1JB
Tel: 045421 242/577
Price guide: £65–£75

Corbet Arms Hotel
High Street
Market Drayton
Shropshire TF9 1PY
Tel: 0630 2037
Price guide: £50–£60

Cottage of Content
Carey
Hereford HR2 6NG
Tel: 0432 840242
Price guide: £42

**Countrymen Restaurant at the
Black Lion Hotel**
Long Melford
Suffolk CO10 9DN
Tel: 0787 312356
Price guide: £60

**The Cricketers' Arms
(The Inn on the Green)**
Rickling Green
Quendon
Saffron Walden
Essex CB11 3YG
Tel: 079988 322/595
Price guide: £60

The Crown
High Street
Southwold
Suffolk IP18 6DP
Tel: 0502 722275
Price guide: £46

**The Crown Inn at Hopton
Wafers**
Hopton Wafers
Cleobury Mortimer
Worcestershire DY14 0NB
Tel: 0299 270372
Price guide: £46

**East Ayton Lodge Hotel
and Restaurant**
Moor Lane
East Ayton
Scarborough
North Yorkshire YO13 9EW
Tel: 0723 864227
Price guide: £40–£80

The Falcon Hotel
St John Street
Lowtown
Bridgnorth
Shropshire WV15 6AG
Tel: 0746 763134
Price guide: £45

Feathers Hotel
High Street
Ledbury
Herefordshire HR8 1DS
Tel: 0531 5266
Price guide: £75–£90

The Five Bells
Wickham
Nr Newbury
Berkshire RG16 8HH
Tel: 0488 38242
Price guide: £35–£45

The Fossebridge Inn
Fossebridge
Nr Cheltenham
Gloucestershire GL54 3JS
Tel: 0285 720721
Price guide: £60–£75

The Fox Country Hotel
Ibstone
Nr High Wycombe
Buckinghamshire HP14 3GG
Tel: 049163 289/722
Price guide: £57-£75

The George at Nunney
Nunney
Nr Frome
Somerset BA11 4LW
Tel: 037384 458
Price guide: £50–£65

The Harbour Inn
Commercial Road
Porthleven
Nr Helston
Cornwall TR13 9JD
Tel: 0326 573876
Price guide: £36–£48

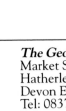

The George Hotel
Market Street
Hatherleigh
Devon EX20 3JN
Tel: 0837 810454
Price guide: £46–£62

Hare & Hounds Country Inn
Bowland Bridge
Grange-over-Sands
Cumbria LA11 6NN
Tel: 04488 333
Price guide: £40–£52

The George Hotel
High Street
Odiham
Basingstoke
Hampshire RG25 1LP
Tel: 0256 702081
Price guide: £65–£75

Holcombe Hotel
High Street
Deddington
Oxfordshire OX5 4SL
Tel: 0869 38274
Price guide: £69–£83

The George Hotel at Buckden
Great North Road
Buckden
Cambridgeshire PE18 9XA
Tel: 0480 810307
Price guide: £55–£70

The Hoops Inn
Horns Cross
Nr Clovelly
North Devon EX39 5DL
Tel: 0237 451222
Price guide: £43–£60

The Granby Inn
Front Street
Longframlington
Morpeth
Northumberland NE65 8DP
Tel: 0665 70228
Price guide: £48–£52

The Hundred House Hotel
Bridgnorth Road
Norton
Nr Shifnal
Telford
Salop TF11 9EE
Tel: 095271 353
Price guide: £65–£80

Green Farm Hotel & Restaurant
Thorpe Market
Norwich
Norfolk NR11 8TH
Tel: 0263833 602
Price guide: £70

The Inn at Whitewell
Forest of Bowland
Clitheroe
Lancashire BB7 3AT
Tel: 02008 222
Price guide: £48–£55

The Green Man Inn
Fownhope
Nr Hereford
Herefordshire HR1 4PE
Tel: 0432 860248
Price guide: £40-£43.50

Inn on the Lake
Ockford Road
Godalming
Surrey GU7 1RH
Tel: 04868 5575
Price guide: £80–£90

The Gretna Chase
Gretna
Carlisle CA6 5JB
Tel: 0461 37517
Price guide: £43–£80

The Jefferson Arms
Thorganby
York
Yorkshire TO4 6DB
Tel: 0904 89316
Price guide: £62.50-£73

The Jersey Arms
Middleton Stoney
Oxfordshire OX6 8SE
Tel: 086989 234
Price guide: £60–£90

Leatherne Bottel Riverside Inn & Restaurant
The Bridleway
Goring-on-Thames
Berkshire RG8 0HS
Tel: 0491 872667
Restaurant only

Jubilee Inn
Pelynt
Nr Looe
Cornwall PL13 2JZ
Tel: 0503 20312
Price guide: £47–£52

The Lugger Hotel
Portloe
Nr Truroe
Cornwall TR2 5RD
Tel: 0872 501322
Price guide: £90–£110

King's Arms Hotel and Restaurant
Market Place
Askrigg
Wensleydale
North Yorkshire DL8 3HQ
Tel: 0969 50258
Price guide: £50–£60

Mallyan Spout Hotel
Goathland
Nr Whitby
North Yorkshire TO22 5AN
Tel: 0947 86206
Price guide: £60–£110

The Kings Arms Inn
Montacute
Somerset TA15 6UU
Tel: 0935 822513
Price guide: £55–£70

The Manor Hotel
West Bexington
Dorchester
Dorset DT2 9DF
Tel: 0308 897616/785
Price guide: £60

Kingshead House Restaurant
Birdlip
Gloucestershire GL4 8JH
Tel: 0452 862299
Restaurant only

The Maynard Arms Hotel
Main Road
Grindleford
Nr Sheffield
South Yorkshire S30 1HP
Tel: 0433 30321
Price guide: £64–£73

The Kingshead Inn and Restaurant
The Green
Bledington
Nr Kingham
Oxfordshire OX7 6HD
Tel: 0608 658365
Price guide: £49

The Milburn Arms Hotel
Rosedale Abbey
Pickering
North Yorkshire YO18 8RA
Tel: 07515 312
Price guide: £72

La Villa Country Hotel and Restaurant
222 Rykneld Road
Littleover
Derby
Derbyshire DE3 7AP
Tel: 0332 510161
Price guide: £70

The Mill Inn
Mungrisdale
Penrith
Cumbria CA11 0XR
Tel: 059683 632
Price guide: £40-£50

The Lamb Inn
Shipton-under-Wychwood
Oxfordshire OX7 6DQ
Tel: 0993 830465
Price guide: £58

The Morritt Arms Hotel
Greta Bridge
Nr Barnard Castle
County Durham DL12 9SE
Tel: 0833 27232
Price guide: £65

The Mortal Man Hotel
Troutbeck
Nr Windermere
Cumbria LA23 1PL
Tel: 05394 33193
Price guide: £80–£90

The Old Swan and Mill Hotel
Minster Lovell
Oxfordshire OX8 5RN
Tel: 0993 776446
Price guide: £120–£166

The New Inn
Tresco
Isles of Scilly TR24 0QQ
Tel: 0720 22844
Price guide: £77–£99

The Oxenham Arms
South Zeal
Nr Okehampton
Devon EX20 2JT
Tel: 0837 840244/577
Price guide: £45–£60

The New Inn
St Owen's Cross
Nr Ross-on-Wye
Herefordshire HR2 8LQ
Tel: 098987 274
Price guide: £50–£80

The Peacock Hotel and Restaurant
Henton
Nr Chinnor
Oxfordshire OX9 4AH
Tel: 0844 53519
Price guide: £60–£90

The Nobody Inn
Doddiscombsleigh
Nr Exeter
Devon EX6 7PS
Tel: 0647 52394
Price guide: £40–£50

The Pheasant Hotel
Seavington St Mary
Nr Ilminster
Somerset TA19 0QH
Tel: 0460 40502
Price guide: £70–£80

The Old Beams Restaurant with Rooms
Waterhouses
Staffordshire ST10 3HW
Tel: 0538 308254
Price guide: £65–£85

The Pheasant Inn
Casterton
Kirkby Lonsdale
Cumbria LA6 2RX
Tel: 05242 71230
Price guide: £55–£60

The Old Bell Hotel
Market Place
Warminster
Wiltshire BA12 9AN
Tel: 0985 216611
Price guide: £50–£60

Quorn Grange
Wood Lane
Quorn
Leicestershire LE12 8DB
Tel: 0509 412167
Price guide: £70–£100

The Old Black Lion
Lion Street
Hay-on-Wye
Hereford
Herefordshire HR3 5AD
Tel: 0497 820841
Price guide: £39

Quy Mill Hotel
Newmarket Road
Stow-cum-Quy
Cambridgeshire CB5 9AG
Tel: 0223 853383
Price guide: £85

The Old Court Hotel
Symonds Yat West
Ross-on-Wye
Herefordshire HR9 6DA
Tel: 0600 890367
Price guide: £58–£66

Ram Jam Inn
Great North Road
Stretton
Oakham
Leicestershire LE15 7QX
Tel: 0780 410776
Price guide: £45

Red House Country Manor
Main Street
Kelham
Newark
Nottinghamshire NG23 5QP
Tel: 0636 705266
Price guide: £55–£65

The Royal Castle Hotel
11 The Quay
Dartmouth
South Devon TQ6 9PS
Tel: 0803 833033
Price guide: £59–£80

The Red Lion Hotel
Bredwardine
Hereford
Herefordshire HR3 6BU
Tel: 09817 303
Price guide: £39–£50

The Royal Oak Inn
Bongate
Appleby-in-Westmorland
Cumbria CA16 6UN
Tel: 07683 51463
Price guide: £40–£55

The Redfern Hotel
Cleobury Mortimer
Shropshire DY14 8AA
Tel: 0299 270395
Price guide: £55–£68

The Royal Oak Inn
Winsford
Exmoor National Park
Somerset TA24 7JE
Tel: 064385 455
Price guide: £77–£87

Rhydspence Inn
Whitney-on-Wye
Nr Hay-on-Wye
Herefordshire HR3 6EU
Tel: 04973 262
Price guide: £46–£50

The Royalist Hotel
Digbeth Street
Stow-on-the-Wold
Gloucestershire GL54 1BN
Tel: 0451 30670
Price guide: £45–£85

The Rising Sun
The Square
St Mawes
Cornwall TR2 5DJ
Tel: 0326 270233
Price guide: £85

The Ryecroft Hotel
Wooler
Northumberland NE71 6AB
Tel: 0668 81459
Price guide: £56

The Rising Sun Hotel
Harbourside
Lynmouth
Devon EX35 6EQ
Tel: 0598 53223
Price guide: £65–£85

The Sea Trout Inn
Staverton
Nr Totnes
Devon TQ9 6PA
Tel: 080426 274
Price guide: £44–£56

The Rose & Crown Hotel
Romaldkirk
Barnard Castle
Teesdale
County Durham DL12 9EB
Tel: 0833 50213
Price guide: £60

The Shaven Crown Hotel
High Street
Shipton-under-Wychwood
Oxfordshire OX7 6BA
Tel: 0993 830330
Price guide: £59–£62

Rose and Crown Hotel
Bainbridge
Wensleydale
North Yorkshire DL8 3EE
Tel: 0969 50225
Price guide: £60

The Ship Inn
Porlock Harbour
Exmoor
Somerset TA24 8PB
Tel: 0643 862636
Price guide: £65-£75

The String of Horses Inn
Faugh
Heads Nook
Carlisle
Cumbria CA4 9EG
Tel: 0228 70297
Price guide: £62–£96

Sun Hotel
Coniston
Cumbria LA21 8HQ
Tel: 05394 41248
Price guide: £65–£70

The Sun Inn
Marston Trussell
Leicestershire LE16 9TY
Tel: 0858 465531
Price guide: £50–£65

The Swan Hotel
Swan Street
Kingsclere
Nr Newbury
Berkshire RG15 8PP
Tel: 0635 298314
Price guide: £80

The Swan Hotel
Newby Bridge
Nr Ulverston
Cumbria LA12 8NB
Tel: 05395 31681
Price guide: £74–£90

The Swan Hotel
The Bull Ring
Thaxted
Essex CM2 2PL
Tel: 0371 830321
Price guide: £70–£90

The Swan Inn
Market Place
Sturminster Newton
Dorset DT10 1AR
Tel: 0258 72208
Price guide: £48

The Talbot Hotel
Yorkersgate
Malton
North Yorkshire YO17 0AA
Tel: 0653 694031
Price guide: £66–£80

The Teesdale Hotel
Market Square
Middleton-in-Teesdale
County Durham DL12 0QG
Tel: 0833 40264
Price guide: £55–£60

Thatchers Hotel and
Restaurant
29/30 Lower High Street
Thame
Oxfordshire OX9 3HJ
Tel: 084421 2146
Price guide: £62.50–£79.50

Thelbridge Cross Inn
Thelbridge
Tiverton
Mid Devon EX17 4SQ
Tel: 0884 860316
Price guide: £50–£70

Trengilly Wartha Country Inn
& Restaurant
Nancenoy
Constantine
Falmouth
Cornwall TR11 5RP
Tel: 0326 40332
Price guide: £46–£52

Tudor Court Hotel
Rye Road
Hawkhurst
Cranbrook
Kent TN18 5DA
Tel: 0580 752312
Price guide: £78–£83

Wasdale Head Inn
Wasdale Head
Nr Gosforth
Cumbria CA20 1EX
Tel: 09467 26229
Price guide: £92

The Wellington Arms Hotel
Stratfield Turgis
Nr Basingstoke
Hampshire RG27 0AS
Tel: 0256 882214
Price guide: £75–£85

The Wensleydale Heifer
West Witton
Leyburn
North Yorkshire DL8 4LS
Tel: 0969 22322
Price guide: £60-£70

The Wheatsheaf Inn
Egton
Nr Whitby
North Yorkshire YO21 1TZ
Tel: 0947 85271
Price guide: £35–£40

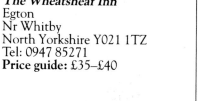

The White Horse At Chilgrove
Chilgrove
Nr Chichester
West Sussex PO18 9HX
Tel: 024359 219
Restaurant only

The Wheatsheaf Inn at Onneley
Barhill Road
Onneley
Staffordshire CW3 9QF
Tel: 0782 751581
Price guide: £42–£52

White Lion Hotel
High Street
Upton-upon-Severn
Worcestershire WR8 0HJ
Tel: 06846 2551
Price guide: £62–£70

The Wheelwrights Arms
Monkton Combe
Nr Bath
Avon BA2 7HD
Tel: 0225 722287
Price guide: £46

The White Swan
The Market Place
Pickering
North Yorkshire YO18 7AA
Tel: 0751 72288
Price guide: £75–£85

The Whipper-In Hotel
The Market Square
Oakham
Rutland
Leicestershire LE15 6DT
Tel: 0572 756971
Price guide: £80–£90

White Swan Hotel
Bondgate-within-Alnwick
Northumberland NE66 1TD
Tel: 0665 602109
Price guide: £70–£80

The White Hart
Ford
Nr Chippenham
Wiltshire SN14 8RP
Tel: 0249 782213
Price guide: £53–£58

Whoop Hall Inn
Burrow-with-Burrow
Kirkby Lonsdale
Carnforth
Lancashire LA6 2HP
Tel: 05242 71284
Price guide: £50–£65

The White Hart Hotel
Market End
Coggeshall
Essex CO6 1NH
Tel: 0376 561654
Price guide: £80–£95

The Wild Duck Inn
Ewen
Nr Cirencester
Gloucestershire GL7 6BY
Tel: 0285 770310/364
Price guide: £65–£75

The White Hart Hotel
The Square
Moretonhampstead
Devon TQ13 8NF
Tel: 0647 40406
Price guide: £53–£58

The Worsley Arms Hotel
Hovingham
York YO6 4LA
Tel: 0653 628234
Price guide: £78

The White Hart Hotel
The Square
Wiveliscombe
Taunton
Somerset TA4 2JP
Tel: 0984 23510
Price guide: £45–£55

Ye Olde Dog and Partridge Inn
High Street
Tutbury
Burton-upon-Trent
Staffordshire DE13 9LS
Tel: 0283 813030
Price guide: £66-£72

The following establishments can be found in *Johansens Recommended Country Houses and Castles in Great Britain and Ireland 1991*:

Beckfoot Country House
Helton
Nr Penrith
Cumbria CA10 2QB
Tel: 09313 241
Price Guide: £44

The Belfry Country Hotel
Yarcombe
Nr Honiton
Devon EX14 9BD
Tel: 040486 234/588
Price Guide: £58

Acomb House
Acomb
Hexham
Northumberland ME46 4PH
Tel: 0434 602596
Price Guide: £30–£35

Biggin Hall
Biggin-by-Hartington
Buxton
Derbyshire SK17 0DH
Tel: 0298 84 451
Price Guide: £40–£75

Ambion Court
The Green
Dadlington
Nuneaton
Warwickshire CV13 6JB
Tel: 0455 212292
Price Guide: £40–£60

**Bishop Field Country
   House Hotel**
Allendale
Hexham
Northumberland NE47 9EJ
Tel: 0434 683248
Price Guide: £54

Appletree Holme Farm
Blawith
Nr Ulverston
South Lakes
Cumbria LA12 8EL
Tel: 022985 618
Price Guide: £90–£105

Blackwell Grange
Blackwell
Shipston-on-Stour
Nr Stratford-upon-Avon
Warwickshire CV36 4PF
Tel: 060882 357
Price Guide: £45

Audley House
Park Gardens
Bath BA1 2XP
Tel: 0225 333110
Price Guide: £60

**Bradfield House Hotel
   & Restaurant**
Bradfield Combust
Bury St Edmunds
Suffolk IP30 0LR
Tel: 028486 301 & 8196
Price Guide: £55–£65

Aydon Grange
Corbridge
Northumberland NE45 5PW
Tel: 0434 632169
Price Guide: £56–£64

Braemont House
Sunny Bank Road
Windermere
Cumbria LA23 2EN
Tel: 09662 5967
Price Guide: £48–£56

The Bauble
Higham
Nr Colchester
Essex CO7 6LA
Tel: 0206 37254
Price Guide: £45–£50

Brattle House
Cranbrook House
Tenterden
Kent TN30 6UL
Tel: 05806 3565
Price Guide: £35–£45

Burghope Manor
Winsley
Nr Bradford-on-Avon
Wiltshire BA15 2LA
Tel: 0225 723557
Price Guide: £60–£70

Crayke Castle
Crayke
York YO6 4TA
Tel: 0347 22285
Price Guide: £80

Chedington Court
Chedington
Nr Beaminster
Dorset DT8 3HY
Tel: 093589 265
Price Guide: £80–£110

Croft Country House Hotel
Great Longstone
Bakewell
Derbyshire DE4 1TF
Tel: 062987 278
Price Guide: £64–£72

Chilvester Hill House
Calne
Wiltshire SN11 0LP
Tel: 0249 813981/815708
Price Guide: £60–£75

Dale Head Hall
Thirlmere
Keswick
Cumbria CA12 4TN
Tel: 07687 72478
Price Guide: £64–£85

The Citadel
Weston-under-Redcastle
Nr Shrewsbury
Shropshire SY4 5JY
Tel: 063084 204
Price Guide: £50–£56

Dunsley Hall
Dunsley
Whitby
North Yorkshire YO31 3TL
Tel: 0947 83437
Price Guide: £60–£66

Colestocks House
Colestocks
Nr Honiton
Devon EX14 0JR
Tel: 0404 850633
Price Guide: £48–£55

Eagle House
Church Street
Bathford
Bath
Avon BA1 7RS
Tel: 0225 859946
Price Guide: £40–£55

Compton House
Townsend
Axbridge
Somerset BS26 2AJ
Tel: 0934 732928
Price Guide: £55

Earles'
Stow Bedon House
Stow Bedon
Attleborough
Norfolk NR17 1BX
Tel: 095383 284
Price Guide: £55–£90

Cove House
2 Cove House
Ashton Keynes
Wiltshire SN6 6NS
Tel: 0285 861221
Price Guide: £35–£42

Easington House Hotel
50 Oxford Road
Banbury
Oxon OX16 9AN
Tel: 0295 270181
Price Guide: £35–£70

Coverdale Country Hotel
Swineside
West Scrafton
Leyburn
North Yorkshire DL8 4RX
Tel: 0969 40601
Price Guide: £46–£59

Ermewood House
Ermington
South Devon PL21 9NS
Tel: 0548 830741
Price Guide: £60

Feldon House
Lower Brailes
Nr Banbury
Oxfordshire OX15 5HW
Tel: 060885 580
Price Guide: £40–£55

Harrop Fold
Bolton-by-Bowland
Clitheroe
Lancashire BB7 4PJ
Tel: 02007 600
Price Guide: £54–£68

Fingals at Old Coombe Manor
Dittisham
Nr Dartmouth
South Devon TQ6 0JA
Tel: 080422 398
Price Guide: £65–£80

Hawksmoor
Lake Road
Windermere
Cumbria LA23 2EQ
Tel: 09662 2110
Price Guide: £34–£50

Gilbert's
Gilbert's Lane
Brookthorpe
Nr Gloucester
Gloucestershire GL4 0UH
Tel: 058476 221
Price Guide: £38–£43

Hernes
Henley-on-Thames
Oxfordshire RG9 4NT
Tel: 0491 573245
Price Guide: £60–£70

The Glebe
Diddlebury
Shropshire SY7 9DH
Tel: 058476 221
Price Guide: £36–£52

High Poplars
Hinton
Darsham
Saxmundham
Suffolk IP17 3RJ
Tel: 050270 528
Price Guide: £36

**The Grange Country
    House Hotel**
Manor Brow
Keswick-on-Derwentwater
Cumbria CA12 4BA
Tel: 07687 72500
Price Guide: £76

Higher House
West Bagborough
Taunton
Somerset TA4 3EF
Tel: 0823 432996
Price Guide: £45–£55

Great Snoring Old Rectory
Great Snoring
Fakenham
Norfolk NR21 0HP
Tel: 0328 820597
Price Guide: £70–£75

Hillards Farmhouse
High Street
Curry Rivel
Langport
Somerset TA10 0EY
Tel: 0458 251737
Price Guide: £44–£50

Halewell Close
Withington
Nr Cheltenham
Gloucestershire GL54 4BN
Tel: 0242 89238
Price Guide: £69–£75

Hipping Hall
Cowan Bridge
Kirkby Lonsdale
Lancashire LA6 2JJ
Tel: 05242 71187
Price Guide: £58–£68

Hams Plot
Beaminster
Dorset DT8 3LU
Tel: 0308 862979
Price Guide: £40–£50

Holme Castle Country Hotel
Holme Village
Nr Holmfirth
West Yorkshire HD7 1QG
Tel: 0484 686764
Price Guide: £47–£60

Hooke Hall
High Street
Uckfield
East Sussex TN22 1EN
Tel: 0825 761578
Price Guide: £55–£90

Little Orchard House
West Street
Rye
East Sussex TN31 7ES
Tel: 0797 223831
Price Guide: £56–£70

Huntsham Court
Huntsham Valley
Nr Bampton
Devon EX16 7NA
Tel: 03986 365/210
Price Guide: £85–£105

Long Cross Victorian Hotel
Trelights
Port Isaac
Cornwall PL29 3TF
Tel: 0208 880243
Price Guide: £55–£65

Kingston House
Staverton
Totnes
South Devon TQ9 6AR
Tel: 080426 235
Price Guide: £80–£90

The Lord Haldon Hotel
Dunchideock
Nr Exeter
Devon EX6 7YF
Tel: 0392 832483
Price Guide: £55–£75

Langar Hall
Langar
Nottinghamshire NG13 9HG
Tel: 0949 60559
Price Guide: £60–£95

Lower House
Adforton
Leintwardine
Shropshire SY7 0NF
Tel: 056886 223
Price Guide: £32–£41

Langshott Manor
Langshott
Horley
Surrey RH6 9LN
Tel: 0293 786680
Price Guide: £100

Maiden Newton House
Maiden Newton
Nr Dorchester
Dorset DT2 0AA
Tel: 0300 20336
Price Guide: £80–£126

Langtry Country House
   Hotel & Restaurant
Washford
Watchet
Somerset TA23 0NT
Tel: 0984 40484
Price Guide: £45–£55

The Malt House
Broad Campden
Chipping Campden
Gloucestershire GL55 6UU
Tel: 0386 840295
Price Range: £60–£80

Laurel Villa
Lake Road
Ambleside
Cumbria LA22 0DB
Tel: 05394 33240
Price Guide: £48–£52

The Manor
Hannington Wick
Nr Highworth
Wiltshire SN6 7RX
Tel: 0285 810009
Price Guide: £52

Little Hodgeham
Smarden Road
Bethersden
Ashford
Kent TN26 3HE
Tel: 0233 850323
Price Guide: £30–£35

The Marsh Country Hotel
Eyton
Leominster
Herefordshire HR6 0AG
Tel: 0568 3952
Price Guide: £93–£110

Marsh Hall Country House Hotel
South Molton
North Devon EX36 3HQ
Tel: 07695 2666
Price Guide: £60–£70

Old Mill Country House Hotel
Harbertonford
Nr Totnes
South Devon TQ9 7SW
Tel: 080423 349
Price Guide: £48–£65

The Moat House
Longnor
Shrewsbury
Shropshire SY5 7PP
Tel: 074373 434
Price Guide: £59

Old Parsonage Farm
Hanley Castle
Nr Malvern
Worcestershire WR8 0BU
Tel: 0684 310124
Price Guide: £37–£39.50

The Moat House
Longdon
Tewkesbury
Gloucestershire GL20 6AT
Tel: 068481 313
Price Guide: £40–£45

The Old Rectory
Blore
Nr Ashbourne
Derbyshire DE6 2BS
Tel: 033529 287
Price Guide: £59

Nanscawen House
Prideaux Road
Nr Blazey
Par
Cornwall PL24 2SR
Tel: 0726 814488
Price Guide: £55–60

The Old Rectory
Martinhoe
Parracombe
Nr Barnstaple
Devon EX31 4QT
Tel: 05983 368
Price Guide: £60–£66

New Capernwray Farm
Capernwray
Carnforth
Lancashire LA6 1AD
Tel: 0524 734284
Price Guide: £50–55

The Old Rectory
St James
Shaftesbury
Dorset SP7 8HG
Tel: 0747 52003
Price Guide: £44–£50

Nolands Farm & Country Restaurant
Oxhill
Warwickshire CV35 0RJ
Tel: 0926 640309
Price Guide: £24-£38

The Old Rectory
Boltongate
Cumbria CA5 1DA
Tel: 09657 647
Price Guide: £58–£64

The Old Cloth Hall
Cranbrook
Kent TN17 3NR
Tel: 0580 712220
Price Guide: £60–£85

The Old Rectory
Ipsley Lane
Ipsley
Redditch
Worcestershire B98 0AP
Tel: 0527 23000/26739
Price Guide: £59–£72

The Old Hall
Jervaulx Abbey
Ripon
North Yorkshire HG4 4PH
Tel: 0677 60313
Price Guide: £55

The Old Rectory
Wolferton
Sandringham
Norfolk PE31 6HF
Tel: 0485 540496
Price Guide: £50–£60

The Old Rectory
Hopesay
Nr Craven Arms
Shropshire SY7 8HD
Tel: 05887 245
Price Guide: £44–£48

The Old Rectory Country House Hotel
St Keyne
Nr Liskeard
Cornwall PL14 4RL
Tel: 0579 42617
Price Guide: £48–£54

The Old Vicarage
Burbage
Marlborough
Wiltshire SN8 3AG
Tel: 0672 810495
Price Guide: £50–£145

The Old Vicarage
Muker
Nr Richmond
North Yorkshire DL11 6QH
Tel: 0748 86498
Price Guide: £69–£80

Otley House
Otley
Ipswich
Suffolk IP6 9NR
Tel: 0473 890253
Price Guide: £40–£46

Ounce House
13 Northgate Street
Bury St Edmunds
Suffolk IP33 1HP
Tel: 0284 761779/255192
Price Guide: £60

Paradise House
Holloway
Bath
Avon BA2 4PX
Tel: 0225 317723
Price Guide: £45–£60

Parrock Head
Woodhouse Lane
Slaidburn
Nr Clitheroe
Lancashire BB7 3AH
Tel: 02006 614
Price Guide: £50–£60

Plestowes House
Hareway Lane
Barford
Nr Warwick
Warwickshire CV35 8DD
Tel: 0926 624503
Price Guide: £50

Robertswood
Farley Hill
Matlock
Derbyshire DE4 3LL
Tel: 0629 55642
Price Guide: £39–£54

Rooking House
Portinscale
Keswick
Cumbria CA12 5RD
Tel: 07687 72506
Price Guide: £36–£40

Rowton Castle
Shrewsbury
Shropshire SY5 9EP
Tel: 0743 884044
Price Guide: £65–£85

Salisbury House
84 Victoria Road
Diss
Norfolk IP22 3JG
Tel: 0379 644738
Price Guide: £52–£65

Sandridge Park
Sandridge
Melksham
Wiltshire SN12 7QU
Tel: 0225 706897
Price Guide: £60–£70

Sedgeford Hall
Sedgeford
Nr Hunstanton
Norfolk PE36 5LT
Tel: 0485 70902/70941
Price Guide: £50–£55

Shearings
Rockbourne
Fordingbridge
Hampshire SP6 3NA
Tel: 07253 256
Price Guide: £39-£42

Shipdham Place
Church Close
Shipdham
Nr Thetford
Norfolk IP25 7LX
Tel: 0362 820303
Price Guide: £45–£90

Thornton Watlass Hall
Ripon
North Yorkshire HG4 4AS
Tel: 0677 22803/24784 or 0904
Price guide: £80–£120

Shires Court Country Hotel
Knayton
Thirsk
North Yorkshire YO7 4BS
Tel: 0845 537210
Price Guide: £44–£50

Upper Court
Kemerton
Nr Tewksbury
Gloucestershire GL20 7HY
Tel: 038689 351
Price Guide: £77

Sid Valley Country Hotel
Sidbury
Sidmouth
Devon EX10 0QJ
Tel: 03957 274
Price Guide: £59–£73.50

Upton House
Upton Snodsbury
Worcester WR7 4NR
Tel: 090560 226
Price Guide: £60

Simonsbath House Hotel
Simonsbath
Exmoor
Somerset TA24 7SH
Tel: 064383 259
Price Guide: £76–£92

Waren House Hotel
Waren Mill
Belford
Northumberland NE70 7EE
Tel: 06684 581
Price Guide: £70–£90

4 South Parade
York YO2 2BA
Tel: 0904 628229
Price Guide: £62–£74

Widbrook Grange
Trowbridge Road
Bradford-on-Avon
Wiltshire BA15 1UH
Tel: 02216 4750
Price Guide: £50–£74

The Steppes
Ullingswick
Nr Hereford HR1 3JG
Tel: 0432 820424
Price Guide: £49–£55

Widdicombe Pixie
Hooke Hall
High Street
Uckfield
East Sussex TN22 1EN
Tel: 0825 761578
Price Guide: Special rates

Tanyard
Wierton Hill
Boughton Monchelsea
Kent ME17 4JT
Tel: 0622 744705
Price Guide: £69

Wigham
Morchard Bishop
Nr Crediton
Devon EX17 6RJ
Tel: 03637 350
Price Guide: £86–£106

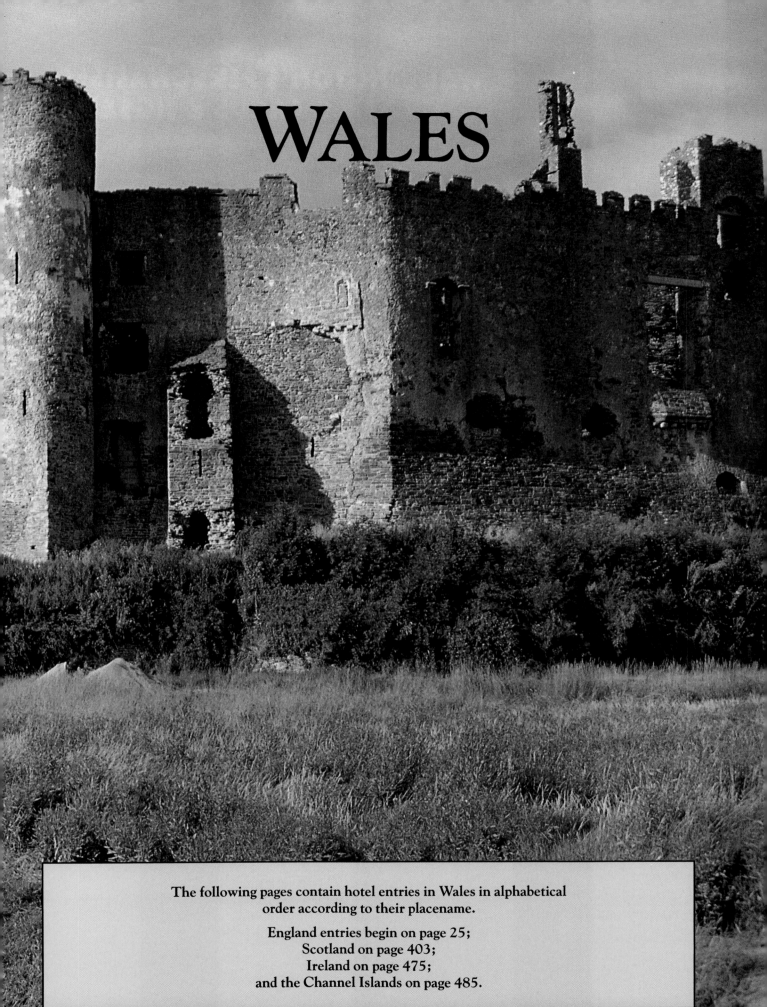

WALES

The following pages contain hotel entries in Wales in alphabetical
order according to their placename.

England entries begin on page 25;
Scotland on page 403;
Ireland on page 475;
and the Channel Islands on page 485.

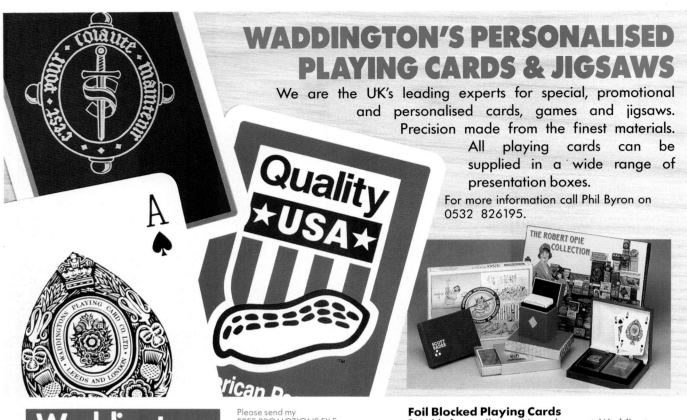
HOW TO PURCHASE A COPY OF THIS GUIDE

Copies of Johansens can usually be purchased direct from the establishment in which you are staying.

Alternatively, all three guides in the Johansens series, *Recommended Hotels*, *Recommended Country Inns and Restaurants* and *Recommended Private Country Houses and Castles*, are now available at all good bookshops throughout the United Kingdom.

If you are still unable to locate a stockist, you may purchase the guides direct from Johansens. Please refer to the order forms to be found at the back of this copy. You may also telephone or fax your requirements through to the Johansens order department on:

Telephone: 0223 354551
Facsimile: 0223 323154

Johansens Limited, FREEPOST, Bateman Street, CAMBRIDGE CB2 1BR

ALLT-YR-YNYS HOTEL
WALTERSTONE, HEREFORDSHIRE HK2 0DU
TEL: 0873 890307 FAX: 0873 890539

Originally the manor house of Robert Cecil, a 9th-century knight of the court of Henry II, Allt-yr-Ynys straddles the England/Wales border with Herefordshire on one side and the Black Mountains of the Brecon Beacons on the other. Today's buildings date from 1550 and retain their original moulded ceilings, oak panelling and massive oak beams. In the bar, adjacent to the jacuzzi and indoor heated swimming pool, there is an ancient, horse drawn cider-press. Period outbuildings have been converted to character suites. The hotel also has an undercover clay pigeon range for which it provides all equipment – shotguns, cartridges and instruction – and it is close to four golf courses. Traditional British fare in the restaurant represents good value for money but chef, Peter Sutton, can also prepare 'special dishes for special occasions' for up to 60 people. Children over 8 are welcome; dogs can be accommodated. Price guide: £65–£80. Directions: Midway between Abergavenny and Hereford, turn off A465 by Pandy Inn. Bear right at Green Barn crossroads (signed to Walterstone).

PORTH TOCYN COUNTRY HOUSE HOTEL

ABERSOCH, PWLLHELI, GWYNEDD LL53 7BU
TEL: 075881 3303 FAX: 075881 3538

Owned and personally run by the Fletcher-Brewer family, Porth Tocyn Country House Hotel stands in 25 acres of farmland and affords magnificent views over Cardigan Bay to Snowdonia. The gardens, tennis court and heated outdoor swimming pool tempt guests to linger, but the Lleyn Peninsula invites exploration: this stretch of Heritage Coastline takes in many different beaches. Inside, the country-style, chintzy furniture and restful decor provide a cosy atmosphere which is enhanced by plentiful fresh flowers and magazines. There are 17 en suite bedrooms. The cuisine is the backbone of Porth Tocyn's reputation. The family works with a team of cooks, producing an interesting menu which changes daily and features many unusual dishes. The hotel fosters a dinner party atmosphere. Nearby are fishing, golf, sailing, horse-riding, Plas-yn-Rhiw (NT) and Plas Glyn-y-Weddw Art Gallery. Open Easter to November. BTA Commended. Price guide: £58–£86. Directions: 2½ miles beyond Abersoch, through Sarn Bach and Bwlchtocyn. Follow signs marked 'Gwesty/Hotel' which lead you to the Porth Tocyn.

BLAS AR GYMRU
TASTE OF WALES

CONRAH COUNTRY HOTEL

RHYDGALED, CHANCERY, ABERYSTWYTH, DYFED SY23 4DF
TEL: 0970 617941 FAX: 0970 624546 TELEX: 35892 CONRAH G

One of Wales' much loved country house hotels, the Conrah is tucked away only minutes from the spectacular Cambrian Coast. Set in 22 acres of landscaped grounds, an atmosphere of quiet luxury pervades the mansion hotel with its country-style furnishings, antiques and fresh flowers. The hotel restaurant (also open to non-residents), is renowned for its imaginative, modern British and traditional Welsh dishes which are made with fresh local, and Conrah kitchen garden, produce. Old-fashioned, high standards of service prevail here and guests' comfort is ensured.

As well as the grander drawing rooms, there is a writing room and a summerhouse. Facilities include a sauna and indoor swimming pool, croquet and table tennis. Golf, pony trekking, fishing, sailing and tennis are available nearby. The bedrooms in both the main house and the Conrah's courtyard annexe are all en suite. Resident proprietors, John and Patricia Heading, extend a warm invitation for a real 'Taste of Wales'. Children over 5 welcome. Closed over Christmas. Price guide: £60–£85. Directions: The Conrah lies 3 miles south of Aberystwyth on the A487.

BONTDDU HALL

BONTDDU, NR BARMOUTH, GWYNEDD LL40 2SU
TEL: 034149 661 FAX: 034149 284

Set in 3 acres of landscaped gardens, 11 acres of mixed woodland and a rhododendron forest, in a superb position in Snowdonia National Park on the Mawddach Estuary, Michael and Margaretta Ball's historic Victorian mansion stands amid some of Britain's finest scenery. The public rooms are richly decorated. High standard cuisine, specialising in the best of fresh local produce, is served in the garden restaurant, which affords views of mountain, river and sea. This is an inviting setting from which to enjoy hill walking, mountain climbing, pony trekking, golf, swimming, bowling, surfing and sailboarding. Quiet, sandy beaches and safe bathing are to be found only a few miles away. The estuary is an ornithologist's dream, and there are numerous historic castles. There is even a gold mine in Bontddu and, for the rail enthusiast, nine narrow-gauge steam railways in the vicinity. Price guide: £80–£98. Directions: Situated halfway between Dolgellau and Barmouth on the A496.

CAER BERIS MANOR

BUILTH WELLS, POWYS LD2 3NP
TEL: 0982 552601 FAX: 0982 552586

Caer Beris Manor dates from before Elizabethan times and is the former home of Lord Swansea. Today's owner, Peter Smith, believes in catering for all tastes. For instance, the gourmet menu includes delicacies such as grilled grapefruit with peppers and Caerphilly cheese. However, guests can opt for plainer fare, such as rack of Welsh lamb. All meals are served in an oak-panelled dining room which still has the Swansea family's heraldic crests hung high on the walls. Guests can curl up in the comfort of the recently built conservatory or take a stroll around the grounds. Mountain bike riding, fishing, shooting and pony trekking are available for more active relaxers and the manor is just 5 minutes' walk away from an 18-hole golf course. One weekend a month, the hotel is given over to families wanting a break from routine – and each other. Play leaders and instructors take younger children on trips – a nature walk, or to visit a farm or dam. Older children may go otter spotting, birdwatching or fossil hunting. All this leaves parents free to discover the beautiful heart of Wales. Price guide: £59.50–£62.50. Directions: By car, A483 or A470. By train the nearest station is Climery. The hotel has a free car service from station.

EGERTON GREY COUNTRY HOUSE HOTEL

PORTHKERRY, NR CARDIFF, SOUTH GLAMORGAN CF6 9BZ
TEL: 0446 711666 FAX: 0446 711690

This lovely, early 19th-century former rectory nestles in a secluded valley in the Vale of Glamorgan. It contains a wealth of antiques: fine porcelain, original Victorian baths and brass work, open fireplaces, ornate mouldings and outstanding mahogany and oak panelling. The en suite bedrooms are individually decorated and provide every thoughtful detail. In the dining room, guests are served the highest quality modern English cuisine. The food is beautifully presented on elegant china, and wine is served in Welsh Royal Crystal. The garden contains a croquet lawn and all-weather tennis court. Riding, fishing, sailing and golf can be arranged and there are delightful walks along the scenic heritage coast. The hotel is just a short drive from the Brecon Beacons and the Gower Peninsular. 'The definitive country house hotel for South Wales . . .' *Egon Ronay* 1990. WTB Highly Commended, AA, RAC, Michelin. Cardiff is only a few miles away. Price guide: £75–£110. Directions: From M4 Junction 33 take A4232; follow airport signs for 10 miles. Take the A4226 towards Porthkerry; turn into lane between two thatched cottages. The hotel is at the end of the lane.

10 rms

BERTHLWYD HALL HOTEL

LLECHWEDD, NR CONWY, GWYNEDD, LL32 8DQ
TEL: 0492 592409 FAX: 0492 572290

Situated in the Snowdonia National Park, above historic Conwy, this charming Victorian manor nestles in the mountains of the picturesque Conwy Valley. The hotel retains many of its original features, such as the splendid oak-panelled entrance hall, magnificent galleried landing and staircase, carved fireplaces and fascinating stained glass windows. The refinement of the hotel is nowhere more apparent than in the luxurious bedrooms, each with their own individuality. The resident proprietors, Brian and Joanna Griffin spent some years in the gastronomic Perigord region of South West France, and in their attractive restaurant,

'Truffles', guests can enjoy imaginative French dishes complemented by a choice of excellent clarets and regional wines. This hotel is an ideal base from which to explore the delights of Snowdonia, the famous Bodnant Gardens and historic Chester (only 35 minutes away). Seven golf courses, fishing, pony trekking and countless wonderful walks are within easy reach. Price guide: £42–£75. Directions: Entering Conwy, over the bridge on the A55, into the centre, turn left into the Sychnant Pass, after 1 mile look for the sign on the left.

7 rms

COED-Y-MWSTWR HOTEL

COYCHURCH, NR BRIDGEND, MID-GLAMORGAN CF35 6AF
TEL: 0656 860621 FAX: 0656 863122

Michael and Barbara Taylor live at Coed-y-Mwstwr as did Michael's parents before him. It is a typical late Victorian mansion set in 17 acres of peaceful grounds containing many fine species of trees and shrubs. The 26 bedrooms and two suites have all the facilities the discerning traveller would expect in a hotel of this calibre, and there is 24-hour room service. The oak-panelled restaurant enjoys an excellent reputation and offers a blend of traditional and modern cuisine complemented by a fine cellar containing 250 bins. Two private dining rooms can seat 12 and 20 people respectively. There is a heated outdoor pool, *en tout cas* tennis court and a snooker room. Royal Porthcawl and Southerndown Golf Course are 10 minutes' drive from the hotel. Weekend break packages are offered all year round. WTB 5 Crowns Commended, member of ILA. Not suitable for small children. Price guide: £90–£150. Directions: Leave M4 at Junction 35, take the A473 towards Bridgend for 1 mile, turn right into Coychurch. At the filling station turn right and follow the signs uphill.

GLIFFAES COUNTRY HOUSE HOTEL

CRICKHOWELL, POWYS NP8 1RH
TEL: 0874 730371 FAX: 0874 730463

Built in 1885 as a private residence, the Brabner family have owned this distinctive house since 1948. It is surrounded by 29 acres of delightful garden and grounds with exceptional trees and shrubs in the middle of a privately owned estate. Lawns provide for putting, croquet and bowls and there is also a golf practice net and a hard tennis court. The hotel commands magnificent views of the surrounding National Park and the fast flowing River Usk. For fishermen, there is a 2½ mile private stretch. Public rooms are elegantly furnished and include a panelled sitting room, a regency-style drawing room, a spacious sun room leading onto the terrace and a billiard room with full-sized table. The dining room has an informal atmosphere and provides a choice of good country cooking, table d'hôte or à la carte. Lunch centres on a cold buffet or bar snacks and afternoon teas are renowned. Price guide: £56–£75. Directions: Gliffaes is signposted from the A40, 2½ miles west of Crickhowell.

HOTEL PLÂS GLYN-Y-MÊL

LOWER TOWN, FISHGUARD, PEMBROKESHIRE SA65 9LY
TEL: 0348 872296

This Georgian mansion stands in 20 acres of grounds and offers views to the River Gwaun. It is within walking distance of old Fishguard harbour and is 3 miles from the Irish ferry terminal at Goodwick. The hotel has been carefully refurbished by the proprietors, Mike and Jenny Moore. Rooms are furnished with many antiques and guests are given a warm, family welcome. All bedrooms have private bathrooms, and the elegant lounge and dining room have typically Georgian proportions. In the winter, fires crackle in the reception rooms' hearths; the bar boasts a particularly fine fireplace. The restaurant is *Good Food Guide* recommended; the meals prepared by a talented team of French and Welsh chefs. A recent addition to the facilities is a heated indoor swimming pool; croquet and fishing are available in the grounds. This is an ideal spot for exploring the Pembrokeshire coastline or to pause en route to Ireland. Price guide: £60–£70. Directions: A487 towards Lower Fishguard harbour, follow hotel's signposts.

HOTEL MAES-Y-NEUADD

TALSARNAU, NR HARLECH, GWYNEDD, LL47 6YA
TEL: 0766 780200 FAX: 0766 780211

This mellow 14th-century manor house stands cradled in 8 acres of landscaped mountainside. Run by the Horsfall and Slatter families, peace and tranquillity pervade the whole building, whether you are relaxing in the pretty beamed lounge or reclining in one of the leather Chesterfields in the bar while enjoying an aperitif. Andrew Taylor is head chef and his delicious English and Welsh dishes are served in the elegant dining room, where diners can admire breathtaking views over the gardens and beyond. The bedrooms vary architecturally from early beams and dormers to later Georgian elegance with full-height windows. Nearby is the quaint Mediterranean-style Portmeirion village, numerous historic castles, and Ffestiniog Railway. The famous Royal St David's golf course is only 3 miles distant and there are special reductions on green fees for hotel residents. Closed 9–19 December. Children over 7 welcome. Dogs by arrangement. Price guide: £90–£120. USA toll free reservations 1-800-635 3602. Directions: The hotel is situated 3½ miles north of Harlech, off the B4573, signposted at the end of the lane.

MILEBROOK HOUSE HOTEL

MILEBROOK, KNIGHTON, POWYS LD7 1LT
TEL: 0547 528632

You can stand in Milebrook's attractive grounds and look across into England, just over the river. Hosts Rodney and Beryl Marsden have created a friendly, informal atmosphere. Rodney is a countryside and wildlife enthusiast and is happy to point out the many species of birds, some very rare, to be seen in the area. The gardens provide fresh vegetables for Beryl's imaginative cooking, which combines traditional and French influences. The handsome house is a mature limestone building dating from around the mid-18th century with 19th-century additions. A comfortable lounge bar leads to the restaurant, while the bedrooms are a good size, well-decorated and attractively furnished. The accent here is on informal comfort and attentive, but unobtrusive service. Guests can take full advantage of the lovely grounds which go down to the river and include formal gardens and a wild flower meadow. The hotel has fly-fishing rights. You can also explore the historic border country around Knighton and walk some of the best stretches of Offa's Dyke. Price guide: £53. Directions: Milebrook is on the A4113, about 1½ miles east of Knighton.

LAKE VYRNWY HOTEL

LAKE VYRNWY, LLANWDDYN, MONTGOMERYSHIRE, MID WALES SY10 0LY
TEL: 069173 692 FAX: 069173 259

The Lake Vyrnwy Hotel occupies a unique position on the hillsides of the Berwyn Mountains and commands awe-inspiring views of the 24,000 acres of Vyrnwy Estate. Built in 1890, the period during which the reservoir was created, it was, and still is, intended very much as a country house and sporting retreat for all country lovers. Each bedroom is individually decorated and furnished to a very high standard; some have four-poster beds, jacuzzis and lounge suites. The restaurant, which has stunning lake views, provides a varied menu which is changed daily, and often features produce from the hotel's market garden plus trout

and game from the estate. Extensive sporting facilities are available as the hotel holds the sole rights to the 24,000 acres of land and the 5-mile long lake, which offer some of the finest trout fishing in Wales, together with a highly acclaimed game shoot. Other recreations within the grounds include clay pigeon shooting, sailing, cycling, birdwatching and walking trails. Price guide: £53–£103. Directions: From Shrewsbury take A458 ring road to Welshpool; turn right on to B4393 just after Ford (signposted Lake Vyrnwy 28 miles).

BODIDRIS HALL

LLANDEGLA, WREXHAM, CLWYD LL11 3AL
TEL: 0978 88434/479 FAX: 0978 88335

Nestled among the wild hills, forest and moorland of Northern Wales, Bodidris Hall features in innumerable legends of Welsh heroes. A fortified building has stood on the site since the year 1100 and Bodidris still harbours a number of historic features including a former prison cell, just large enough for one person, a priest hole and a staircase on which duels were fought. It is also rumoured that the house is haunted by a knight in armour! The spacious bedrooms are individually designed and have luxurious bathrooms. Guests can opt for a room with a four-poster bed and spa bath. The restaurant affords magnificent views and has a large open fireplace (sometimes used to roast a whole lamb). Here guests are offered Continental and British dishes, with occasional exotic additions, all created with fresh produce from the locality or the estate. Bodidris has beautiful gardens and an ornamental lake which is a haven for wildfowl. The Hall is an ideal base for exploring North Wales, or enjoying walks on nearby Offa's Dyke. Riding, game shooting and trout fishing are available too. Price guide: £65–£90. Directions: Bodidris Hall is ½ mile off the main A5104 Chester–Corwen road, 2 miles west of the junction with the A525.

TYDDYN LLAN COUNTRY HOUSE HOTEL

LLANDRILLO, NR CORWEN, CLWYD LL21 0ST
TEL: 049084 264 FAX: 049084 264

Tyddyn Llan, owned and run by Peter and Bridget Kindred, is a delightful 18th-century country house hotel in the ancient Vale of Edeyrnion, and is set amid scenery of unrivalled beauty. The bedrooms with their restful views of the surrounding Berwyn Mountains are all individual in style and decor. Each is elegantly furnished with antiques and interesting period furniture. The much-acclaimed restaurant features both Welsh and international cuisine, prepared with flair and imagination by David Barret, and there is an excellent cellar providing guests with a choice of fine wines. Situated between Bala and Llangollen it is an ideal centre for exploring the wealth of historic attractions of North and Mid Wales. The hotel offers a variety of sporting activities ranging from fishing on its own 1½-mile stretch of the River Dee, guided walks via ancient routes and old droving roads, and shooting in season, to croquet in its lovely gardens. Price guide: £98–£110 including dinner. Directions: Llandrillo is midway between Corwen and Bala on B4401, 4 miles from A5 at Corwen.

BODYSGALLEN HALL

LLANDUDNO, GWYNEDD, NORTH WALES LL30 1RS
TEL: 0492 584466 FAX: 0492 582519 TELEX: 617163 HHHG

Standing in its own grounds to the south of Llandudno with stunning views of Snowdonia, Bodysgallen Hall offers not only all that is best in country house hospitality but also secluded cottage accommodation. The beautiful grounds include a rare 17th-century Knot garden, a large walled rose garden, a shady rock garden and a cooling cascade. The Hall has been skilfully and sympathetically restored and furnished with antiques and fine paintings to evoke an atmosphere of warmth and relaxation. Bedrooms are spacious and elegantly furnished and have gleaming brass Edwardian fitments in the bathrooms. In the dining room,

imaginative food, prepared from fresh local produce, is served with fine wines. A former stable block adjacent to the hotel has been converted into a roomy split-level conference hall. There are nine picturesque cottages grouped around a secluded courtyard bright with flowers. Beautifully appointed sitting rooms and comfortable bedrooms provide self-contained accommodation for those seeking extra privacy. Highly commended. Welcomes children over 8. Price guide: £121.50–£166.50. Directions: Take A55 to junction A470, then A470 towards Llandudno. The hotel is 1 mile on the right.

St Tudno Hotel

PROMENADE, LLANDUDNO, GWYNEDD LL30 2LP
TEL: 0492 874411 FAX: 0492 860407 TELEX: 61400

Without doubt one of the most beautiful small hotels to be found on the coast of Britain, the St Tudno is highly recommended. Not merely because it is elegant, beautifully and lovingly furnished with meticulous attention to detail, but because of the warmth of the welcome you will receive from owners Martin and Janette Bland and their talented, friendly staff. All the fully equipped bedrooms are quite delightful with individual decor. The air-conditioned, no smoking Garden Room Restaurant is the perfect setting for the excellent cuisine, for which a prestigious AA Rosette has been awarded. This AA Red Star hotel has won a host of other awards for excellence ranging from the Best Seaside Resort Hotel in Great Britain and national winner of the AA's Warmest Welcome Award through to having the Best Hotel Loos in Great Britain. The St Tudno remains open for Christmas and the New Year but closes for the first 2 weeks in January. Long and short breaks available. Price guide: £60–£105. Directions: On the promenade opposite the pier entrance and gardens.

THE LAKE COUNTRY HOUSE
LLANGAMMARCH WELLS, POWYS LD4 4BS
TEL: 05912 202 FAX: 05912 457

The Lake is a riverside country house set in 50 acres of beautiful grounds with sweeping lawns, woods, riverside walks and a large well-stocked lake. The reception hall and drawing room are spacious and well proportioned, and are enhanced by log fires and antiques. Excellent imaginative food, prepared from fresh local produce, is served in the elegant dining room and accompanied by one of the finest wine lists in Wales. The award-winning Lake offers all that is best in country house hospitality and satisfied guests return again and again. It is a fisherman's paradise, with trout in the hotel's own lake, and salmon and trout in the Rivers Wye and Irfon. The region is well known to birdwatchers and is an ideal centre for walkers. There are spectacular drives in all directions. Nearby are three full-size golf courses, the Brecon Beacons and the Wye Valley. Clay pigeon shooting and horse-riding are also available. AA and RAC 3 Stars and Merit Award, BTA Commended. Children over 10 welcome. Dogs by arrangement. Price guide: £85–£120. Directions: From the A483, follow signs to Llangammarch Wells and then to the hotel.

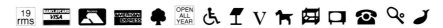

MEADOWSWEET HOTEL

STATION ROAD, LLANRWST, GWYNEDD LL26 0DS
TEL: 0492 640732

Providing high standards of personal service is the aim of the proprietors of this very individual hotel. It lies on the edge of the market town of Llanrwst overlooking the Conwy Valley towards Snowdonia. Noted for its superb cuisine, every dish is prepared only from fresh produce, complemented by one of the most outstanding wine lists in the country with over 500 bins. Salmon fishing, horse-riding, golf and the North Wales coast are all within easy reach and Llanrwst is the starting point for many forest and mountain walks. Several of Snowdonia's most pictures-que lakes are nearby. There are many local opportunities for days out, including Caernarfon Castle, scene of the investiture of the Prince of Wales, and the Ffestiniog Railway, one of Wales' most famous 'little trains'. Price guide: £50–£70. Directions: The Meadowsweet Hotel is on the A470, on the corner of Parry Road.

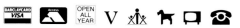

LLANGOED HALL

LLYSWEN, BRECON, POWYS, WALES LD3 0YP
TEL: 0874 754525 FAX: 0874 754545

The history of Llangoed Hall dates back to 560 AD when it is thought to have been the site of the first Welsh Parliament. Now there stands a great country house, the Edwardian masterpiece of Sir Clough Williams-Ellis, hardly changed since he designed it in 1914. Nestled deep in a secret valley of the Wye, surrounded by a walled garden, it commands breathtaking views of the Black Mountains and Brecon Beacons beyond. Here you will find many of the comforts and pleasures that greeted guests 70 years ago: the rooms are warm and welcoming, filled with antiques and period rugs. These are complemented by an outstanding collection of paintings collected by Sir Bernard Ashley, the current owner. If eating well is important to you, the prize-winning dishes of head chef, Mark Salter, are worth the visit. So is the cellar of over 300 superb wines. Tennis and croquet are available at the hotel, and nearby there is golf, fishing, riding, shooting, and some of the best mountain walking and gliding in Britain. Stabling and kennelling are available. For expeditions, there are the Wye Valley, the antiquarian bookshops of Hay, Border castles, Hereford and Leominster. 'Most Auspicious Hotel Opening' . . . *Good Hotel Guide*, 1990. Children over 8 welcome. Price guide: £115–£165. Directions: Hotel is 9 miles west of Hay, 11 miles north of Brecon on A470.

YNYSHIR HALL COUNTRY HOUSE HOTEL

EGLWYSFACH, MACHYNLLETH, POWYS SY20 8TA
TEL: 0654 781209

This captivating Georgian manor house, once used by Queen Victoria, perfectly blends modern comfort and luxury with old-world elegance. Its 12 acres of picturesque, landscaped gardens, nestling amid the mountains that grace the Dyfi Estuary, offer an oasis of peace and tranquillity. The enchanting vistas outside are balanced by beauty inside; there is a luxurious drawing room, an elegant dining room and a bar furnished with comfortable sofas, antiques, oriental rugs and works of art. The ten en suite bedrooms, including one on the ground floor and a four-poster room, are all individual in style and decor but are furnished in keeping with the period of the house. Guests enjoy a personal service from hosts, Rob and Joan Reen, the hallmark of a good family run hotel, while the much-acclaimed restaurant serves a tempting range of English, French and Welsh dishes. Rob is an established artist whose paintings decorate the walls of the hotel. He also makes the most of this wonderful setting for creative work by running art courses in the spring and autumn. AA and RAC 3 Star. Price guide: £60–£120. Directions: Off the main road between Aberystwyth and Machynlleth.

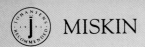

MISKIN MANOR

MISKIN, MID-GLAMORGAN CF7 8ND
TEL: 0443 224204 FAX: 0443 237606

Miskin Manor opened in 1986 after being totally restored and refurbished. Peace and seclusion are guaranteed here as this mellow old house nestles in 20 acres of tranquil parkland. The public rooms are superbly proportioned and have fine fireplaces, panelled walls and ornate ceilings, all enhanced by rich drapery and comfortable furniture. The bedrooms all have en suite bathrooms and full facilities. In the 1920s, one of the de luxe suites was host to the Prince of Wales (later King Edward VIII). His room is now the Prince of Wales Suite. The restaurant serves high quality cuisine which is complemented by an extensive wine list. Within the hotel's grounds is the popular Fredericks sports club available for use by Miskin Manor's guests. There is an indoor heated swimming pool, gymnasium, spa whirlpool bath, sauna, solarium and steam room; badminton, squash and snooker are also available. The hotel can cater for seminars or conferences for up to 150 delegates (40 residential). No catering facilities 26 – 30 December. A Hidden Hotel. Price guide: £104. Directions: From Junction 34 of the M4, follow hotel signs. Drive is 1 minute from the motorway roundabout.

BLAS AR GYMRU
TASTE OF WALES

THE CROWN AT WHITEBROOK

WHITEBROOK, MONMOUTH, GWENT NP5 4TX
TEL: 0600 860254 FAX: 0600 860607

Roger and Sandra Bates' romantic auberge is ideally situated for those wishing to savour peace and tranquillity. Set in the wooded Whitebrook Valley, on the edge of Tintern Forest and 1 mile from the River Wye, The Crown offers guests the opportunity to unwind amid unparalleled views. The public rooms are all tastefully decorated, the Manor Room being furnished in locally handmade ash furniture. The Egon Ronay, AA and Michelin recommended restaurant is deservedly famous; your meal may begin with a terrine of game birds marinated in Madeira, brandy and red wine, followed by local salmon poached in wine and herbs, served in a brandy and cream sauce, rounded off with a Normandy crêpe flamed in Calvados. Vegetarian and most other diets can also be catered for. The warm atmosphere of the restaurant complements the French cuisine perfectly. Golf can be played at Monmouth and there are horse-riding facilities nearby. Price guide: £50 including dinner. Directions: Whitebrook is situated between the A466 and the B4293 approximately 5 miles south of Monmouth.

12 rms · BARCLAYCARD VISA · Access · AMERICAN EXPRESS · Diners

NORTON HOUSE HOTEL AND RESTAURANT

NORTON ROAD, MUMBLES, SWANSEA SA3 5TQ
TEL: 0792 404891 FAX: 0792 403210

This elegant Georgian hotel, set in well-kept gardens only a few hundred yards from the seashore of Swansea Bay, provides a comfortable and peaceful base from which to explore the Welsh countryside. Resident proprietors, Jan and John Power, have earned a reputation for providing tasteful surroundings and attentive staff. The rooms all have private facilities and four particularly spacious rooms house four-poster beds. Guests enjoy quality food and a fine selection of wines and liqueurs as they dine in the restaurant overlooking the terrace and gardens. There is a 7-hole putting green in the grounds and clay pigeon shooting and horse-riding can be arranged locally. Conference facilities can be provided for up to 20 people. The unspoiled Gower Peninsular is nearby with its scores of coves and bays. Mumbles village is only a short walk away, while the city of Swansea is alive with galleries, theatres, good shopping and its famous market and maritime quarter. Price guide: £70–£80. Directions: From London, leave M4 at Junction 42. After Briton Ferry Bridge take A483 to Swansea, then A4067 alongside Swansea Bay. A mile beyond the Mumbles sign, hotel sign is on the right-hand side.

THE CELTIC MANOR HOTEL

COLDRA WOODS, NEWPORT, GWENT NP6 2YA
TEL: 0633 413000 FAX: 0633 412910 TELEX: 497557

This beautifully developed Victorian manor house has held the highest Egon Ronay rating in Wales since it opened in 1982. There is a stylish lounge for relaxation, two spacious bars, and a splendid terrace where guests can rest with a drink while enjoying the pastoral views over acres of mature parkland. There are two excellent restaurants – Hedley's, with its French à la carte menu, and the Patio. Elegant extensions which blend with the original building have brought it into the 1990s, so that it now has an unrivalled selection of flexible banqueting and conference facilities. Two large suites plus meeting rooms for the latter can be adapted to suit all requirements and any budget. There is an indoor heated swimming pool, sauna, gym and solarium complex, plus woodland walk and jogging track on site. The hotel can also arrange for guests to take part in various pursuits, from clay pigeon shooting to archery. Nearby places of interest include Tintern Abbey, the Wye Valley, Cardiff, Chepstow and Caerphilly Castles. Price guide: £95–£165. Directions: Leave M4 at Junction 24 and the hotel is 400 yards along A48, towards Newport, on the right-hand side.

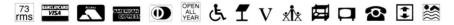

PENALLY ABBEY
PENALLY, TENBY, PEMBROKESHIRE
TEL: 0834 3033

This beautiful country house lies in 5 acres of gardens and woodland on the edge of the Pembrokeshire National Park, just over a mile from Tenby. From its elevated position, the hotel overlooks Carmarthen Bay and Caldey Island. The bedrooms in the main building and in the adjoining coach house are exquisitely furnished, most with four-poster beds – ideal for a special occasion. Dinner is a romantic candle-lit affair with mouthwatering dishes to choose from. The emphasis here is on relaxation, and guests can enjoy late breakfast and dine at their leisure. To aid further relaxation, there is an elegant, sunlit lounge, secluded gardens with a ruined chapel, a small indoor pool and a snooker room. For the more energetic guest there are plenty of opportunities nearby to fish, water-ski, surf or horse-ride. Tenby also has a championship golf course. Quite simply, Penally Abbey combines elegant surroundings with a warm, friendly atmosphere, making this a superb place to stay. Price guide: £88–£100 including dinner. Directions: Penally Abbey is adjacent to the church on the Penally village green.

THE COURT HOTEL & RESTAURANT

LAMPHEY, NR TENBY, PEMBROKE, PEMBROKESHIRE SA71 5NT
TEL: 0646 672273 FAX: 0646 672480 TELEX: 48587

Relax and – if you want to – get fit at The Court Hotel. It has an indoor heated swimming pool with shallow toddler's area, sauna, solarium and mini-gym. If you prefer to play in open waters, the hotel provides yacht and boat hire on a daily basis and nearby Milford Haven Waterway offers a range of other water-borne activities. The hotel has special arrangements for golf at nearby Tenby Golf Club and you can also try your hand at sea, coarse or fly-fishing, horse-riding, tennis or squash during your stay. If you are a rambler, you could walk some of the 180 mile long Pembrokeshire Coast Footpath. You can also spend time browsing for bargains in local crafts and antiques shops, soak up some history with visits to Caldey Island Monastery, St David's Cathedral and the 13th-century Bishop's Palace at Lamphey or just unwind in the seclusion of the hotel's extensive gardens and enjoy the luxury of being waited on. Seafood is a speciality here with Llawhaden trout getting pride of place. Choose from the daily country house menu or dine à la carte in the hotel's candle-lit Georgian Room. Call the conferences and meetings services division for details of their business facilities. Price guide: £84–£95. Directions: A477 from Carmarthen. Left at Milton village for Lamphey.

ST BRIDES HOTEL
SAUNDERSFOOT, DYFED SA69 9NH
TEL: 0834 812304 FAX: 0834 813303 TELEX: 48350

Discover this beautiful hotel in the unspoiled grandeur of the Pembrokeshire Coast National Park. Dramatic views can be enjoyed from the clifftop Commodore Restaurant, taking in the hotel swimming pool, the bustling harbour below and the sea beyond. Both the table d'hôte and the à la carte menus feature locally caught fish, Angle Bay lobsters and crab, Teifi salmon and flambé dishes cooked at the table. There are 45 bedrooms, all with private en suite facilities. Five of the rooms are suites. The Lady Hamilton suite has a large four-poster bed, and the Admiral's Quarters, Bosun's Cabin and the Stateroom all offer magnificent views over the harbour and the golden sands of Saundersfoot. All bedrooms have tea and coffee trays, hair dryers and satellite TV. St Brides Hotel also has three air-conditioned conference suites with facilities for up to 160 persons theatre-style, on request. Golf, sailing, deep-sea fishing, wind-surfing, and walking are among the many activities which can be enjoyed close by. Open all year. Welcomes guests with disabilities, children and dogs. Price guide: £70–£100. Directions: 40 miles from M4, A477 from St Clear. A476 from Fishguard – follow signs to Saundersfoot.

WARPOOL COURT HOTEL

ST DAVIDS, PEMBROKESHIRE, DYFED SA62 6BN
TEL: 0437 720300 FAX: 0437 720676

Warpool Court Hotel overlooks the wild Atlantic on a remote peninsula of rugged beauty, steeped in history and famous for the variety of its bird life and wild flowers. The hotel is surrounded by delightfully peaceful grounds with a heated, covered swimming pool and first-class all-weather tennis court. A gym, sauna, table tennis and pool table are housed in a separate building. The food, in the finest traditions of British country house cooking, comprises only the best quality ingredients. Local produce is used whenever possible and salmon and mackerel are smoked on the premises. The restaurant affords glorious views of the coast at St Bride's Bay, and the residents' lounge overlooks the Italian gardens and the sea. Warpool Court is famous for its antique armorial and pictorial tile collection. Wind-surfing, birdwatching and walking on the Pembrokeshire Coast Path are all easily accessible. Price guide: £66–£120. Directions: In St Davids, bear left by Midland Bank in Cross Square, down the hill, then follow signs to hotel.

FAIRYHILL

REYNOLDSTON, GOWER, NR SWANSEA, WEST GLAMORGAN SA3 1BS
TEL: 0792 390139

This tranquil retreat is set in 24 acres of park and woodland on the 5-mile wide Gower peninsular, Britain's first designated area of outstanding natural beauty. Sheep and wild ponies roam free here and often stray into the hotel's grounds. Fairyhill is first and foremost a family home and has an uncommercial feel to it. The restaurant is excellent and attracts diners from a wide area. All the ingredients are fresh and the menu is changed weekly. The service is efficient and friendly and the absence of head, and wine waiters is deliberate. The proprietors, the Fraynes, feel that such staff give too formal an atmosphere. Hill and beach walking are a must for visitors; golf and horse-riding can be arranged by the hotel. Price guide: £75–£85. Directions: Exit Junction 47 off M4. Follow signs to Gorseinon. At traffic lights turn left. Go 1½ miles to Gowerton. At lights, turn right. Continue for about 12 miles. Fairyhill on left.

11 rms ♣ ⌷ V ✕ 🐕 ⬚ ☎ 🐋

TYNYCORNEL HOTEL

TAL-Y-LLYN, TYWYN, GWYNEDD LL36 9AJ
TEL: 0654 77282

Situated in the breathtaking Snowdownia National Park, Tynycornel overlooks its own 222-acre natural lake, whose waters reflect the grandeur of Cader Idris. Originally constructed in the 1500s as a farmhouse, the hotel has been extensively and sensitively refurbished in a way which is sympathetic to the historic origins of the building. The spacious lounge affords pleasant views of the lake, and is comfortably and attractively furnished. The en suite bedrooms enable guests to relax in peace and comfort. Further pleasures are provided by a sauna, solarium and swimming pool within the hotel's grounds. Tynycornel is an anglers' paradise, with brown trout, seasonal salmon and sea trout fishing readily available; and among the hotel's amenities are six petrol powered boats, tackle hire and freezing facilities. The stunning landscape opens opportunities for shooting, walking, birdwatching and photography, while the wider area of Mid Wales and the Snowdonia National Park is steeped in history and offers a splendid variety of pastimes. Price guide: £98–£104 including dinner. Directions: Tal-y-Llyn is signposted from the main A487 Machynlleth to Dolgellau road. The hotel is on the lake shore.

CWRT BLEDDYN HOTEL AND COUNTRY CLUB

TREDUNNOCK, NR USK, GWENT, SOUTH WALES NP5 1PG
TEL: 063349 521 FAX: 063349 220

This idyllic country house hotel rests serenely in 17 acres of undulating Welsh countryside in south east Wales. The emphasis here is on fine foods and comfort. The Country Club leisure centre has enviable facilities: squash, tennis, swimming, sauna, steam room, gymnasium, solarium, restaurant, bar and a snooker room. The hotel offers Country House Weekend Breaks which includes two nights' accommodation, breakfast, evening meal and temporary membership of the Country Club. The bedrooms are individually designed; the suites have whirlpool baths. There are purpose-built banqueting and conference facilities for 10–200 persons; ideal for special occasions and the business community. The Cwrt Bleddyn has facilities for seminars, product launches, banquets, wedding receptions, Christmas celebrations and other functions. There is 24-hour room service plus a laundry, shoe cleaning and maid service. Children are particularly welcome and facilities include a pleasant children's play area at the rear of the hotel. Golf, shooting and wind-surfing are available nearby. Price guide: £85–£115. Directions: The hotel is 3 miles north of Caerleon on the road to Usk.

Llwyn Onn Hall

CEFN ROAD, WREXHAM, CLWYD LL13 0NY
TEL: 0978 261225 FAX: 0978 261225

Originally a manor house, built around 1700, Llwyn Onn Hall has been converted into a very comfortable hotel. Set in substantial parkland with gardens and views, Llwyn Onn Hall is a peaceful place to stay and is personally run by Eric and Jane Moore. Individually furnished bedrooms have comfort and charm. The snug bar boasts a listed carved fireplace. In the elegant restaurant you will find an interesting menu and the chef will be happy to cook to order. Vegetables are home-grown. The dining room overlooks the lawn with its traditional ha-ha. The hotel stands close to the market town of Wrexham, Clwyd and among many interesting places nearby are Chirk Castle, Erddig Hall and Chester. Golf is available locally. Country walks available on owners' surrounding farmland. Price guide: £80–£94. Directions: The hotel is situated on Cefn Road which forms the east side of Wrexham. Approaching Wrexham from Whitchurch, turn right off A525 after Marchwiel, or from Nantwich, left off the A534 at the Greyhound Inn. From Chester or Shrewsbury on A48, take the Nantwich turn-off, follow A5156 to the A534 and turn right, following instructions above.

The following establishments can be found in *Johansens Recommended Country Inns and Restaurants in Great Britain 1991:*

The Griffin Inn
Llyswen
Brecon
Powys LB3 0UR
Tel: 0874 754241
Price guide: £39–£50

The Hand Hotel
Llanarmon DC
Nr Llangollen
Clwyd LL20 7LD
Tel: 069176 666
Price guide: £70

The Bear Hotel
High Street
Cowbridge
South Glamorgan CF7 7AF
Tel: 04463 4814
Price guide: £49

The Hawk and Buckle Inn
Llannefydd
Nr Denbigh
Clwyd LL16 5ED
Tel: 074579 249
Price guide: £48–£50

Castle Hotel
Llandovery
Dyfed SA20 0AW
Tel: 0550 20343
Price guide: £55–£70

The New Inn
Newbridge-on-Wye
Powys LD1 6HY
Tel: 059789 211
Price guide: £52

Castle View Hotel
16 Bridge Street
Chepstow
Gwent NP6 5EZ
Tel: 0291 270349
Price guide: £53–£63

The Plough Inn
Rhosmaen
Llandeilo
Dyfed SA19 6NP
Tel: 0558 823431
Price guide: £40–£45

The Golden Pheasant Hotel
Glyn Ceiriog
Nr Chirk
North Wales LL20 7BB
Tel: 069172 281
Price guide: £65–£103

The West Arms Hotel
Llanarmon DC
Nr Llangollen
Clwyd LL20 7LD
Tel: 069176 665
Price guide: £54

The Grapes Hotel
Maentwrog
Gwynedd
North Wales LL41 4HN
Tel: 076685 208/365
Price guide: £37

Ye Olde Bulls Head Hotel
Castle Street
Beaumaris
Anglesey
Gwynedd LL58 8AP
Tel: 0248 810329
Price guide: £62

The following establishments can be found in *Johansens Recommended Country Houses and Castles in Great Britain and Ireland 1991:*

Parva Farmhouse & Restaurant
Tintern
Chepstow
Gwent NP6 6FQ
Tel: 0291 689411
Price guide: £39-£52

Plas Bodegroes
Pwllheli
Gwynedd LL53 5TH
Tel: 0758 612363
Price Guide: £90–£110

**Borthwnog Hall Country
House & Restaurant**
Bontddu
Dolgellau
Gwynedd LL40 2TT
Tel: 034149 271
Price Guide: £60–£75

Spring Farm
Brockweir
Chepstow
Gwent NP6 7NU
Tel: 0291 689439
Price Guide: £40–£44

Eyarth Old Railway Station
Llanfair DC
Ruthin
Clwyd LL15 2EE
Tel: 08242 3643
Price Guide: £35

Tan-y-Foel
Capel Garmon
Nr Betws-y-Coed
Gwynedd LL26 0RE
Tel: 0690 710507
Price Guide: £50–£60

Llanwenarth House
Govilon
Abergavenny
Gwent NP7 9SF
Tel: 0873 830289
Price Guide: £51–£52

Tower
Nercwys Road
Mold
Clwyd CH7 4ED
Tel: 0352 700220
Price guide: £50–£60

Minffordd Hotel
Tal-y-Llyn
Tywyn
Gwynedd LL36 9AJ
Tel: 0654 761665
Price Guide: £82–£92

Ty'n Rhos
Llanddeiniolen
Caernarfon
Gwynedd LL55 3AE
Tel: 0248 670489
Price Guide: £36–£56

The Old Rectory
Llanrwst Road
Llansanffraid Glan Conwy
Gwynedd LL28 5LF
Tel: 0492 580611
Price Guide: £104–£124

Tŷ Mawr Country House Hotel
Brechfa
Dyfed SA32 7RA
Tel: 0267 202332
Price Guide: £67

"You can't go home without Walkers shortbread."

For a delectable memory of Scotland, Walkers shortbread is perfect.

The recipe is as it has been since 1898 – flour, pure creamery butter, sugar, salt and fresh eggs. Not an additive, flavouring or colouring in sight. The result is magnificent.

You can buy your shortbread in Fingers, Petticoat Tails and Highlanders. You can also try Walkers excellent fruit cakes, oatcakes and biscuits. And you can choose from a wide range of gift packs and tins. Wherever you're from, wherever you're bound, take home the best shortbread in the world – Walkers.

Walkers
pure butter
shortbread & oatcakes

Our picture, reproduced by permission of Dundee City Museum, is a detail from "Lochaber No More" by J. B. MacDonald RSA. It depicts the departure from Scotland of Bonnie Prince Charlie, who failed to win the British throne in the rebellion of 1745.

SCOTLAND

The following pages contain hotel entries in Scotland in alphabetical
order according to their placename.

England entries begin on page 25;
Wales on page 365;
Ireland on page 475;
and the Channel Islands on page 485.

ATKINS RESTAURANT AT FARLEYER HOUSE HOTEL

ABERFELDY, PERTHSHIRE PH15 2JE
TEL: 0887 20332 FAX: 0887 29430

Farleyer House stands amid mature woodland overlooking the Tay Valley. Resident owners Bill and Frances Atkins moved here in 1989 from their Buckinghamshire restaurant and there is no doubt that the Home Counties' loss has been Scotland's gain. Twice a week, Frances visits Glasgow market to select fruit, vegetables, scallops, lobster and crayfish. The wonderful food, which won the *Good Food Guide's* Tayside Restaurant of the Year 1990 Award, is produced by Frances and her chef-partner, Tony Heath. The house itself offers 'a warm, luxurious feel with soft-pile carpets, full-bodied drapes, clusters of paintings and scattered *objets d'art*'

(Tovey). There are 70 acres of woods and parkland, already popular with grouse shooters. Deerstalking, fishing, horse-riding, sailing and wind-surfing can all be arranged and there is a 9-hole practice golf course in the grounds. Dogs are accommodated separately from the main house. The central location makes it the perfect base for touring Scottish beauty spots and historic towns. Price guide: £160–£225 (includes dinner). Directions: Drive through Weem on the B846 past Castle Menzies and Farleyer is on the Kinloch–Rannoch road.

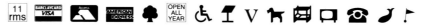

SUMMER ISLES HOTEL

ACHILTIBUIE, ROSS-SHIRE IV26 2YG
TEL: 085482 282

Mark and Geraldine Irvine run this individual, sophisticated hotel which has belonged to their family since the late 60s. Over the years the hotel has established itself as an oasis of civilisation hidden away in a stunningly beautiful, still wild and untouched landscape.

Nearly everything you eat here is home-produced or caught locally. There are scallops, lobsters, langoustines, crabs, halibut, turbot, salmon, venison and big brown eggs plus wholesome brown bread fresh from the oven.

Access to such wonderfully fresh ingredients allows chef, Chris Firth-Bernard, to create delicious and healthy fare – he strives for perfection with every course. The good food, the guaranteed refreshing sleep and the chance to relax in beautiful surroundings is so theraputic that many guests return year after year.

There is a marvellous amount of 'nothing to do' in Achiltibuie. After breakfast, Mark or Geraldine are happy to talk to their guests about fishing, walking or birdwatching and details of tried, favourite walks, varying in length from 3 to 30 miles, are available for guests in their bedrooms. Also, guests can go for a sail around the islands on the cruiser *Island Lass*, to see the seals and rare birds. Inverewe Gardens, the Inverpolly Nature Reserve and the coast of Sutherland can all be visited comfortably from Summer Isles Hotel. The sands of Achnahaird are nearby and there is always a sheltered rock handy if you just want to sit down and enjoy the tranquillity.

The ambience of the hotel is relaxing. People unwind easily and find themselves among friends. Although most guests like to change for dinner, the atmosphere is informal. So that the full flavour of the freshly cooked food can be appreciated, dinner is served promptly at 8pm.

Mark and Geraldine like their guests to make the most of this beautiful wilderness of islands and mountains; the landscape is not suitable for children under 8 or the over-80s. The owners recommend that you take your wellingtons, sensible shoes, and even your dog if you like – as long as he does not appear in the dining room or lounge – plus sunglasses, midge cream, cameras, paintboxes, binoculars, Thermos flasks and comfortable, old clothes. Although the mild Gulf Stream flows at the foot of the croft, the weather can change from Aegean to Arctic within a week!

Open Easter–October. Price guide: £62–£75. Directions: 10 miles north of Ullapool, turn along the twisting single-track road that skirts Lochs Lurgain, Badagyle and Oscaig under the eye of Stac Polly.

After 15 miles, you will come upon a straggle of white cottages which afford views of the bay at the Summer Isles, and beyond to the Hebrides. This is Achiltibuie. A few hundred yards past the post office, you will find the hotel.

INVERCRERAN COUNTRY HOUSE HOTEL

GLEN CRERAN, APPIN, ARGYLL PA38 4BJ
TEL: 063173 532

Viewed from the outside, it is difficult to believe that the Invercreran Country House Hotel has only seven guest bedrooms. Once inside, it is easy to see why, as the public rooms, bedrooms and their en suite bathrooms are very spacious. The hotel, which nestles against a hillside, stands in 25 acres of shrub garden and woodland and offers spectacular views of mountainous Glen Creran. There are many lovely walks in the hills and glen to be enjoyed. The Kersley family are involved in all aspects of the day-to-day running of the house. Their son, Tony, is the chef, and exquisite Scottish fare is cooked to order. It is served in the semicircular, marble-floored dining room. Oban and Fort William are nearby, but many guests spend much of their stay soaking up the peace and tranquillity of the hotel and glen. Closed mid-November to beginning of March. Price guide: £120–£135 (includes dinner). Directions: A828 to Invercreran, at head of Loch Creran. Hotel is just under a mile on the left.

CRAIGENDARROCH HOTEL AND COUNTRY CLUB

BRAEMAR ROAD, BALLATER, ROYAL DEESIDE AB3 5XA
TEL: 03397 55858 FAX: 03397 55447 TELEX: 739952

A palatial experience awaits you at Craigendarroch, which offers a range of accommodation and activities second to none. Choose from 50 beautiful bedrooms with every facility and many thoughtful extras. Dine in baronial style on local game and seafood in the elegant Oaks Restaurant – one of three within the hotel. The Country Club facilities include two indoor pools, spa pool, squash, trimnasium, snooker, crèche, children's games room, health and beauty salon, sauna and solarium, dry ski-slope and an all-weather tennis court. The magnificent Crathie Suite is available for conferences and functions. Salmon fishing in the Dee, shooting, stalking, orienteering, birdwatching, climbing, walking, pony trekking and gliding are all nearby. Glenshee and Lecht Ski Centres are within 30 minutes. AA and RAC 4 Stars. STB 5 Crowns Highly Commended. Price guide: £115–£145. Directions: Craigendarroch is on the slopes of Craigendarroch Hill, just above the village of Ballater.

TULLICH LODGE
BY BALLATER, ABERDEENSHIRE AB3 5SB
TEL: 03397 55406 FAX: 03397 55397

Few hotels offer the complete experience of a country house. The proprietors feel that Tullich, the former residence of a Victorian gentleman, does just that. From wild mountain pass down through heather-clad moor to the straths of Dee and Don there is something to stimulate all. Visit fortified houses or ruined castles or play golf. Take a stroll under ancient Scots pines on a misty day or picnic by a tumbling burn under an ever-changing sky and watch the days sail by; the possibilities are endless. The menu at Tullich is without choice – though not Hobson's Choice! – and cooked freshly for the table. Vegetarian and other diets are, with a little notice, a pleasure to prepare. Fish, meat and game are bought locally and vegetables picked from the kitchen garden. A guide book described Tullich thus: 'If it is the duty of an hotel to be all things to all men, it fails. However, if it is regarded as a private house, furnished in striking but admirable taste and admitting a paying public to rooms and meals, it succeeds triumphantly'. The hotel is closed December–March. Price guide: £155 including dinner. Directions: The hotel is situated 1 mile east of Ballater on the A93 Aberdeen to Braemar road.

INVERY HOUSE

BANCHORY, ROYAL DEESIDE, KINCARDINESHIRE
TEL: 03302 4782 FAX: 03302 4712 TELEX: 73737

The early 19th-century mansion house of Invery, AA Scottish Newcomer of the Year 1988, is set in 40 acres of delightful grounds. The 14 bedrooms have been individually designed using the finest fabrics and antique furniture. The cuisine is in keeping with the surroundings, offering Scotland's finest fish, meat and game; the gardens supply the fruit and vegetables. The discerning diner will love selecting wine from some of the 400 bins or may wish to savour one of the numerous Scottish malt whiskies. Exclusive business meetings and small conferences are catered for in the Garden Room where excellent facilities including a translator are available. Invery House has fishing rights on several beats of the River Dee. The surrounding area offers the finest shooting with grouse moors, pheasant shoots and deerstalking. There are also many excellent golf clubs nearby, as is Balmoral Castle. A chauffeur-driven car and helicopter pad complete the facilities of this splendid hotel. The hotel welcomes children over 8. Dogs can be kept in the kennels. Closed from 4–26 January. Price range: £95–£165. Directions: Invery House lies on the B974 out of Banchory.

RAEMOIR HOUSE HOTEL

BANCHORY, KINCARDINESHIRE AB3 4ED
TEL: 03302 4884/4923 FAX: 03302 2171 TELEX: 73315 CHACOM G

Beautifully sheltered by the historic Hill of Fare, this elegant 18th-century mansion house is set in a 3,500-acre estate with shooting, game fishing and stalking by arrangement. The famous Ha' Hoose dates back to the 16th century and is now part of this unique, family-run hotel which is furnished with many valuable antiques. Sporting facilities abound in the area – riding, pony trekking, golf, water-skiing, gliding, squash, swimming and bowling. The famous ski centre of Aviemore is 70 miles away.

For relaxation the hotel has 70 acres of beautiful gardens and parkland. There are numerous fine castles to visit nearby including Balmoral on Royal Deeside. However you decide to spend your day, you will appreciate the excellent Scottish fare presented with a very high standard of service and cuisine. Private helipad available. Price guide: £90–£130. Directions: The Raemoir House Hotel is on the A980 Raemoir road from Banchory.

THE KILDONAN HOTEL

BARRHILL, AYRSHIRE KA26 0PU
TEL: 046582 360 FAX: 046582 292

Nestling in 83 acres of rolling wooded countryside, this grand and imposing Edwardian mansion hotel is certainly far from the madding crowd. The nearest town is 11 miles away. However, for a fast connection to or from Glasgow city centre, the hotel does have its own helipad. The hotel's owner is very much a family man and welcomes children of all ages; there is a wide range of baby equipment available. The hotel's chef, Rolf Mueller, is Master Chef of Great Britain and has many AA Rosettes and Egon Ronay awards to his credit. Whatever your sport or indulgence, the hotel's Country Club can provide it. There is an indoor swimming pool, trimnasium, sauna and solarium as well as beauty treatments and hairdressing. As well as shooting, a nine-hole golf course, all-weather tennis court, snooker table and squash court, the hotel often arranges special sporting weekends with an invited tennis coach or professional golfer. Fishing, horse-riding and deer stalking can all be arranged on the nearby Drumlamford 6,500-acre estate. Conference facilities for up to 100 delegates. Price guide: £85–£115 (special rates for stays of 2 and 5 consecutive nights). Directions: The hotel is on the A714 between Girvan and Newton Stewart.

KINLOCH HOUSE HOTEL

BY BLAIRGOWRIE, PERTHSHIRE PH10 6SG
TEL: 0250 84237 FAX: 0250 84333

This elegant example of a Scottish country home, situated in beautiful Perthshire countryside, has a fabulous galleried hall with an ornate glass ceiling, plus fine paintings and antiques in the public rooms. A recently added wing echoes the style of older parts of the house with its oak panelling and ornate friezes. To match this style, chef Bill McNicoll has built a reputation for fine Scottish fare – lamb, fish, shellfish, wildfowl and game are all available in season. The cocktail bar – which stocks over 130 malt whiskies – is adjacent to the conservatory and is the hotel's focal point. Sarah and David Shentall host Kinloch House personally and offer equally warm welcomes to guests who wish simply to enjoy the beauty of the area, or take advantage of local pursuits – golf, fishing and shooting. Closed Christmas. Price guide: £115–£145 including dinner. Directions: The hotel is 3 miles west of Blairgowrie, off the A923 Dunkeld Road.

DALMUNZIE HOUSE
SPITTAL O'GLENSHEE, BLAIRGOWRIE, PERTHSHIRE PH10 7QG
TEL: 0250 85224

Dalmunzie House enjoys a glorious position in the Scottish Highlands 18 miles north of Blairgowrie and 15 miles south of Braemar. It stands in its own 6,000-acre sporting estate and is run by Simon and Alexandra Winton. The hotel has a relaxed, family atmosphere which, together with unobtrusive service and attention, ensures a comfortable stay. The bedrooms here are all individual. Some are large and spacious, others are small and cosy. Some bedrooms have turrets, some have antique furnishings, they are all tastefully decorated and have private bathrooms. Delicately cooked, traditional Scottish fare made from locally produced ingredients is always available in the dining room and meals are complemented with wines from the hotel's well-stocked cellar. The menu changes every day. The hotel offers many facilities including its own nine-hole golf course – the highest in Britain – and tennis court plus shooting for grouse, ptarmigan and pheasant. River and loch fishing, stalking for red deer and pony trekking are available too. Cross country and downhill skiing is available at the Glenshee ski centre, 6 miles away. Closed 1 November to 28 December. Price guide: £54–£68. Directions: Dalmunzie is on the A93 at the Spittal O'Glenshee just a little south of Braemar.

DALHOUSIE CASTLE HOTEL

BONNYRIGG, EDINBURGH EH19 3JB
TEL: 0875 20153 FAX: 0875 20153 TELEX: 72380

Historic Dalhousie Castle Hotel nestles in 12 acres of gardens adjoining parkland and farming estates 8 miles south of Edinburgh, and is one of the finest hotels in the area. The family seat of the Ramsays of Dalhousie (built about 1450 on the banks of the South Esk river) has been converted into a luxurious hotel, while retaining many of its finest features. Ornate plasterwork, fine panelling, stone walls and rich drapes adorn the public rooms, while the ancient dungeons offer a unique setting for a candle-lit dinner. There are full conference, banquet and wedding suites for up to 100 people, a helicopter landing pad, and landing facilities for private planes at the nearby airport. Limousine hire is available. The hotel is only 20 minutes drive from Edinburgh, and there are opportunities for shooting, salmon and trout fishing, horse-riding, dry skiing, clay pigeon shooting, archery and golf. Price guide: £110–£135. Directions: A7 Edinburgh–Eskbank; 1 mile further turn right towards Carrington, then left at first crossroads. Hotel signposted 200 yards on.

ROMAN CAMP HOTEL

CALLANDER, PERTHSHIRE FK17 8BG
TEL: 0877 30003 FAX: 0877 31533 TELEX: 9312132123

Roman Camp Hotel, dating from 1625, was originally built as a hunting lodge for the Dukes of Perth, and takes its name from a nearby Roman encampment. Reminiscent of a French château, the hotel's turrets house myriad period features, including a tiny turret chapel, linenfold, wood panelling and ornate ceilings. It is set in 20 acres of superb gardens bordered by the River Teith. The public rooms, the drawing room, the sun lounge and the library, are characterised by grand proportions, ornate ceilings and fine views over the river and gardens. The bedrooms are individually and tastefully furnished. The restaurant provides a well-chosen menu and an extensive wine list in traditional Scottish surroundings. Fishing is available on a private stretch of water. Golf and walks are within easy reach as are the Trossachs, Doune Castle and Aberfoyle. Dogs welcome by prior arrangement. Price guide: £75–£135. Directions: Approaching Callander on the A84, the entrance to the hotel is between two cottages in Callander's main street.

COUL HOUSE HOTEL

CONTIN, BY STRATHPEFFER, ROSS-SHIRE IV14 9EY
TEL: 0997 21487 FAX: 0997 21945

Visitors are guaranteed a warm Highland welcome here, not only from the management but also from two lovable labradors, Skye and Raasey, and the summer evening piper! The hotel offers a number of 'Highland Passport' breaks, which include free admissions to places of interest: a cruise of Loch Ness, a visit to Cawdor Castle, a sailing trip to the Summer Isles, or following Highland Heritage trails to the Glenfiddich Distillery or Culloden battlefield. There are golf holidays with unlimited golf on the local course, salmon and trout fishing breaks, pony trekking, guided rambling, and autumn, winter and spring breaks (the latter being the best season to see the Highlands, say the owners). Guests sip pre-dinner malts in Mackenzies Cocktail Bar before enjoying hearty Scottish fare in the candle-lit Chef Bentley's restaurant – smoked seafood, succulent roasts, steaks, fresh salmon and venison. Conference facilities for up to 12 are available. Price guide: £47–£67. Directions: From south, bypassing Inverness, continue on A9 over Moray Firth Bridge. After 5 miles, take second exit at roundabout on A835. Follow to Contin. Hotel is ½ mile along private drive to the right.

CRAIGELLACHIE HOTEL
CRAIGELLACHIE, BANFFSHIRE AB38 9SR
TEL: 0340 881204 FAX: 0340 881253

It is no exaggeration to say that there is something for everyone at this enterprising hotel. Located in one of the most beautiful villages in Moray and lying at the confluence of the Fiddich and Spey rivers, this lovingly restored Victorian building has blazing log fires and a homely public bar, plus fine fabrics and quality period furnishings in its 30 en suite rooms (including four family rooms). There is also a billiards room, weights room, sauna and solarium. Craigellachie specialises in personalised packages including wedding and celebration parties, traditional Scottish Christmas and New Year events, golf breaks with private tuition, fishing and shooting breaks. Welcome hampers, private dining, exclusive distillery visits and tastings, and a traditional Scottish breakfast are all possible elements in a stay here, together with an early morning call courtesy of a Scottish piper! The hotel is surrounded by 15 inexpensive golf courses and innumerable well-known whisky distilleries. Conference facilities for up to 22 people. Price guide: £90–£100. Directions: Just off A95 between Granton-on-Spey (24 miles) and Elgin (12 miles).

DOLPHINTON HOUSE HOTEL

DOLPHINTON, NR WEST LINTON, PEEBLESSHIRE EH46 7AB
TEL: 0968 82286 FAX: 0899 20456

Dolphinton House, which was started in 1801, is set in 160 acres of parkland. The unexcavated remains of an Iron Age fort lie in the grounds and, from the top, guests can look out over both the Tweed and Clyde rivers. The hotel is operated by Arthur and Susan Bell, owners of Scottish Gourmet which supplies top quality Scottish meats by mail order from their factory. The gourmet theme is echoed at the hotel where master chef Roy Ellis changes the menu daily to take advantage of fresh, seasonal produce. The good food is complemented by a comprehensive wine list based on research done by leading wine experts. Arthur Bell's philosophy is that it is better to offer good wine at a reasonable price than to ruin a good meal with plonk! Some bedrooms have their own lounges which, together with extra touches like a selection of books and a bottle of the hotel's own spring water, enhance the hotel's relaxing atmosphere. Guests can unwind before a crackling log fire in the lounge, or in the small snug bar which offers a wide selection of aged malt whiskies. Recently, a delightful bar and steakhouse called The Watering Hole has been created from an 18th century stable block. There are conference facilities for up to 14 delegates. Children and dogs welcome. Price guide: £120–£130 including dinner. Directions: 20 minutes from Edinburgh; 7 miles east of Biggar on the A702.

       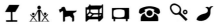

BARJARG TOWER

AULDGIRTH, DUMFRIESSHIRE DG2 0TN
TEL: 0848 31545 FAX: 0848 30918

Barjarg Tower, standing in over 40 acres of magnificent grounds, was originally built in the 16th century. The house has been lovingly refurbished retaining period features such as the fine oak-panelling and superb fireplaces. At this small but lavishly appointed hotel, guests are unobtrusively cossetted by the owners and the staff. The bedrooms, each tastefully and individually furnished, combine the charm of a bygone era with up-to-date comfort. The elegant dining room offers traditional British cuisine, with a menu which, relying largely on fresh local produce, changes daily and is complemented by a carefully chosen wine list. Private fishing on the River Nith and shooting in season are available on several local estates. There are several golf courses nearby too. Drumlanrig Castle, Maxwelton House and Dumfries are a short drive away. The hotel is ideal for visitors travelling from the north or south, as it is just inside the Scottish border. Welcomes older children. Closed Christmas to 1 April. Price guide: £100–£140. Directions: Leave the A76 at Thornhill on the Moniaive Road. Turn left at Penpont. The house is on the right, 4 miles south through Keir, on the road to Auldgirth.

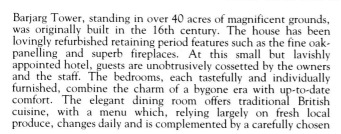

ARDFILLAYNE HOTEL AND RESTAURANT

WEST BAY, DUNOON, ARGYLL PA23 7QJ
TEL: 0369 2267 FAX: 0369 2501

Built in 1835, Ardfillayne was originally the author's retreat of Robert Buchanan, a professor at Glasgow University, better known as A D Fillan, writer of romantic novels about the Jacobite rebellions of 1715–1745. Picturesquely placed in acres of wooded grounds, this professionally converted hotel enjoys panoramic views over the West Bay, Dunoon and the Firth of Clyde. It houses 'Beverley's Restaurant', a turn-of-the-century art nouveau delight, which produces a nightly à la carte menu with venison, salmon, Loch Fyne scallops and Scottish beef much in evidence. Its Edwardian charm is enhanced with crisp napery, lace, crystal, fresh flowers and candelabra. 4 Crowns, Highly Commended, an AA 500 top restaurant, and a Scotland's Heritage Hotel. Price guide: £95 including dinner, bed and breakfast. Directions: M8 from Glasgow Airport to Gourock Ferry, 1 mile from ferry terminal on Innellan Road.

ENMORE HOTEL

MARINE PARADE, KIRN, DUNOON, ARGYLL PA23 8HH
TEL: 0369 2230

This attractive house overlooking the Clyde was originally built in 1785 as a summer house for a wealthy cotton merchant and has been completely restored by owners David and Angela Wilson. Furnishings, decor and appointments are of a very high standard, and the bedrooms contain such luxuries as towelling robes, fruit, chocolates and flowers. Four of the bedrooms have four-poster beds and one has a water bed and whirlpool bath. The menu in the hotel's restaurant puts the emphasis on fresh local produce and traditional Scottish dishes, such as Arbroath Smokie, haggis soup, kippers or steak with Drambuie and cream. David Wilson, chef/patron, offers a table d'hôte each evening, featuring his own home-made bread, ice cream and after dinner mints. The Enmore has good leisure facilities with two international-standard squash courts. Guests can even improve their game by watching themselves on the video playback. Shooting can be arranged, while fishing and sailing are available a short drive away. Dunoon has its own 18-hole championship golf course. Closed Christmas and New Year. Dogs by arrangement. Price guide: £74–£106. Directions: Kirn is on the A815, north west of Dunoon (A885).

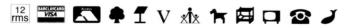

CHANNINGS

SOUTH LEARMONTH GARDENS, EDINBURGH EH4 1EZ
TEL: 031–315 2226 FAX: 031–332 9631

Channings is only 10 minutes' walk from the centre of Edinburgh and offers easy access to the host of shops on Princes Street and the timeless grandeur of Edinburgh Castle. Originally five Georgian town houses, the hotel has had original features restored and has an atmosphere akin to an exclusive country club. Here you can relax in one of the peaceful lounges with a coffee or afternoon tea. An elegant brasserie restaurant provides varied menus from light lunches to full evening meals. The hotel has its own terraced, patio gardens to the rear and the main entrance fronts on to a cobbled street. The hotel lies opposite Learmonth Gardens. Price guide: £66–£97. Directions: Go North West from Queensferry Street, over Dean Bridge on to Queensferry Road. Take third turning on right down South Learmonth Avenue, turn right at end into South Learmonth Gardens.

THE HOWARD

32–36 GREAT KING STREET, EDINBURGH EH3 6QH
TEL: 031–557 3500 FAX: 031–557 6515

The Howard Hotel has been refurbished from attic to basement and now offers top quality service in top quality surroundings. However, the hotel has lost none of its Georgian town house character, and the 16 bedrooms, including two suites, are furnished with antiques, while the fine drawing room is dominated by a superb crystal chandelier. The restaurant, Number 36, seats up to 50 people and offers guests the very best in Scottish cuisine, simply presented in elegant surroundings. There are also two meeting rooms, the Oval Room and the Cumberland Room, which can accommodate 12–24 guests for business or social occasions. In keeping with its town house style, the main entrance door is kept closed at all times; guests obtain entry by ringing the bell. The Howard also has the distinction of being an integral part of the largest classified historic monument in the British Isles, Edinburgh's New Town. The Howard is an ideal base from which to explore Edinburgh, from its castle to the shops on Princes Street. Price guide: £145–£185. Directions: Take the third road on the left off Princes Street into Frederick Street. Go right into George Street, then left into Hanover Street. At the third set of lights, go right into Great King's Street. Hotel is on left.

THE NORTON HOUSE HOTEL

INGLISTON, EDINBURGH EH28 8LX
TEL: 031–333 1275 FAX: 031–333 5305 TELEX: 727232

This Scottish Victorian mansion dates back to 1861. Situated in 55 acres of parkland, this hotel combines modern conveniences with more than a touch of old-world charm and elegance. The 49 en suite bedrooms are bright, airy and spacious, with complementary decor and furniture. The cuisine combines the best of French and Scottish traditions; the menu is very wide-ranging. Nearby, in the hotel's grounds, a former stable block has been converted into a tavern, providing drinks and snacks for families and friends. Set in walled gardens, it is ideal for the barbecues which are a regular feature in the summer months. The patio, veranda, library and study are perfect for smaller gatherings, while the Linlithgow Suite caters for larger scale events such as banquets, weddings and conferences of up to 200 people. Golf, fishing and clay pigeon shooting can be arranged. The hotel is 1 mile from Edinburgh Airport and 6 miles from the city centre and is a convenient base from which to explore the Trossachs, Borders and Lothians. Price guide: £88–£150. Directions: From Edinburgh take A8 past the airport and hotel is ½ mile on left. From Glasgow, follow M8 to its close, take first exit off roundabout following signs for Ratho then turn left at top of hill.

BORTHWICK CASTLE

NORTH MIDDLETON, BORTHWICK, EDINBURGH EH23 4QY
TEL: 0875 20514 FAX: 0875 21702 TELEX: 72422 BORCAS

Sir Walter Scott called this illustrious castle, built in 1430, 'the finest example of a twin-tower keep'. Only 12 miles south of Edinburgh in a pastoral setting, its massive towers rise 110 feet and dominate the hamlet of Borthwick. Once the refuge of Mary Queen of Scots and the Earl of Bothwell, and besieged by Cromwell, its mediaeval ambience has been lovingly maintained. Guests dine by candle light and log fires in the grandeur of Scotland's most beautiful great hall and delight in cuisine that is *nouvelle* inspired – but with larger portions. A *gastronomique* menu is available. The castle is internationally renowned for its overall excellence and has become a unique venue, not only for tourists but for top-level conferences and private parties. Exclusive use of this stately home and grounds is a special feature. Riding, golf, shooting and fishing nearby. Price guide: £55–£155. Directions: 12 miles south of Edinburgh at North Middleton, follow signs for Borthwick. A private road leads to the castle gates.

JOHNSTOUNBURN HOUSE

HUMBIE, NR EDINBURGH, EAST LOTHIAN EH36 5PL
TEL: 087533 696 FAX: 087533 626

Johnstounburn is surrounded by acres of lawns, gardens and picturesque farmland at the foot of the Lammermuir Hills, and only 15 miles away from bustling Edinburgh. Guests can well appreciate the depth of Scotland's heritage once they step inside the 17th-century stone walls. There they are warmed by the open fires, and treated to an outstanding menu made with fresh local produce. Johnstounburn has 20 well-appointed bedrooms, conference rooms for as many delegates, an exquisite 19th-century pine-panelled dining room and a singularly relaxing wood-panelled lounge. In the grounds there is a first-class clay pigeon shoot and a trout-filled loch for fishing. There are also all-terrain vehicles which guests may drive over the Johnstoun 'burn' and through the fields. Golfers have a choice of 15 courses nearby, including the famous Championship Links at Gullane and Muirfield. The hotel offers easy access to Edinburgh, Tantallon Castle, Abbotsford and Traquair House for guests who wish to explore the area. Price guide: £110–£135. Directions: From Edinburgh take the A68 through Dalkeith and Pathhead to Fala. Turn left onto B6457. After 1½ miles turn right at T-junction, Johnstounburn is then on the left.

SHIELDHILL HOTEL

QUOTHQUAN, BIGGAR, LANARKSHIRE ML12 6NA
TEL: 0899 20035 FAX: 0899 21092 TELEX: 777308

An imposing mansion house dating back to the 12th century, Shieldhill stands in extensive grounds with wide lawns and woodland pathways. The imaginative restoration of Shieldhill by the owners, Christine Dunstan and Jack Greenwald, gives guests a flavour of the house's original elegance. The spacious bedrooms and suites, richly decorated with Laura Ashley fabrics and wallpapers, overlook the hotel gardens and distant Scottish hills. Some also have a jacuzzi. The cuisine of chef Brian Graham, who joined Shieldhill in late May 1989, and his Scottish culinary team is becoming well known. Brian returned from Singapore with a silver medal for his culinary skills. Reputedly haunted, the oak-panelled sitting room, magnificent dining room and other public rooms have an atmosphere of comfort and luxury unaffected even by the 'Grey Lady of The Old Keep'. Ideal for a romantic and peaceful holiday, the hotel also has excellent facilities for small executive conferences. Children over 12 welcome. Price guide: £104–£138. Directions: Take the A702 to Biggar, then the B7016 towards Carnwath, and follow the signs to Shieldhill House.

MANSION HOUSE HOTEL

THE HAUGH, ELGIN, MORAY IV30 1AW
TEL: 0343 548811 FAX: 0343 547916

Overlooking the quietly flowing River Lossie stands this former baronial mansion, built in the mid-19th century. In the grounds are many beautiful trees, including a copper beech dating back to the reign of Charles I. The fine Victorian building, carefully restored by its resident owners, now provides first-class hotel facilities including an indoor pool with gym, jacuzzi and sauna, a ballroom leading out onto riverside lawns, comfortable public rooms and well-furnished, highly appointed bedrooms offering a choice of four-posters, family rooms and suites. The creative, imaginative menu provides a range of original dishes requiring a high degree of culinary art. There is a wide selection of appetisers, fish, chicken, lamb, beef and game, with a well-chosen wine menu to accompany the meal. Almost 100 bins are on offer, from vintage French labels to the new labels of the southern hemisphere. The Moray landscape is rich in walks, castles and a variety of country pursuits. The famous Whisky Trail is nearby, as is the historic town of Elgin itself. Price guide: £80–£100. Directions: In Elgin, turn off the main A96 road into Haugh Road. The hotel is at the end of this road by the river.

KIRROUGHTREE HOTEL
NEWTON STEWART, SOUTH WEST SCOTLAND DG8 6AN
TEL: 0671 2141 FAX: 0671 2425

Built in 1719 and full of traditional character, this hotel is regarded as one of Britain's most luxurious country house hotels. You will find a selection of books, and a welcoming glass of sherry, in each bedroom on arrival. This is indicative of the hotel's friendly and relaxing atmosphere. In its two elegant dining rooms – one exclusively reserved for non-smokers – guests really can experience gastronomic excellence. Spend the night in one of the hotel's 'draped canopy suites' which, in keeping with the general standards of the Kirroughtree, are elegant, spacious and a reminder of those days of more gracious living. Free golf at two courses is included in the price and there is easy access to Turnberry, Prestwick and Troon. The area is also an excellent centre for trout and salmon fishing, plus deerstalking and shooting. Closed 2 January–mid-February. Welcomes children over 10. Price guide: £120. Directions: The hotel is signposted 1 mile outside Newton Stewart on the A75.

CALLY PALACE HOTEL

GATEHOUSE OF FLEET, DUMFRIES & GALLOWAY DG7 2DL
TEL: 0557 814341 FAX: 0557 814522

Set in 100 acres of forest and parkland, this 18th-century country house has been restored to its former glory by the McMillan family, the proprietors since 1981. On entering the hotel, you will first be struck by the grand scale of the interior. Two huge marble pillars support the original moulded ceiling of the entrance hall. All the public rooms have intricately ornate ceilings, original marble fireplaces and fine reproduction furniture. Combine these with fine, traditional Scottish cuisine and you have a hotel *par excellence*. The 55 en suite bedrooms have all been individually decorated. Some are suites with a separate sitting room; others are large enough to comfortably accommodate a three piece suite. In the hotel grounds, there is a hard surface tennis court, a putting green and a loch where guests can fish or go boating. Guests are offered free golf on three local courses: Gatehouse of Fleet, Newton Stewart and Kirkcudbright. An indoor leisure complex comprising a heated swimming pool, sauna, solaria and a jacuzzi is under construction. Special weekend and over 60s breaks are available out of season. Closed January and February. Price guide: £70–£90. Directions: 60 miles west of Carlisle, 1–1½ miles from either Gatehouse of Fleet junction on the main A75 road.

CASTLETON HOUSE HOTEL

EASSIE, GLAMIS BY FORFAR, ANGUS DD8 1SJ
TEL: 030784 340 FAX: 030784 506

Castleton House Hotel, set in 11 acres of garden and woodland in the heart of the Angus countryside, makes an ideal retreat for those seeking peace and tranquillity. Each bedroom is furnished and decorated to the highest standard for your comfort and relaxation. The hotel offers excellent cuisine using only fresh produce – the fruit, vegetables and herbs are picked daily from the walled garden. A carefully chosen wine list matches the high standards of cuisine. The hotel makes an excellent base from which to explore the glens, and Glamis Castle is only 3 miles away. You can drive from the hotel to Edinburgh in an hour and Perth and Dundee are also within easy reach. The hotel can arrange fishing, golf – St Andrews, Gleneagles, Carnoustie and Rosemount are all nearby – game shooting and stalking. Price guide: £75. Directions: The hotel is situated on the A94 between Forfar and Coupar Angus.

ONE DEVONSHIRE GARDENS

1 DEVONSHIRE GARDENS, GLASGOW G12 0UX
TEL: 041–339 2001 FAX: 041–337 1663

One Devonshire Gardens – a country house near the city – was voted best City Hotel and Hotel of Style by the *Scottish Hotel Guide 1989*. It is set in the heart of Glasgow's distinctive West-end, amid Victorian mansions and graceful terraces. At The Devonshire, guests are accorded old-fashioned values of personal service and comfort. Each suite in the hotel has been individually designed, with careful attention to detail. The proprietors have developed a cuisine which matches the fine quality of the house, and the wine cellar can be relied upon to complement the good food. Quite simply, this is a hotel for those who expect and appreciate fine standards. First-class amenities, such as shopping, art, golf and tennis, are within easy reach of the hotel. The historic city of Glasgow has many fascinating museums and other attractions. Price guide: £105–£175. Directions: From Junction 18 of the M8, take the A82 towards Dumbarton and Kelvinside. This is the Great Western Road which runs through Glasgow. Going towards Anniesland from the city centre turn left into Hyndland Road, then first right into Hughenden Road following it round, then right into Devonshire Gardens.

THE TOWN HOUSE HOTEL

54 WEST GEORGE STREET, GLASGOW G2 1NG
TEL: 041–332 3320 FAX: 041–332 9756

Part of the Hidden Hotels group of country houses, the 34 bedrooms and suites of The Town House are distinctive for their lavish use of unusual fabrics and flowers wherever you turn. Whether it is dinner for two or formal lunch for 80, the same high standards are applied. Diners sit beneath an impressive mid-19th century ornate high ceiling and sparkling chandeliers, drinking from elegant glass and fine china as the gentle splashing of a fountain contributes to an atmosphere of relaxed geniality. The head chef makes the best use of local produce in his modern British cuisine. Situated in the very heart of the city overlooking St George's Church, the hotel is close to central stations and a minute's walk from the St Enoch Shopping Centre. Flexible conference facilities allow for small meetings or larger events of up to 150. Baby-minding and child care services are also provided. Glasgow Cathedral, Burrell Collection, Botanic Gardens, Loch Lomond and Glasgow Airport are a short trip from the hotel. Price guide: £103–£160. Directions: Follow city centre signs to George Square. The hotel is situated on the side adjacent to Buchanan Street.

COZAC LODGE

GLEN CANNICH, BY BEAULY, INVERNESS-SHIRE IV4 7LX
TEL: 04565 263

Set in a remote and beautiful Highland glen, this former Edwardian shooting lodge, built by the Chisholm of Chisholm, offers a standard of comfort and cuisine seldom found in such splendid isolation. The warm, cosy atmosphere is complemented by period furniture and a mahogany-panelled dining room with chandeliers. The seven delightful bedrooms all have private facilities. Everywhere are spectacular views of loch and mountains. Glen Cannich is famous for its marvellous wildlife, which includes red deer and rare golden eagles. Nearby glens Affric and Strathfarrar also offer excellent walking in superb scenery. Stalking is available in season on local estates, and pony trekking and fishing can be arranged. Menus in the dining room change daily and rely on fresh local produce, fish and game in season. Dogs by arrangement. Price guide: £82–£98 (including dinner). Directions: Take the A82 from Inverness to Drumnadrochit then following A831 to Cannich, there find signpost to Cozac Lodge.

KINTAIL LODGE
GLENSHIEL, ROSS-SHIRE IV40 8HL
TEL: 059981 275

Kintail Lodge is a former Georgian shooting lodge on the shores of Loch Duich, nestling in a spectacular setting at the foot of the Five Sisters of Kintail. The hotel, which is surrounded by 3 acres of walled garden and woodland, is in an area of outstanding interest to historians and naturalists. It offers guests peace and tranquillity in an informal and relaxing atmosphere which will particularly appeal to those wishing to walk and climb in an area which epitomises, for many, the scenery of the West Highlands. The hotel is very comfortably furnished with three different lounges in which guests can relax. The dining room offers a daily change of menu containing a wide variety of fresh local produce, including wild salmon, shellfish, venison and other game. The hotel is an excellent centre for visiting Skye, Plockton, Torridon and Glenelg with Eileann Donan Castle just 7 miles away. Dogs by prior arrangement. Closed Christmas and New Year. Price guide: £80–£96 including dinner. Directions: On the A87, 64 miles west of Inverness, 16 miles east of Kyle of Lochalsh.

DUNAIN PARK

INVERNESS IV3 6JN
TEL: 0463 230512 FAX: 0463 224532

This elegant, listed Georgian country house is situated 1 mile from Inverness in 6 acres of beautiful gardens and woodland. The atmosphere here is relaxed and the general feeling of comfort is enhanced by antique furnishings, oil paintings and, in cooler weather, crackling log fires. The cuisine is a unique combination of Scottish traditional with a French influence. The unusual menus have proven popular: the hotel was awarded the Decanter MacAllen Scottish Restaurant of the Year Award 1989/90. Work up an appetite with a swim in the hotel's indoor pool, or ask the hotel to arrange for you to go horse-riding, shooting or fishing or to play croquet or golf. The hotel comes highly recommended by the Scottish Tourist Board (they awarded it 4 Crowns), the British Tourist Authority, Egon Ronay and other leading independent guides. Dogs by arrangement. Price guide: £110–£130.

KINGSMILLS HOTEL

CULCABOCK ROAD, INVERNESS IV2 3LP
TEL: 0463 237166 FAX: 0463 225208 TELEX: 75566

Built in 1785, this historic hotel has been thoughtfully extended to offer a unique blend of luxury and elegance nestling in 3 acres of sleepy gardens, adjacent to Inverness Golf Course – only 1 mile from the town centre. The beautifully appointed bedrooms have all modern facilities and, in addition to many spacious family rooms, the hotel has six luxury two-bedroomed villas which overlook the golf course. The hotel also boasts a magnificent indoor swimming pool and leisure complex, encompassing spa bath, steam room, sauna, fitness room, sunbed and three hole minigolf course. The hotel never closes and throughout the year offers exceptional five and seven night holidays in addition to the ever popular Breakaway Weekends. During Christmas, New Year and Easter, special packages are offered. Places to visit include Loch Ness, Culloden and Cawdor Castle. USA Representative – Thomas McFerran, tel: toll free 800 215 443 7990. Price guide: £85–£110. Directions: Take the left turn off the A9 signposted Kingsmills and Culcabock, turn right at first roundabout, left at second roundabout and the hotel is situated on the left just past the golf course.

CULLODEN HOUSE HOTEL

INVERNESS IV1 2NZ

TEL: 0463 790461 FAX: 0463 792181 TELEX: 75402

This handsome Georgian house, with its strong historical links with Bonnie Prince Charlie, perfectly blends modern comfort and old-world elegance. Its 40 acres of parkland, sweeping lawns and woodland offer peace and tranquillity. In the magnificent bedrooms (one with jacuzzi), flowers, fruit and other luxuries await you. The hotel is internationally renowned for its gourmet food and pleasant service which guests can appreciate in the fine Adam dining room. Chef Michael Simpson trained at Gleneagles Hotel and the Hamburg Congress Centre. A private dining room is available for dinner parties of up to 20 people, and is also ideal for weddings or conferences (up to 40). There is a tennis court, solarium, sauna and a full-size snooker table. Fishing, shooting, golf, and boat trips to Loch Ness can be arranged. Cawdor Castle, the Clava Cairns and Culloden Battlefield Centre are nearby. Dogs by arrangement. Price guide: £125–£165. Directions: Take A96 road (Inverness Airport and Nairn) and turn off at signs to Culloden. Turn again at the little white church.

UIG HOTEL
UIG, ISLE OF SKYE IV51 9YE
TEL: 047042 205 FAX: 047042 308

Grace Graham and her son David Taylor welcome guests to their delightful hotel, set in 3 acres of grounds on a hillside overlooking Uig Bay on the mystical Isle of Skye. Grace is responsible for the tasteful decor which includes watercolours and etchings by well-known artists, while David is responsible for the day-to-day running of the hotel. The Island, nearly 70 miles long, is a wildlife haven of bays, moors and glens. Uig is the departure point for the Hebridean Ferry to the Outer Hebrides, North and South Uist, Harris and Lewis. The hotel organises pony trekking. Guests ride out each morning and afternoon using quiet, sturdy Highland ponies which are descended from the Highland Garron, the native working pony. In the west of Skye, near Dunvegan Castle, the ancestral seat of the MacLeods, are beautiful white coral beaches. Portree, the small central town has a heated indoor swimming pool, squash court and tennis court. There is a 9-hole golf course at Sconser. The Uig Hotel is open from Easter to mid-October. Dogs can be accommodated by arrangement. Price guide: £65–£75. Directions: Approaching Uig from Portree, the hotel is on the right beside a striking white church.

EDNAM HOUSE HOTEL
BRIDGE STREET, KELSO, ROXBURGHSHIRE TD5 7HT
TEL: 0573 24168 FAX: 0573 26319

Situated in 3 acres of gardens overlooking the River Tweed, this 18th-century mansion is one of the finest examples of Georgian architecture in the country. The hotel has been owned and managed by the same family for over 60 years. Despite the grandiose splendour, there is a homely atmosphere throughout the large and comfortable public rooms and bars. The bedrooms are all fully equipped and many have been refurbished. The light and airy dining room offers a table d'hôte menu which changes daily. The accent is on traditional cuisine with a choice of hot dishes, cold meats and home-made soups. The cellar is stocked with a wide selection of interesting and reasonably priced wines. Being popular with lovers of hunting, shooting and fishing – the Borders are salmon and trout country – the hotel has 11 single rooms, ideal for sports enthusiasts, as well as 21 high quality double rooms. The area, popularised by Sir Walter Scott, is exceptionally rich in grand country houses, most of which are open from Easter to end of September. Price guide: £59.40–£71.50. Directions: Kelso is approached from the south via the A698; from the north via the A68. The hotel is just off the market square by the river.

SUNLAWS HOUSE HOTEL

KELSO, ROXBURGHSHIRE TD5 8JZ
TEL: 0573 5331 FAX: 0573 5611 TELEX: 728147

Converted by the owner, the Duke of Roxburghe, into a small luxury hotel of charm and character, Sunlaws House is situated in some 200 acres of lovely grounds on the banks of the Teviot. All 22 bedrooms are tastefully decorated and the spacious public rooms are furnished with the same care and elegance. The menu, which is changed daily, reflects the hotel's position at the source of some of the world's finest fish, meat and game – salmon and trout from the waters of the Tweed or grouse, pheasant and venison from the Duke's estate – complemented with wines from the Duke's own cellar. The Library Bar, with its log fire and leather-bound tomes, offers a fine selection of whiskies. The hotel will be pleased to arrange a full sporting and cultural programme, and no stay would be complete without a visit to one of the many woollen mills to see tartans being made. Member of Scotland's Heritage Hotels, Scotland's Commended Country Hotels and Inns. Price guide: £84–£130. Directions: The hotel is at Heiton, just off the A698 Kelso–Jedburgh road.

ARDSHEAL HOUSE
KENTALLEN OF APPIN, ARGYLL PA38 4BX
TEL: 063174 227 FAX: 063174 342

Situated high on a peninsula overlooking Loch Linnhe and the mountains of Morvern, this historic home of the Stewarts of Appin is set in 900 acres of hills, woods and shore-front. The 1760 house has oak panelling, open fires and is furnished with antiques. There are 13 individually decorated bedrooms, all with private bathrooms. Commended by the leading guide books, the food at Ardsheal House has won high praise both in Britain and abroad, and the new garden conservatory dining room makes the meals even more enjoyable. The relaxed, congenial atmosphere allows guests to enjoy their stay at Ardsheal House to the full. A BTA Commended Country Hotel, run by the owners, Robert and Jane Taylor. Closed November to Easter. Price guide: £116–£160 (includes dinner). Directions: Ardsheal lies on the A828 4 miles south of the Ballachulish bridge on the way towards Oban.

ARDANAISEIG

KILCHRENAN, BY TAYNUILT, ARGYLL PA35 1HE
TEL: 08663 333 FAX: 08663 222

The hotel is set in 32 acres of idyllic rhododendron and shrub gardens beneath the peaks of Cruachan and on the shores of Loch Awe, with a private pier. Built in 1834 for a member of the Clan Campbell, Ardanaiseig has been the home of the Brown family since 1963 and is now run by Jonathan and Jane Brown. The rooms are invitingly decorated with big chintzy chairs, polished tables and fresh flowers. The cuisine is outstanding – and award-winning – thanks to the team of talented young chefs who have made dining at Ardanaiseig a memorable experience with their flair and skilful use of fresh produce. Outside, there is fishing, Highland croquet and a clay pigeon trap; indoors, a billiard room, plenty of games and books and a grand piano. An ideal centre for touring the West Coast's dramatic scenery. Open mid-April to end of October. Children over 8 welcome. Price guide: £144–£210 (including dinner). Directions: Kilchrenan is on the B845, (leave A85 at Taynuilt).

MONTGREENAN MANSION HOUSE HOTEL

MONTGREENAN ESTATE, KILWINNING, AYRSHIRE KA13 7QZ
TEL: 0294 57733 FAX: 0294 85397 TELEX: 778525

A superb mansion house, 19 miles from Glasgow off the A736, set in 48 acres of mature woodlands and gardens. The house, built in 1817, stands on the estate which dates back to the 14th century. A family home till 1980, it still retains a family atmosphere. The cuisine is highly acclaimed and features fresh Scottish salmon, lobster, game and beef. An award-winning wine list of 150 bins will complement your meal perfectly. There are over 30 golf courses within 45 minutes' drive, Glasgow and Prestwick Airport are only 30 minutes' drive. The hotel offers all the conveniences of the modern day combined with the elegance and grace of the past. With a billiard room, tennis court, croquet lawn, and 5-hole golf course for residents' use, it is a place for that weekend break. Special rates available. Price guide: £73. Directions: From the A736 take the B785 Kilwinning road and turn right at Benslie. Montgreenan Estate is then on your left.

THE KINLOCHBERVIE HOTEL

KINLOCHBERVIE, BY LAIRG, SUTHERLAND IV27 4RP
TEL: 097182 275 FAX: 097182 438

The Kinlochbervie Hotel nestles between the last sea lochs on the west coast of Scotland, a short distance below Cape Wrath and its majestic cliffs, affording a welcoming base for your stay in this exciting yet solitary land. Resident owners, Rex and Kate Neame, with their helpful, enthusiastic staff, ensure guests enjoy their stay. Central heating throughout maintains a warm, cosy atmosphere even during the wild winter storms. The lounges and bars are relaxed and comfortable and the dining room imparts exactly the right atmosphere in which to savour the delights of

the renowned Kinlochbervie kitchens and cellars. Seafood from the nearby market and the meats for which Scotland is famous figure prominently on the hotel menus, complemented by an extensive and expertly managed wine cellar. The remote land of Sutherland offers a paradise for naturalists, ornithologists and geologists (Lewisian gneiss-banded rocks of the Pre-Cambrian age are visible at roadsides and cliffs), and all kinds of leisure pursuits. A restricted service is offered from November to March. Price guide: £70–£90. Directions: 50 miles from Lairg; B851 via A838.

THE LOG CABIN HOTEL
KIRKMICHAEL, PERTHSHIRE PH10 7NB
TEL: 025081 288

The Log Cabin Hotel, which is built of Norwegian pine logs, stands 900 feet above sea level in a setting of Highland heather and pine forest high in Glen Derby, and commands panoramic views. Newly refurbished, the hotel features pine furnishings and a landscaped front garden with fountains. This is a hotel for lovers of the great outdoors. The Glen abounds with wildlife and offers walking, horse-riding, pony trekking, trout fishing on the hotel's own loch, stalking, game and clay pigeon shooting on 3,000 acres of private grouse moor. The Edelweiss Restaurant provides cordon bleu dishes using the freshest produce, particularly local game, in a beautiful setting overlooking The Glen. The Log Cabin Hotel makes an ideal centre for touring Perthshire and for skiing at nearby Glenshee. STB Commended. Price guide: £68 including dinner. Directions: The hotel is equidistant from Blairgowrie and Pitlochry on the A924.

GLEDDOCH HOUSE

LANGBANK, RENFREWSHIRE PA14 6YE
TEL: 047554 711 FAX: 047554 201 TELEX: 779801

Standing in a magnificent position within its own 250 acres, Gleddoch House commands dramatic views across the River Clyde to the Lomond Hills beyond. Each of the 31 bedrooms is named after a Scottish bird and is individually designed. Some rooms have four-poster beds while others are designed for the executive customer; they have a leather inlaid desk and a little extra space. The Garden Room is the perfect venue for luncheons and dinners; there are views across the terrace to the gardens. There is an original marble fireplace and ornate plasterwork in the drawing room. The Restaurant holds an AA Rosette for its modern Scottish cuisine. The food is prepared from fresh local produce, plus herbs and spices from the hotel's gardens. The menu is complemented by a carefully selected wine list. Hotel guests have use of the Gleddoch Golf and Country Club situated in the grounds. The Club has an 18-hole, par-72 golf course (reduced rate green fees available), as well as squash, sauna, snooker and riding facilities. Special price, 2-night golf breaks are available: £66 per person, per night, including dinner, bed and breakfast. Price guide: £126.50–£165. Directions: M8 towards Greenock. Take the B789 Langbank/Houston exit. Follow signs to left and then right after ½ mile. Hotel on right.

INVER LODGE HOTEL

LOCHINVER, SUTHERLAND IV27 4LU
TEL: 05714 496 FAX: 05714 395 TELEX: 75206

This superb hotel was opened in April 1988 by the Chairman of the Scottish Tourist Board, it has been awarded AA and RAC 3 Stars and is STB 4 Crowns Commended. It stands in ½ an acre of heather garden and lawn and commands breathtaking, panoramic views across Loch Inver Bay to the Hebrides. The mountains of Suilven and Canisp (the hotel's two magnificent suites are named after them) are in the background. No expense has been spared in furnishing the rooms, and attention has been given to every comfort – even bathrobes are provided. The cooking by chef John Robertson is Scottish with a French influence. The hotel's facilities include a sauna, solarium and billiards room. Golf and sailing are available nearby and guests can cast for salmon in any of three rivers and for trout in the nearby lochs. Places of interest include Ardvreck Castle, Inverpolly Nature Reserve and Cape Wrath. Welcomes children over 7. Open 1 May to end October. Price guide: £94–£140 excluding service. Directions: Take A837 into Lochinver, first turning on the left after the village hall. Inver Lodge sits approximately 100 yards above the village.

DRYFESDALE HOTEL
LOCKERBIE, DUMFRIESSHIRE DG11 2SF
TEL: 05762 2427 FAX: 05762 4187

The Dryfesdale Hotel stands in 7 acres of landscaped grounds and overlooks the bustling market town of Lockerbie in beautiful Border country. It makes an ideal base for the exploration of the wild mountains, heather moors and sandy creeks of Dumfries and Galloway. It is an 18th-century former manse and is run with warmth and flair by the Smith family. It has a light and airy feel to it. The bedrooms are comfortable, the public rooms, sun lounge, cocktail lounge and drawing room, have log fires. Of the 15 bedrooms, six are suitable for people with disabilities. The cuisine is excellent and is complemented by a varied wine list. Anglers are well served here: fishing from boat or bank is available on several nearby lochs and rivers. Also, Lockerbie has its own golf course and a curling rink. Yachting and water-skiing are available on Castle Loch, Lochmaben. Nearby castles worth a visit include Caerlaverock and Drumlanrig, where Bonnie Prince Charlie rested on his retreat from Culloden. Glasgow and Edinburgh are a short drive away. Price guide: £60. Directions: Just off the A74, 1 mile north of Lockerbie.

BALBIRNIE HOUSE

BALBIRNIE PARK, MARKINCH, BY GLENROTHES, FIFE KY7 6NE
TEL: 0592 610066 FAX: 0592 610529

Balbirnie is a historic 18th-century mansion house set in 416 acres of parkland, and is flanked by the front and back nines of Balbirnie Park Golf Course to which guests have access. Formerly the ancestral seat of the Balfours of Balbirnie, the house now offers spacious and versatile accommodation. Bedrooms are all en suite and range in size from comfortable to extremely large. There are two restaurants, the East and West Rooms, which serve a range of international cuisine. High quality bar meals are available in the Gamekeeper's Inn. The gracious public rooms afford the feeling of a large country house rather than that of a hotel. Conferences, weddings, dinner dances and receptions for up to 120 people can be accommodated in the Ballingal Suite. A range of weekend breaks is available throughout the year; from Champagne weekends to golf outings; from off-track driving, shooting and fishing packages to Christmas and New Year house parties. Away from the pleasures of the park, which include nature trails, a craft centre and horse-riding facilities, you can explore the nearby Scottish Deer Centre, Kellie Castle and the British Golf Museum at St Andrews. Price guide: £94. Directions: A92, East Fife Regional Route, goes from the M90 at Junction 3. Follow signs for Tay Bridge, turn right opposite Tullis Russell Paper Mill following signs to Balbirnie Park.

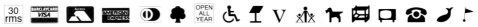

KNIPOCH HOTEL

BY OBAN, ARGYLL PA34 4QT
TEL: 08526 251 FAX: 08526 249

This lovely neo-Georgian building lies on the shores of Loch Feochan, an arm of the sea stretching 4 miles inland. All the fully equipped bedrooms enjoy a magnificent view of the Loch. The hotel is owned and personally supervised by the Craig family, who go out of their way to see that guests enjoy their stay. Food is of special interest with daily menus of Scottish specialities. Not only is there an extensive – and informative – wine list, but guests are given a copy to study at their leisure rather than hurriedly scan it before ordering. In addition, there is an excellent range of malt whiskies. Sports facilities available locally include fishing, sailing, yachting, golf, tennis, pony trekking and skiing. Oban Highland Games, a spectacular traditional Scottish event renowned for its solo piping competition, is held here every year. The hotel is an ideal base for touring the magnificent countryside and lochs. Birds of prey, deer and otter abound in the area. Closed mid-November–mid-February: open for New Year. Price guide: £98. Directions: On the A816, 6 miles south of Oban.

THE LODGE ON THE LOCH

CREAG DHU, ONICH, NR FORT WILLIAM, INVERNESS-SHIRE PH33 6RY
TEL: 08553 237/8 FAX: 08553 463 TELEX: 94013 696

This distinctive Highland hotel is set near the shores of Loch Linnhe in 5 acres of sheltered grounds, where palm trees and rhododendrons flourish. A mild climate is a benefit of the warm Gulf Stream which flows into the bay at the head of the loch. Surrounded by spectacular views, you can feast your eyes on the scenery while you enjoy exceptional Scottish cuisine. Local salmon, seafood, game and venison, wholefoods plus real home baking are regulars on the menu which also includes a vegetarian choice each day. Most rooms have local views and the hotel has a purpose-built, ground-floor bedroom with wheelchair access for guests with disabilities. You can drive around the romantic Western Highlands in a day using The Lodge as your base. Sea and loch fishing for salmon and trout, golf and horse-riding facilites are available locally. In the winter, skiing is available at the Nevis Range development. Closed Nov–Feb; open Christmas and New Year. Price guide: £59–£92. Directions: 10 miles south of Fort William and 4 miles north of Ballachulish on the A82.

CRINGLETIE HOUSE HOTEL
PEEBLES EH45 8PL
TEL: 07213 233 FAX: 07213 244

This fine mansion, turreted in the Scottish Baronial style, sits in 28 acres of beautifully maintained gardens and woodland. All the bedrooms are tastefully furnished, with magnificent views, and five have been completely redesigned to give superb colour co-ordination. There is a panelled lounge with an impressive carved-oak and marble fireplace and painted ceiling, and a bar, which was once the library, with a log fire. Imaginative food using fresh local ingredients including fruit and vegetables from the 2-acre walled garden, has given the hotel a consistent reputation for good food. As well as the hotel's own sporting facilities, there is an attractive golf course, an indoor swimming pool at nearby Peebles, and fishing available by permit on the River Tweed. Cringletie is an excellent centre from which to visit Edinburgh and to tour the scenic and historically rich Border country. The hotel is closed from January to early March. A lift is available to the first and second floors. Price guide: £72. Directions: The hotel is on the A703 Peebles to Edinburgh road, about 2 miles from Peebles.

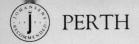

THE MURRAYSHALL COUNTRY HOUSE HOTEL

SCONE, PERTHSHIRE PH2 7PH
TEL: 0738 51171 FAX: 0738 52595 TELEX: 76197

The Murrayshall Country House Hotel is set in 300 acres of magnificent parkland and wooded hillside, with decor and furnishings of a traditional style. The Old Masters' Restaurant, hung with Dutch paintings, is a visual delight, well suited to complement the artistry of the hotel's award-winning Master Chef. Vegetables from the hotel's walled garden and an abundance of local produce form the ingredients for the menus with a Scottish flavour and a hint of modern French cuisine. The bedrooms have been designed to suit the varied demands of holiday-makers, honeymooners, fishermen, golfers and business travellers alike. There is an 18-hole golf course adjacent to the hotel with its own superb club house, tennis, croquet, bowls and snooker, and published walks start from the hotel. Fishing, shooting, gillies, transport and tackle hire can be arranged. Not suitable for children under 12. Dogs by arrangement. Price guide: £70–£195. Directions: Signposted 1 mile out of Perth on the A94.

BALLATHIE HOUSE HOTEL

KINCLAVEN BY STANLEY, NR PERTH, PERTHSHIRE PH1 4QN
TEL: 025083 268 FAX: 025083 396 TELEX: 76216

The Ballathie House Hotel offers its guests a taste of the 'charm and tranquillity of a more gracious age'. The building itself has a splendid French baronial facade and the public rooms are spacious and elegant. The drawing room overlooks the extensive lawns which slope to the riverside, while the morning room is an airy retreat with a view of the fine gardens and croquet lawn. The hotel has recently added a suite and two new bedrooms; all are on the ground floor and are suitable for guests with disabilities. The cuisine at the hotel is of a high standard, with imaginative and varied use made of the best of fresh local produce; Tay salmon and local game are seasonal delicacies. Ballathie House is ideally placed for nearby Perth, Blairgowrie or Scone Palace, and Edinburgh is only an hour's drive away. A variety of activities are available on the Estate including trout and salmon fishing, clay pigeon shooting. Or guests can choose from numerous renowned golf courses. Dogs by prior arrangement. Price guide: £114–£169 (includes dinner and VAT). Directions: From A93 at The Beech Hedges signposted for Kinclaven and Ballathie, or off the A9, 2 miles north of Perth through Stanley.

THE GREEN PARK HOTEL

PITLOCHRY, PERTHSHIRE PH16 5JY
TEL: 0796 3248

The Green Park is the only hotel on the banks of beautiful Loch Faskally, set in magnificently laid-out gardens only 5 minutes' walk from the centre of Pitlochry. A luxurious semicircular lounge overlooks the loch. The bright and spacious dining room offers an exciting and varied menu including excellent traditional Scottish dishes. All rooms have large picture windows and most overlook the loch and gardens. Amenities at the hotel include sailing, sail-boarding, putting, table tennis, bar billiards, and fishing from the hotel garden's bankside. There is a play area for children, for whom special rates apply. Golf courses abound locally and there are facilities for pony trekking. Pitlochry Festival Theatre offers a wide variety of entertainment from May to October. Open 27 March–1 November. Price guide: £62–£84. Directions: North end of Pitlochry, turn left at 'D' restriction sign, the hotel is 50 yards down to the lochside.

PINE TREES HOTEL

STRATHVIEW TERRACE, PITLOCHRY, PERTHSHIRE PH16 5QR
TEL: 0796 2121 FAX: 0796 2460

Pine Trees is a captivating Victorian mansion, built in 1892 and set amid a garden of pine trees in the heart of the Scottish Highlands. The MacLellans, resident owners, take pride in the way in which their guests are warmly welcomed and helpfully treated during their stay. The atmosphere is relaxing and homely throughout, the bedrooms well appointed and quiet. In the restaurant you can choose from a menu compiled by a chef noted for his culinary skills. Pine Trees is an ideal centre for exploring this beautiful region. Blair Castle and the famous Festival Theatre are nearby, as are numerous facilities for golf, fishing, shooting and riding. Closed January and February. Price guide: £64–£70. Directions: From the main Inverness–Perth road in Pitlochry, turn down Larchwood Road, take first left and the hotel is straight ahead.

THE HAVEN HOTEL

INNES STREET, PLOCKTON, ROSS-SHIRE IV52 8TW
TEL: 059 984 223/334

Built over 100 years ago as a merchant's residence, this small hotel has been carefully converted and extended, retaining its character and elegance. Situated in the charming lochside village of Plockton, Haven Hotel offers its guests peace and relaxation in beautiful surroundings. There are 13 bedrooms, all with private bathrooms and fully equipped with tea and coffee-making facilities, hair dryers and trouser presses. There are two lounges, one where open fires burn on cooler evenings, a conservatory and a candle-lit dining room serving fresh local produce – salmon, prawns, venison, beef and home-baking. Packed lunches are available for guests who wish to go out for a day's fishing or walking. Plockton, 'Jewel of the Highlands', enjoys some of the finest scenery in the Western Highlands: mountains, glens, waterfalls, sea-scapes, lochs and castles. Local wildlife includes herds of wild goats and red deer. Walk, climb, fish, trek, and relax. Visit the National Trust gardens at Inverewe, the island of Skye or Dunvegan or Eilean Donan Castles. STB 4 Crowns Highly Commended; AA 2 Stars. Welcomes children over 7. Price guide: £64–£84 (includes dinner). Directions: Plockton is on the A87 north of Fort William. The hotel is on the left as one drives into Plockton.

KNOCKINAAM LODGE

PORTPATRICK, WIGTOWNSHIRE DG9 9AD
TEL: 077681 471 FAX: 077681 435

Knockinaam Lodge stands in 30 acres of rocky grassland – wonderful for walking and picnics – and has gardens running down to a small private beach. Guests here can enjoy magnificent views of the Irish coastline and observe the changing moods of the elements – sea, sky and sun. During the Second World War, Sir Winston Churchill chose the Lodge for a secret meeting with General Eisenhower and their chiefs of staff. The hotel has ten sumptuous bedrooms – four master bedrooms, six standard – all with en suite bathrooms. The restaurant makes enticing use of the very best, fresh ingredients and has received some of the highest accolades for the quality of its French cuisine. Open fires in cooler weather, a welcoming oak-panelled bar, antiques, polished mahogany furniture and many paintings all contribute to the feeling of luxury, comfort and relaxation created by owners Marcel and Corinna Frichot. Their aim is to make their guests' stay the most pleasant of experiences. Open Easter to January. Children aged up to 11 are welcome at high tea but only children over 12 can be accommodated for dinner in the dining room. Dogs by prior arrangement. Price guide: £140–£170 including dinner. Directions: Please ask for them when booking.

BARON'S CRAIG HOTEL

ROCKCLIFFE BY DALBEATTIE, KIRKCUDBRIGHTSHIRE DG5 4QF
TEL: 055663 225

Baron's Craig, a late 19th-century mansion set in lush gardens ablaze with colour, has a unique and spectacular setting in the heathered hills and woodlands overlooking the Solway and the Rough Firth. The imposing granite structure of 1880 has been extended to provide a new wing of modern rooms to complement those in the old house. The interesting character of the building has been retained, while inside luxury abounds; decor is of the highest period quality, public rooms are grand and spacious, and the bedrooms are beautifully furnished. Traditional and Continental cuisine is served in the dining room with its splendid views. As with all else, service is excellent. Guests can enjoy swimming from the beach; sailing, water-skiing, fishing and golf are available nearby. Places of interest are numerous, such as Castle Douglas and New Abbey, and of course, the beauty of the local cliffs and sands must be explored during any stay at Baron's Craig. Open Easter to mid-October. Price guide: £80–£106. Directions: Rockcliffe is a small village just off the A710 south of Dalbeattie.

THE QUEEN OF SCOTS
42A QUEEN STREET, EDINBURGH EH2 3PS
TEL: 031–220 6441/Freefone 0800 838539 FAX: 031–220 6422

The Queen of Scots is the most luxurious train in Britain, guaranteeing travellers the trip of a lifetime through Scotland's most spectacular scenery. With the ambience of a country house on wheels, guests can stretch their legs in the stylish comfort of the large, panelled observation car while sipping whisky and enjoying the beautiful mountains and glens. Or, if they wish, guests can read in the quiet seclusion of the family saloon. Both carriages were built at the turn-of-the-century to take aristocratic families from London to their Scottish estates. There are 3, 4 and 6-day tours available, with a changing itinerary according to their length. Breakfast, lunch and dinner are served in the 100 year-old dining car in which guests can sample the best of Scottish fare, complemented by specially chosen wines. Fresh provisions are taken on board each day. Service is, at all times, of the highest standard. Guests are encouraged to dress for dinner, with at least one formal evening meal served on each tour. Guests are not confined to the train alone. They may leave the train to experience, for example, the local hospitality, or to take cocktails with Lord Strathnaver at Dunrobin Castle; visit the Cardhu Whisky Distillery or wander over the battlefield of Culloden. Each night the train rests in a quiet country siding, so guests can sleep undisturbed in the luxury and elegance of a state room or Imperial state room, each with en suite bathroom and twin beds. Operational: April–November. Four-week waiting list. Fully inclusive price: £2,670 for two people for two nights.

    V

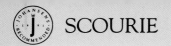

THE EDDRACHILLES HOTEL

BADCALL BAY, SCOURIE, SUTHERLAND IV27 4TH
TEL: 0971 2080

Superbly situated on Badcall Bay in 320 acres, this listed 200 year-old former manse has been completely refurbished, providing every comfort. The 11 bedrooms are decorated in pale pastel shades and have practical modern furniture. You can relax in the charming sun room and enjoy magnificent views of the Bay which is dotted with small islands. You can hire a boat to explore the Bay, and, if you wish, do some fishing. The loch is good for wind-surfing too, but you must take your own board. Handa Island has a bird sanctuary, which together with the native seals, otters, roe and red deer makes the area a Mecca for wildlife photographers. The rugged countryside is ideal for hill walkers and climbers, providing both challenging spots for serious trekkers and gentle walks along sandy shores. The hotel can provide maps, packed lunches and, if you wish, can put you in touch with local guides for a day out in the hills. Also, in case the worst happens and it rains, the hotel has a special drying room for soggy clothing and boots. Local beauty spots you must not miss are Sandwood Bay, reputedly haunted, and the waterfalls of Eascoul-Aluin which, with a fall of 685 feet, are the tallest in Britain. Afterwards, try some good home cooking in the hotel's fully licensed, characterful dining room with its stone walls and flag-stoned floors. Fish and venison have pride of place on the menu here, but there is always a vegetarian choice as well. AA 2 Stars; STB 4 Crowns. Ideally located for touring the North and West. Closed November–February. Price guide: £60–£70. Directions: The hotel is reached via the A894 south of Scourie.

462

MANOR PARK HOTEL

SKELMORLIE, AYRSHIRE PA17 5HE
TEL: 0475 520832

Under new ownership since June 1990, the hotel has retained all of the features that have long made it such a comfortable and convenient base from which to explore some of Scotland's finest attractions. Manor Park was built in 1840 and although it provides all the modern amenities expected today, it also retains a feeling of gracious living with its oak staircase, imposing portals and log fires. Residents are always fascinated to learn that the Cowal Room was the very room in which Winston Churchill and General Eisenhower met to plan the D-Day landings. Every room has views over 13 acres of formal and wild gardens and, beyond that, the Firth of Clyde and a panorama of mountains and lochs. Chef, Graeme Lavery, prepares a first-class menu including traditional dishes but also Scottish specialities. For the dedicated malt lover, there are more than 190 whiskies to sample. The nearby Largs resort offers watersports, yachting, boating, fishing and golf. For those wishing to tour the Clyde area, ferry services to Argyll, Bute, the Cumbraes and Arran are only a short drive away – as is Burns country. One day conference facilities can accommodate up to 50; residential, 25. Price guide: £81.75–£105. Directions: Hotel is off the A78, 3 miles north of Largs Pier.

THE FOUR SEASONS HOTEL

ST FILLANS, PERTHSHIRE PH6 2NF
TEL: 076485 333

The charming village of St Fillans is set in the beauty of Highland scenery, yet Edinburgh and Glasgow are within 1½ hours' drive. The light and airy public rooms and most of the spacious bedrooms of The Four Seasons command glorious views over Loch Earn, 'the jewel in the crown of Perthshire lochs'. Six chalets on the wooded hillside behind the hotel offer freedom and privacy. Each accommodates three adults or a family of four; there is car access to the door in most cases. The Scott family and staff take pleasure in the company of their guests, and are always on hand, be it to offer a suggestion for a day's outing or about the choice of wine to complement a meal. Chef Andrew Scott and his team prepare imaginative fare, making full use of fresh, Scottish produce with an emphasis on game and seafood. The menu is changed daily and guests' preferences are considered with individually prepared dishes to please the adventurous diner, as well as those with more traditional tastes. The hotel has its own jetty and the area is ideal for water sports, fishing, golf and hill walking. Also, guests can explore by car on the easy roads which link charming villages or the narrow tracks which entice you up peaceful glens. Closed January and February. Price guide: £58–£75. Directions: St Fillans is 13 miles from Crieff on the A85.

CHAPELTOUN HOUSE
STEWARTON, AYRSHIRE KA3 3ED
TEL: 0560 82696 FAX: 0560 85100

Two brothers, Colin and Graeme McKenzie, run this friendly hotel with a personal, informal touch. The house was built to be the family home for a wealthy Scots industrialist and his young English wife: to celebrate this match, a romantic theme of thistles and roses was incorporated into the ornate plasterwork and masonry. A welcoming atmosphere is immediately apparent on arrival in the spacious oak-panelled hall, which is vibrant with the crackle of an open log fire in cold weather. There are splendid dining rooms and bedrooms with views across the gardens to the river. Chapeltoun has gained an international reputation for producing very good food and for looking after people. This has been acknowledged by The Scottish Tourist Board (4 Crowns, Highly Commended), as well as numerous travel guides and food critics. The fabulous Burrell Collection, Royal Troon, ferries to Arran and Cumbrae and the wonderful collections of Dean Castle are all within 30 minutes' drive. Culzean Castle and Burns Country are less than 1 hour's drive away. Children over 12 welcome. Dogs by arrangement. Price guide: £99–£125. Directions: The hotel is 18 miles south of Glasgow and 30 minutes from Glasgow Airport, off the Stewarton–Irvine road (B769).

PARK LODGE HOTEL

32 PARK TERRACE, STIRLING FK8 2JS
TEL: 0786 74862

Facing south and situated in a delightful part of the town overlooking Stirling Castle and the golf course and with panoramic views of the Campsie Fell Hills, this Georgian country house is a find indeed. The luxurious furnishings and decor throughout reflect a bygone era of gracious elegance. In the truly splendid Heritage Restaurant, a short walk from the hotel, the finest in haute cuisine is served using the best fresh produce, and the wine cellars present a choice to delight the most discerning palate. A special selection of malt whiskies tempts the connoisseur into the exquisite bar. Michelin recommended, and just 5 minutes' walk from Stirling city centre, the hotel has splendidly furnished garden and drawing rooms, both afford fine views of the walled garden. Price guide: £75. Directions: The hotel faces the golf course in the centre of Stirling.

STONEFIELD CASTLE HOTEL
TARBERT, LOCH FYNE, ARGYLL PA29 6YJ
TEL: 0880 820836 FAX: 0880 820929

This 19th-century castle, from which there are fantastic views over Loch Fyne, stands in 60 acres of wooded grounds. While retaining its dignity and historic charm, it offers guests every comfort, and is under the personal supervision of Kevin and Janet Reid. The traditional Scottish menu features local lobster, oysters, prawns, salmon, venison, game and the famed Loch Fyne herring. The gardens are renowned for their exotic shrubs and the Himalayan rhododendrons and azaleas that flourish in the mild, balmy climate. All bedrooms but one have private bathrooms and a baby-listening system is available. Facilities include a library, bar, sauna, solarium, children's playground and games room, yacht moorings, sea and loch fishing and riding. There are five golf courses within 40 miles of the hotel and ferry trips to Arran, Islay, Gigha, Mull and Iona are also available. There is a helicopter landing pad (book via Glasgow Airport on 041–887 8726). STB 4 Crowns Commended; AA and RAC 3 Stars. USA bookings: toll free 800-2211-1074. Price guide: £50–£88. Directions: From Lochgilhead take Tarbert road south; 10 miles further to Stonefield Castle.

PIERSLAND HOUSE HOTEL

CRAIGEND ROAD, TROON, AYRSHIRE KA10 6HD
TEL: 0292 314747 FAX: 0292 315613

This historic listed building, built for the grandson of Johnnie Walker, founder of the Scotch whisky firm, is as attractive inside as out. All the public rooms are spacious and inviting with an array of original features, such as oak panelling and a frieze of Jacobean embroidery. Retaining their original charm, the bedrooms are tastefully decorated in a period style with soft colourings. Afternoon cream teas are served in the veranda, an airy sunlounge opening onto beautiful grounds which contain a Japanese water garden. Guests can choose from the very best classic and Continental cuisine in the warm, intimate atmosphere of the restaurant, and can select from wines provided by Scotland's oldest established wine firm. There is a croquet lawn in the gardens and for those who enjoy golf, the hotel is surrounded by championship courses, such as Royal Troon, Turnberry and Old Prestwick. Ayr – the birthplace of Robert Burns – Kilmarnock and Irvine are all nearby and offer facilities for shooting and fishing. Culzean Castle is 19 miles away. Glasgow, Stirling and Edinburgh are just a short journey away, as are Loch Lomond, the Trossachs, and the isles of the Firth of Clyde where Brodick Castle can be found. Price guide: £80–£100. Directions: The hotel is on the B749, just beside Royal Troon golf club.

HOUSTOUN HOUSE HOTEL

UPHALL, WEST LOTHIAN EH52 6JS
TEL: 0506 853831 FAX: 0506 854220

This 17th-century laird's fortified tower near Edinburgh is now an internationally renowned hotel and restaurant enjoying a peaceful location in 20 acres of its own beautiful wooded grounds. Some bedrooms are traditionally furnished with original 18th-century panelling, while others have a more modern look; but all are equipped with every facility one could wish for. In the dining room the emphasis is on the finest fresh Scottish produce, expertly prepared using home-grown herbs and spices. The wine cellar is one of Britain's largest, containing approximately 10,000 bottles. The vaulted bar dates from 1737, has a huge log fire and an extensive range of malt whiskies. The superb gardens are still surrounded by the original yew hedges and the enormous cedar tree on the main lawn was grown from a Lebanese seed. Price guide: £105–£130. Directions: 10 minutes from Edinburgh Airport, taking the Broxburn road from Ingliston roundabout on A89. Uphall is reached from Glasgow via the M8, turning off at Junction 4 and left at first roundabout. Follow signs to Broxburn and turn left at traffic lights on A89. The hotel is signposted from Uphall.

KNOCKIE LODGE HOTEL
WHITEBRIDGE, INVERNESS-SHIRE IV1 2UP
TEL: 04563 276 FAX: 04563 389

Built as a shooting lodge in 1789, Knockie Lodge stands close to Loch Ness, 25 miles south of Inverness, in an area of outstanding beauty and utter peace and quiet. It is now very much the home of Ian and Brenda Milward. With its ten bedrooms, each comfortably and individually furnished, its drawing and dining rooms filled with antique furniture and family paintings, the new billiard room and, of course, superb food prepared from a wide range of local produce, you can be assured of a real welcome and a very relaxed atmosphere. For the brown trout fly-fisherman, there is excellent fishing on two lochs close to the house. You can also cast for salmon on Loch Ness or, by arrangement, in local salmon rivers. Other activities: deerstalking in the autumn, birdwatching, sailing, pony trekking and hill walking. AA 2 Red Stars; STB 3 Crowns Highly Commended. Open end April–end October. Children over 10 welcome. Dogs by arrangement. From USA (reservations only) 1-800-635 3603. Price guide: £120–£170 including dinner. Directions: The hotel stands 8 miles north of Fort Augustus on B862.

The following establishments can be found in *Johansens Recommended Country Inns and Restaurants in Great Britain 1991:*

Ardentinny Hotel
Loch Long
Nr Dunoon
Argyll PA23 8TR
Tel: 036981 209/275
Price guide: £50–£80

The Birnam Hotel
Birnam
Dunkeld
Perthshire PH8 0BQ
Tel: 03502 462
Price guide: £60–£85

The Burns Monument Hotel
Alloway
Ayr
Ayrshire KA7 4PQ
Tel: 0292 42466
Price guide: £60–£70

Burts Hotel
Melrose
Roxburghshire TD6 9PN
Tel: 089682 2285
Price guide: £60–£64

Cluanie Inn
Glenshiel
Skye and Lochalsh
Glenmoriston
Inverness-shire IV3 6YW
Tel: 0320 40257/228/238
Price guide: £54–£64

Fernhill Hotel
Heugh Road
Portpatrick
Dumfries & Galloway DG9 8TD
Tel: 0776 81220
Price guide: £60–£85

Inchnadamph Hotel
Loch Assynt
By Lairg
Sutherland IV27 4HL
Tel: 05712 202
Price guide: £49.50–£60.50

Kilfinan Hotel
Kilfinan
Nr Tighnabruaich
Argyll PA21 2AP
Tel: 070082 201
Price guide: £50

The Killiecrankie Hotel
Pass of Killiecrankie
By Pitlochry
Perthshire PH16 5LG
Tel: 0796 3220
Price guide: £67.40

Kirkhouse Inn
Strathblane
Glasgow G63 9AA
Tel: 0360 70621
Price guide: £70

Kirklands Hotel
West Stewart Place
Hawick
Roxburghshire TD9 8BH
Tel: 0450 72263
Price guide: £60

Moffat House Hotel
High Street
Moffat
Dumfriesshire DG10 9HL
Tel: 0683 20039
Price guide: £54–£60

Moorings Hotel
Fort William
Inverness–shire PH33 7LY
Tel: 0397 772797
Price guide: £66–£76

Murraypark Hotel
Connaught Terrace
Crieff
Perthshire PH7 3DJ
Tel: 0764 3731
Price guide: £53

The Ord Arms Hotel
Great North Road
Muir of Ord
Ross-shire IV6 7XR
Tel: 0463 870286
Price guide: £38.50-£44

The Pickwick Hotel
19 Racecourse Road
Ayr
Ayrshire KA7 2TD
Tel: 0292 260111
Price guide: £35–£40

Western Isles Hotel
Tobermory
Isle of Mull
Argyll PA75 6PR
Tel: 0688 2012
Price guide: £59–£83

The Portland Arms
Lybster
Caithness
Tel: 05932 208
Price guide: £42

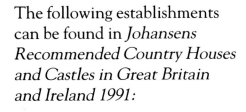

The following establishments can be found in *Johansens Recommended Country Houses and Castles in Great Britain and Ireland 1991:*

Potarch Hotel
By Banchory
Royal Deeside AB3 4BD
Tel: 03398 84339
Price guide: £35–£40

Allt-Chaorain Country House Hotel
Crianlarich
Perthshire FK20 8RU
Tel: 08383 283
Price Guide: £66–£78

Queens View Hotel and Restaurant
Strathtummel
By Pitlochry
Perthshire PH16 5NR
Tel: 0796 3291
Price guide: £51.20–£61.20

Ardvourlie Castle
Aird a Mhulaidh
Isle of Harris
Western Isles PA85 3AB
Tel: 0859 2307
Price Guide: £88–£98

Scourie Hotel
Scourie
Sutherland IV27 4SX
Tel: 0971 2396
Price guide: £50–£56

Balcary Bay Hotel
Auchencairn
Nr Castle Douglas
Dumfries & Galloway DG7 1QZ
Tel: 055664 217/311
Price Guide: £50–£75

Selkirk Arms Hotel
High Street
Kirkcudbright
Dumfries & Galloway DG6 4JG
Tel: 0557 30402
Price guide: £65

Ballachulish House
Ballachulish
Argyll PA39 4JX
Tel: 08552 266
Price Guide: £45–£60

The Sun Inn
Lothianbridge
Nr Dalkeith
Midlothian EH22 4TR
Tel: 031-663 2456
Price guide: £50–£55

The Cairn Lodge
Orchil Road
Auchterarder
Perthshire PH3 1LX
Tel: 0764 62634
Price Guide: £75

Tormaukin Hotel
Glendevon
By Dollar
Perthshire FK14 7JY
Tel: 025981 252
Price guide: £56–£58

Contin House
Contin
Strathpeffer
Ross-shire IV14 9EB
Tel: 0997 21920
Price Guide: £66–£77

Corrour House Hotel
Inverdruie
Aviemore
Scotland PH22 1QH
Tel: 0479 810220
Price Guide: £70–£80

Ladyburn
By Maypole
Ayrshire KA19 7SG
Tel: 06554 585/586
Price Guide: £110–£150

**Druimnacroish Country
House Hotel**
Dervaig
Isle of Mull
Argyll PA75 6QW
Tel: 06884 274
Price Guide: £65

Loch Melfort Hotel
Arduaine by Oban
Argyll PA34 4XG
Tel: 08522 233
Price Guide: £85–£110

The Dryburgh Abbey Hotel
St Boswells
Roxburghshire TD6 0RQ
Tel: 0835 22261
Price Guide: £78–£95

Nivingston House
Cleish
Kinross-shire KY13 7LS
Tel: 05775 216
Price Guide: £75

Gean House Hotel
Tullibody Road
Alloa
Stirling FK10 2HS
Tel: 0259 219275
Price Guide: £110–£200

Polmaily House Hotel
Drumnadrochit
Inverness-shire IV3 6XT
Tel: 04562 343
Price Guide: £90

Glenfeochan House
Kilmore
By Oban
Argyll PA34 4QR
Tel: 063177 273
Price Guide: £90–£112

Port-an-Eilean House
Strathtummel
Nr Pitlochry
Perthshire PH16 5RU
Tel: 08824 233
Price Guide: £52

Guinach House
By 'The Birks'
Aberfeldy
Perthshire PH15 2ET
Tel: 0887 20251
Price Guide: £60

Purves Hall Hotel
Greenlaw
Berwickshire TD10 6UJ
Tel: 089084 558
Price Guide: £60–£65

Harburn House
Harburn
West Calder
West Lothian EH55 8RN
Tel: 0506 410742
Price Guide: £100

Sciberscross Lodge
Strath Brora
Rogart
Sutherland IV28 3YQ
Tel: 04084 246
Price Guide: £70–£80

Kinnaird
Kinnaird Estate
Dunkeld
Perthshire PH8 0LB
Tel: 079682 440
Price Guide: £110–£150

Tiroran House
Isle of Mull
Argyll PA69 6ES
Tel: 06815 232
Price Guide: £154–£192

Why not?   Lanson

IRELAND

The following pages contain hotel entries in Ireland in alphabetical
order according to their placename.

England entries begin on page 25;
Wales on page 365;
Scotland on page 403;
and the Channel Islands on page 485.

THE DUNADRY

DUNADRY, CO ANTRIM BT41 2HA
TEL: 08494 32474 FAX: 08494 33389 TELEX: 747245

Now set in 10 acres of gardens in the heart of beautiful Antrim countryside, The Dunadry is of considerable historic interest. The name means The Middle Fort (Dun-Eddery), so called because of its position as the middle of three forts on the road which ran from Tara to Dunseverick, where Conal Cernach, the most valiant of the legendary Red Branch Knights of Ulster lived. The Dunadry occupies the site of the village which grew up around the mill on the river, powering first a paper-mill and then a linen-mill. Retaining old-world charm, while offering every modern luxury, many of the spacious bedrooms have French windows leading out into the garden or inner courtyard. The main restaurant with its open log fire overlooks the Six Mile Water (or River of the Rushes, by its old Irish name), and the extensive menu offers something to suit the most discerning palate. With the main restaurant, bar and many of the bedrooms on the ground floor, any guests with a disability will be able to move around with ease. RAC Grade A. AA 4 Star. The hotel is pleased to offer activity breaks, including golf and shooting. Price guide: IR£90–IR£120. Directions: 4 miles from Belfast's International Airport, on the Templepatrick to Antrim road.

MARLFIELD HOUSE HOTEL

GOREY, CO WEXFORD
TEL: 055 21124 FAX: 055 21572 TELEX: 80757

Staying at Marlfield House is a memorable experience. Set in 34 acres of woodland and gardens, this former residence of the Earl of Courtown, built in 1820, preserves the Regency lifestyle in all its graciousness. It is recognised as one of the finest country houses in Ireland, and is supervised by the welcoming host/proprietors, Raymond and Mary Bowe. The suites all have period fireplaces where open fires blaze in cooler weather, and have been built in a traditional, very grand style. All the bedroom furniture is of the Regency period and the roomy beds are draped with ruffled, sumptuous fabrics. The bathrooms are made of highly polished marble and have large freestanding bathtubs. There is a luxurious drawing room, an impressive curved Richard Turner conservatory, and an opulent dining room. The hotel's gastronomic delights have earned it numerous awards. Located 2 miles from fine beaches, the hotel is central to many touring high points: Powerscourt Demesne, Mount Usher Gardens and the Devil's Glen. The hotel is 1½ hour's drive from Dublin; 1 hour from Rosslare. When phoning from the British mainland, dial 010 353 55 21124. Price guide: IR£90–IR£127. Directions: On the Gorey–Courtown road, just over a mile east of Gorey.

RELAIS & CHATEAUX — Prestige Hotel

PARK HOTEL KENMARE

KENMARE, CO KERRY
TEL: 064 41200 FAX: 064 41402 TELEX: 73905 PARK EI

Set in the lovely lake district of Killarney, this hotel was originally built as a railway hotel in 1897. The hotel stands high on a hillside, has an impressive entrance reached by a flight of steps beneath an awning, plus beautiful terraced gardens and walkways leading down to fields, woods and the estuary of the Kenmare River. The hotel features many items of antique furniture. There is a handsome cistern decorated with mythological figures and supported by gilded seahorses and dolphins in the hall, and the bedrooms feature magnificent carved beds. The public rooms contain comfortable sofas, open fires in cooler weather and beautiful paintings. There is a hexagonal-shaped bar and, in the sitting room, a pianist plays each evening. In the hotel's elegant restaurant, where all the meals are served by seamlessly efficient staff, fish dishes are a speciality. There is a tennis court, 9-hole golf course and a croquet lawn in the grounds; salmon fishing, hunting and horse-riding are available locally. Nearby are the Dingle Peninsula, Ring of Kerry and Beara. Price guide: IR£160–IR£226. Directions: Take the N22 from Cork through Macroom to Loo Bridge. Turn left through Kilgarven to Kenmare. If ringing from the UK dial 010 353 64 41200.

AGHADOE HEIGHTS HOTEL
AGHADOE, KILLARNEY, CO KERRY
TEL: 064 31766 FAX: 064 31345 TELEX: 73942

In the heart of Ireland's beautiful County Kerry, in a landscape of mountains and lakes, stands the Aghadoe Heights Hotel, sister hotel to Fredrick's of Maidenhead. Aghadoe Heights reflects owner Fredrick Losel's influence: rich tapestries, crystal chandeliers, paintings and antiques. Much attention has been given to the hotel's bedrooms. The furniture is of mahogany, ash or cherry wood and there are soft drapes and deep carpets. Great cuisine and fine wines are offered at Fredrick's at the Heights, the hotel's rooftop restaurant. Fresh local produce is used for the innovative dishes of chef, Robin Suter. There are three function rooms offering conference facilities for up to 60 delegates. Whether for business or leisure, the Aghadoe Heights makes a good base for tours of Kerry and for those wishing to play South West Ireland's premier golf courses such as Killarney, Waterville and Ballybunion. Irish music is offered in season in the hotel's Abbey Bar which is named after the ruined 7th-century Aghadoe Cathedral next to the hotel. The hotel has its own stretch of river for salmon fishing and there is a tennis court in its 8½ acres of gardens. When ringing from the British mainland dial 010 353 64 31766. Pony trekking and lake fishing are also available nearby. Price guide: IR£90–IR£120. Directions: 10 miles from Kerry airport; 3 miles from Killarney.

NEWPORT HOUSE

NEWPORT, CO MAYO, IRELAND
TEL: 098 41222 FAX: 098 41613 TELEX: 53740

This Georgian mansion, owned by Kieran and Thelma Thompson, has private fisheries on the tidal Newport river and Lough Beltra and affords views over the quay. The original bow-fronted mansion is encased in an extremely grand edifice; the interiors reflect this grandeur. The chandelier-hung sitting room contains a fine fireplace and, via huge doors, opens into the dining room. While fish dishes, including home-smoked salmon, take pride of place on the menu, vegetables from the walled garden and cheeses also feature; the food is complemented by an extensive range of wines. The vast inner hall is flooded with daylight from a heat-retaining skylight and an elegant staircase rises to the galleried landing; all the bedrooms lead off this. Each room has private facilities and 12 of the 19 bedrooms are in the main house; the remainder are in an adjacent courtyard building. Billiards and snooker are available indoors. Outdoors: excellent salmon and trout fishing on the river and local lakes; golf, riding, diving and hang-gliding nearby. Open March–September. Price guide: IR£76–IR£96. Directions: From Dublin, take Mullinger–Longford Road; continue to Newport. Hotel one hour's drive from Connaught Airport. When phoning from the UK, dial 010 353 98 41222.

RATHMULLAN HOUSE
LOUGH SWILLY, RATHMULLAN, CO DONEGAL
TEL: 074 58188 FAX: 074 58200

This gracious Georgian mansion is set amid ancient oaks, weeping elms and award-winning gardens on the sandy shores of Lough Swilly in the wild and beautiful county of Donegal. The owners of Rathmullan, Bob and Robin Wheeler, undertook a grand refurbishment to restore the house and grounds to their former glory. An outstanding feature is the flowing silk, Arabian tent-design dining room, where the cooking is in Irish country house style, and seafood is a speciality. There are many other elegant rooms inside the antique-filled house, which features intricate pargeted ceilings, crystal chandeliers, rich oil portraits and white marble log-burning fireplaces. Many of the bedrooms are richly furnished with comfortable antique furniture and some afford views across the lake to the Inishowen Peninsula. Overlooking the gardens are the hotel's Egyptian Baths, housing an indoor pool of ionised salt water, a sauna and a steam room. There are also four golf courses nearby. Member of Irish Country Houses and Restaurants Association. Price guide: IR£65–IR£95. Directions: Take the T72 Ramelton road from Letterkenny. Turn right after the bridge in Ramelton, take L77 to Rathmullan. If phoning from the British mainland, dial 010 353 74 58188.

TINAKILLY HOUSE HOTEL
RATHNEW, CO WICKLOW
TEL: 0404 69274 FAX: 0404 67806

Less than an hour's drive from Dublin stands Tinakilly House, set in beautiful coastal country known as the Garden of Ireland. Owners William and Bee Power provide a house party atmosphere for their guests. The bedrooms are a perfect blend of Victorian splendour and modern comfort, featuring beautifully sculptured timber windows and doors; the restaurant is internationally recognised for its blend of country house cooking and nouvelle cuisine, with an excellent cellar. Seven acres of pleasure gardens enhance the peace of this extensively restored house, built in 1870. Nearby are Glendalough 6th-century monastic settlement, Avondale (home of Charles Parnell), the Vale of Avoca, Powerscourt Gardens, Russborough, Mount Usher Gardens at Ashford, several racecourses and the Wicklow mountains. Dublin, with its splendid shopping, atmospheric pubs, theatres and entertainment to suit all tastes, is well worth a visit. Price guide: IR£88–IR£132. Directions: Take the N11 from Dublin through Rathnew village. The hotel is on the left-hand side as you come out of the village. If ringing from the British mainland, dial 010 353 404 69274.

MARKREE CASTLE AND KNOCKMULDOWNEY RESTAURANT

COLLOONEY, CO SLIGO
TEL: 071 67800 FAX: 071 67840

Markree Castle is one of Ireland's architectural masterpieces and is set in 1,000 acres of breathtakingly beautiful countryside, with gardens leading down to the River Unsin. Home of the Cooper family for over 300 years, it has been carefully and sensitively restored, offering guests every modern comfort combined with the atmosphere of a bygone age. Since 1989, the original dining room, with its lofty ceiling, has been re-gilded with gold leaf to its original beauty. The Knockmuldowney Restaurant is renowned for its superb menu complemented by an extensive wine list. Markree Castle is an ideal base for tours of the magnificent west of Ireland and a variety of sporting activities, including horse-riding, can be enjoyed nearby. Price guide: IR£78–IR£84. Directions: South of Sligo just off the N4 at Collooney. If phoning from the British mainland, dial 010 353 71 67800.

The following establishments can be found in *Johansens Recommended Country Houses and Castles in Great Britain and Ireland 1991:*

Clohamon House
Bunclody
Co Wexford
Tel: 054 77253
Price Guide: IR£60–IR£68

Coopershill House
Riverstown
Co Sligo
Tel: 071 65108
Price Guide: IR£70–IR£75

Ballyvolane House
Castlelyons
Fermoy
Co Cork
Tel: 025 36349
Price Guide: IR£97

Enniscoe House
Castlehill
Nr Crossmolina
Ballina, Co Mayo
Tel: 096 31112
Price Guide: IR£100–IR£104

Bantry House
Bantry
Co Cork
Tel: 027 50047
Price Guide: IR£70

Glendalough House
Caragh Lake
Co Kerry
Tel: 066 69156
Price Guide: IR£50–IR£56

Caragh Lodge
Caragh Lake
Co Kerry
Tel: 066 69115
Price Guide: IR£60–IR£75

The Old Rectory Country House & Restaurant
Wicklow
Co Wicklow
Tel: 0404 67048
Price Guide: IR£74

THE
CHANNEL ISLANDS

The following pages contain hotel entries in the Channel Islands in alphabetical order according to their placename.

England entries begin on page 25;
Wales on page 365;
Scotland on page 403;
and Ireland on page 475.

HOTEL L'HORIZON

ST BRELADE'S BAY, JERSEY
TEL: 0534 43101 FAX: 0534 46269 TELEX: 419228

Hotel L'Horizon nestles in St Brelade's Bay, considered to be one of the most beautiful in Europe with its fine beach and golden sands. The luxurious bedrooms are kept in pristine condition, offering guests every comfort, and most have balconies overlooking the bay. The Crystal Room and the Star Grill both enjoy high accolades for service and cuisine, where the presentation of fresh local produce is of paramount importance. The food is complemented by an extensive wine list. An efficient business centre and special conference facilities are available in the Clipper Suite. For the health conscious the hotel has a new leisure centre, Club L'Horizon, featuring an indoor pool, gymnasium, saunas, spa baths and steam rooms; you can recover afterwards in the comfortable Brasserie. Swimming, golf, riding and a variety of sea sports are close at hand. The hotel has its own 40-foot yacht with full-time skipper available for charter to explore the Islands and coast of France. Jersey itself has a wealth of beauty, interest and history to offer and, with the delightful climate, there is much to entertain the visitor. Price guide: £120. Directions: Take the main road to the right out of Jersey Airport towards Red Houses, and St Brelade's Bay is 2 miles along the road.

THE LITTLE GROVE HOTEL
RUE DE HAUT, ST LAWRENCE, JERSEY
TEL: 0534 25321 FAX: 0534 25325

Straight off the plane and into the Rolls-Royce or Renault 5 Espace that will convey you to the hotel, or to your place of business – a foretaste of the sophistication and high standard of service you can expect at the Little Grove where the pursuit of excellence is taken seriously. Set amid landscaped gardens and fragrant orchards, the 19th-century pink granite building houses comfortable, tastefully furnished rooms that provide a haven of peace, with real log fires in winter. In the Old Masters' Restaurant (the name inspired by its original Dutch paintings), the resident pianist plays soft classical music while you enjoy an exquisite menu of artistically presented dishes created by the head chef. For those on business, there is an elegant boardroom and private rooms for a working meal. In warmer weather, the garden terrace provides an idyllic setting for breakfast, lunch or drinks. Suitable for children over 12. Price guide: £107–£142.50. Directions: The hotel is in quiet surroundings between the airport and St Helier.

LA FRÉGATE HOTEL

LES CÔTILS, ST PETER PORT, GUERNSEY, CHANNEL ISLANDS
TEL: 0481 24624 FAX: 0481 20443

La Frégate Hotel, a charming 18th-century manor house, is tucked away on a garden hillside overlooking the harbour of St Peter Port and the offshore islands of Herm, Jethou and Sark. It is within 5 minutes' walk of the main town and shopping centre with its old markets selling fresh, local and traditional produce. Eleven of the 13 bedrooms overlook the harbour; all have private bathrooms, TV, hair dryers and trouser press. Some now offer the added attraction of double-glazed patio windows leading on to private balconies. You can also enjoy panoramic harbour views from the hotel's terraced lawns, a good place to relax with a drink. The excellent French menu features local shellfish, various seafood and fresh vegetables. This is complemented by an extensive and well-balanced wine list together with service of the highest standard. La Frégate is for discerning people, those who appreciate good food and peaceful surroundings in an unspoiled setting. Price guide: £96–£109. Directions: Please ask the hotel to supply a map.

13 rms | BARCLAYCARD VISA | Access | AMERICAN EXPRESS | ◐ | ♣ | OPEN ALL YEAR | V | ▯ | ☏ | 🐎

OLD GOVERNMENT HOUSE HOTEL

ANN'S PLACE, ST PETER PORT, GUERNSEY, CHANNEL ISLANDS
TEL: 0481 24921 FAX: 0481 24429 TELEX: 4191144

Affectionately known as the 'OGH', the hotel was, from the middle of the 18th century, the official residence of the governors of Guernsey. Constantly modernised since 1858, when it became a hotel, it now offers all modern amenities and comforts yet its traditional style and decor retain an atmosphere of gracious living. The OGH can justly claim not only one of the finest restaurants but also the most favoured setting in Guernsey with its breathtaking views over Herm, Sark and Jethou. Gentlemen are requested to wear a jacket and tie at dinner. Proud to have been awarded 5 Crowns, the accommodation throughout is of the very highest standard. Many of the bedrooms have sea views. There is dancing regularly in the Centenary Bar and in Scarlett's Nightclub situated in the soundproofed basement. There are comprehensive facilities for business travellers. Executive breaks available October–March, and a fully inclusive Christmas programme is offered. Price guide: £68–£146. Directions: The OGH is situated in the centre of St Peter Port.

ST PIERRE PARK HOTEL

ROHAIS, ST PETER PORT, GUERNSEY, CHANNEL ISLANDS
TEL: 0481 28282 (Freefone: 0800 373321) FAX: 0481 712041 TELEX: 4191662

Guernsey's fabulous 5-Crown hotel is situated on the outskirts of St Peter Port in a 40-acre estate with its own lake and fountain in the grounds. Other facilities deserving mention include a 9-hole par-3 golf course designed by Tony Jacklin, a driving range, hair and beauty salon, shopping arcade, snooker, and a health suite which includes saunas, solaria, massage facilities, a well-equipped exercise room, spa pool and impulse showers and rest room. These fine facilities are complemented by the high standards of cuisine served in both of the two restaurants: the Victor Hugo French à la carte restaurant and Pierrot's Brasserie which caters for meals at any time throughout the day until late evening. Pierrot's nightspot has its own bar and live musical entertainment. Guernsey and the St Pierre Park are the ideal place for a short break, sporting or family holiday. Price guide: £115. Directions: The hotel is centrally situated only 15 minutes' drive from the airport and 5 minutes' drive from St Peter Port, the capital of Guernsey. Take the Rohais road westbound out of St Peter Port.

GREENHILL COUNTRY HOTEL
ST PETER'S VALLEY, JERSEY, CHANNEL ISLANDS
TEL: 0534 81042

Facing south, the hotel is situated in lovely countryside away from traffic. This is a friendly and welcoming hotel, ideal for a quiet holiday or business trip. Owners Rita and Barry Lane are always on hand to help you feel at ease. You can relax beside the heated swimming pool in the walled, suntrap garden and soak up the tranquillity of your surroundings. Extensive à la carte and varied table d'hôte, mainly French menus together with fine wines are offered in the dining room and make it popular with local residents. All bedrooms have pleasing decor, en suite facilities, colour TV with BSB and SKY satellite channels, radio, tea and coffee-making facilities, telephone, trouser presses and hair dryers. St Peter's Valley boasts one of the Island's largest strawberry farms and is just 10 minutes from St Helier via A11 and C112. Closed mid-December – mid-February. Price guide: £70. Directions: 10 minutes from St Helier via A11 and C112.

Hotels with Conference Facilities

(Note: the number of delegates quoted refers to the maximum number for which the hotel can cater in either theatre or boardroom style)

England

Wales

Scotland

Ireland

Channel Islands

Hotels with wheelchair access

Children of all ages welcome

Hotels With Golf

Wales

Scotland

Ireland

Channel Islands

Relais Chateaux members

Prestige members

Pride of Britain Members

Index of Advertisers

GUEST SURVEY REPORT

To: Johansens Limited, FREEPOST
Bateman Street, Cambridge CB2 1BR

Name and address of hotel: _____

Name and address of guest: _____

Date(s) of visit: _____ Purpose of visit (please tick): Business ☐ Pleasure ☐ Both ☐

Please tick one box in each category below:	Faultless	Excellent	Good	Disappointing	Poor
Bedrooms					
Public rooms					
Restaurant/Cuisine					
Service					
Welcome/Friendliness					
Value for money					

Additional comments: _____

Establishment(s) you would like to see in a Johansens guide:

Name: _____

Address or location: _____

Tel no (if known) _____

☐ Please send me free of charge the *Excellent Secrets* newsletter

Your own Johansens 'inspection' gives reliability to our guides

Please return your Guest Survey Report form

GUEST SURVEY REPORT

To: Johansens Limited, FREEPOST
Bateman Street, Cambridge CB2 1BR

Name and address of hotel: _____

Name and address of guest: _____

Date(s) of visit: _____ Purpose of visit (please tick): Business ☐ Pleasure ☐ Both ☐

Please tick one box in each category below:	Faultless	Excellent	Good	Disappointing	Poor
Bedrooms					
Public rooms					
Restaurant/Cuisine					
Service					
Welcome/Friendliness					
Value for money					

Additional comments: _____

Establishment(s) you would like to see in a Johansens guide:

Name: _____

Address or location: _____

Tel no (if known) _____

☐ Please send me free of charge the *Excellent Secrets* newsletter

Your own Johansens 'inspection' gives reliability to our guides

Please return your Guest Survey Report form

GUEST SURVEY REPORT

To: Johansens Limited, FREEPOST
Bateman Street, Cambridge CB2 1BR

Name and address of hotel: _____

Name and address of guest: _____

Date(s) of visit: _____ Purpose of visit (please tick): Business ☐ Pleasure ☐ Both ☐

Please tick one box in each category below:	Faultless	Excellent	Good	Disappointing	Poor
Bedrooms					
Public rooms					
Restaurant/Cuisine					
Service					
Welcome/Friendliness					
Value for money					

Additional comments: _____

Establishment(s) you would like to see in a Johansens guide:

Name: _____

Address or location: _____

Tel no (if known) _____

☐ Please send me free of charge the *Excellent Secrets* newsletter

Your own Johansens 'inspection' gives reliability to our guides

Please return your Guest Survey Report form

ORDER FORM Please send me:

Title	Qty	Price	Total
Johansens Recommended Hotels in Great Britain & Ireland 1991 (508 pages) Softback (819)		£14.95	£
Hardback (822)		£19.95	£
Johansens Recommended Country Inns and Restaurants in Great Britain 1991 (164 pages) (820)		£6.95	£
Johansens Recommended Private Country Houses and Castles in Great Britain & Ireland 1991 (148 pages) (821)		£6.95	£
Posting and handling charges UK:1 book £2.95, 2 books £3.95, 3 or more books £4.95 Rest of world: 1 book £4.50, 2 books £8.50, 3 or more books £12.50			£
Prices valid until 31/12/91		TOTAL	£
Special Discount (deduct £5 if all three books purchased)			£
BUY ALL THREE GUIDES AND SAVE £5.00 ON YOUR FINAL PAYMENT		GRAND TOTAL	£

☐ Please supply free of charge the Johansens newsletter *Excellent Secrets*

To: Johansens Limited, FREEPOST,
Bateman Street, Cambridge CB2 1BR

All payments must be made in pounds sterling

☐ I enclose a cheque/Eurocheque for £ _____ made payable to **Johansens Limited**

☐ Please charge my credit card account *(please tick)*

☐ Visa ☐ Access ☐ AmEx ☐ Diners

Card no _____

Expiry date _____

Signature _____

Name _____

Address _____

Postcode _____ Telephone _____

Please allow 28 days for delivery of UK orders.

If you would like to send part or all of your order as a gift to a friend, please supply the delivery address on a separate sheet of paper and enclose it with your order form.

ORDER FORM Please send me:

Title	Qty	Price	Total
Johansens Recommended Hotels in Great Britain & Ireland 1991 (508 pages) Softback (819)		£14.95	£
Hardback (822)		£19.95	£
Johansens Recommended Country Inns and Restaurants in Great Britain 1991 (164 pages) (820)		£6.95	£
Johansens Recommended Private Country Houses and Castles in Great Britain & Ireland 1991 (148 pages) (821)		£6.95	£
Posting and handling charges UK:1 book £2.95, 2 books £3.95, 3 or more books £4.95 Rest of world: 1 book £4.50, 2 books £8.50, 3 or more books £12.50			£
Prices valid until 31/12/91		TOTAL	£
Special Discount (deduct £5 if all three books purchased)			£
BUY ALL THREE GUIDES AND SAVE £5.00 ON YOUR FINAL PAYMENT		GRAND TOTAL	£

☐ Please supply free of charge the Johansens newsletter *Excellent Secrets*

To: Johansens Limited, FREEPOST,
Bateman Street, Cambridge CB2 1BR

All payments must be made in pounds sterling

☐ I enclose a cheque/Eurocheque for £ _____ made payable to **Johansens Limited**

☐ Please charge my credit card account *(please tick)*

☐ Visa ☐ Access ☐ AmEx ☐ Diners

Card no _____

Expiry date _____

Signature _____

Name _____

Address _____

Postcode _____ Telephone _____

Please allow 28 days for delivery of UK orders.

If you would like to send part or all of your order as a gift to a friend, please supply the delivery address on a separate sheet of paper and enclose it with your order form.

ORDER FORM Please send me:

Title	Qty	Price	Total
Johansens Recommended Hotels in Great Britain & Ireland 1991 (508 pages) Softback (819)		£14.95	£
Hardback (822)		£19.95	£
Johansens Recommended Country Inns and Restaurants in Great Britain 1991 (164 pages) (820)		£6.95	£
Johansens Recommended Private Country Houses and Castles in Great Britain & Ireland 1991 (148 pages) (821)		£6.95	£
Posting and handling charges UK:1 book £2.95, 2 books £3.95, 3 or more books £4.95 Rest of world: 1 book £4.50, 2 books £8.50, 3 or more books £12.50			£
Prices valid until 31/12/91		TOTAL	£
Special Discount (deduct £5 if all three books purchased)			£
BUY ALL THREE GUIDES AND SAVE £5.00 ON YOUR FINAL PAYMENT		GRAND TOTAL	£

☐ Please supply free of charge the Johansens newsletter *Excellent Secrets*

To: Johansens Limited, FREEPOST,
Bateman Street, Cambridge CB2 1BR

All payments must be made in pounds sterling

☐ I enclose a cheque/Eurocheque for £ _____ made payable to **Johansens Limited**

☐ Please charge my credit card account *(please tick)*

☐ Visa ☐ Access ☐ AmEx ☐ Diners

Card no _____

Expiry date _____

Signature _____

Name _____

Address _____

Postcode _____ Telephone _____

Please allow 28 days for delivery of UK orders.

If you would like to send part or all of your order as a gift to a friend, please supply the delivery address on a separate sheet of paper and enclose it with your order form.

GUEST SURVEY REPORT

To: Johansens Limited, FREEPOST
Bateman Street, Cambridge CB2 1BR

Name and address of hotel: _____

Name and address of guest: _____

Date(s) of visit: _____ Purpose of visit *(please tick)*: Business ☐ Pleasure ☐ Both ☐

Please tick one box in each category below:	Faultless	Excellent	Good	Disappointing	Poor
Bedrooms					
Public rooms					
Restaurant/Cuisine					
Service					
Welcome/Friendliness					
Value for money					

Additional comments: _____

Establishment(s) you would like to see in a Johansens guide:

Name: _____

Address or location: _____

Tel no (if known) _____

☐ Please send me free of charge the *Excellent Secrets* newsletter

Your own Johansens 'inspection' gives reliability to our guides

Please return your Guest Survey Report form

GUEST SURVEY REPORT

To: Johansens Limited, FREEPOST
Bateman Street, Cambridge CB2 1BR

Name and address of hotel: _____

Name and address of guest: _____

Date(s) of visit: _____ Purpose of visit *(please tick)*: Business ☐ Pleasure ☐ Both ☐

Please tick one box in each category below:	Faultless	Excellent	Good	Disappointing	Poor
Bedrooms					
Public rooms					
Restaurant/Cuisine					
Service					
Welcome/Friendliness					
Value for money					

Additional comments: _____

Establishment(s) you would like to see in a Johansens guide:

Name: _____

Address or location: _____

Tel no (if known) _____

☐ Please send me free of charge the *Excellent Secrets* newsletter

Your own Johansens 'inspection' gives reliability to our guides

Please return your Guest Survey Report form

JOHANSENS RACE DAY NEWMARKET
WEDNESDAY 17th APRIL 1991

To: Johansens Limited
Bateman Street, Cambridge CB2 1LZ

☐ I would like further particulars about the race day

☐ Please send me details of hotels planning race day parties for the Johansens Guides Wood Ditton Stakes with prices

Name: _____

Address: _____

_____

No. in party: _____

Daytime tel no: _____

Accommodation required: _____ Double _____ Single room(s)

Special requirements: _____

503

ORDER FORM
Please send me:

Title	Qty	Price	Total
Johansens Recommended Hotels in Great Britain & Ireland 1991 (508 pages) Softback (819)		£14.95	£
Hardback (822)		£19.95	£
Johansens Recommended Country Inns and Restaurants in Great Britain 1991 (164 pages) (820)		£6.95	£
Johansens Recommended Private Country Houses and Castles in Great Britain & Ireland 1991 (148 pages) (821)		£6.95	£
Posting and handling charges UK:1 book £2.95, 2 books £3.95, 3 or more books £4.95 Rest of world: 1 book £4.50, 2 books £8.50, 3 or more books £12.50			£
Prices valid until 31/12/91		TOTAL	£
Special Discount (deduct £5 if all three books purchased)			£
BUY ALL THREE GUIDES AND SAVE £5.00 ON YOUR FINAL PAYMENT		GRAND TOTAL	£

☐ Please supply free of charge the Johansens newsletter *Excellent Secrets*

To: **Johansens Limited, FREEPOST,** Bateman Street, Cambridge CB2 1BR

All payments must be made in pounds sterling

☐ I enclose a cheque/Eurocheque for £ _____ made payable to **Johansens Limited**

☐ Please charge my credit card account (*please tick*)

☐ Visa ☐ Access ☐ AmEx ☐ Diners

Card no _____

Expiry date _____

Signature _____

Name _____

Address _____

_____

Postcode _____ Telephone _____

Please allow 28 days for delivery of UK orders.

If you would like to send part or all of your order as a gift to a friend, please supply the delivery address on a separate sheet of paper and enclose it with your order form.

ORDER FORM
Please send me:

Title	Qty	Price	Total
Johansens Recommended Hotels in Great Britain & Ireland 1991 (508 pages) Softback (819)		£14.95	£
Hardback (822)		£19.95	£
Johansens Recommended Country Inns and Restaurants in Great Britain 1991 (164 pages) (820)		£6.95	£
Johansens Recommended Private Country Houses and Castles in Great Britain & Ireland 1991 (148 pages) (821)		£6.95	£
Posting and handling charges UK:1 book £2.95, 2 books £3.95, 3 or more books £4.95 Rest of world: 1 book £4.50, 2 books £8.50, 3 or more books £12.50			£
Prices valid until 31/12/91		TOTAL	£
Special Discount (deduct £5 if all three books purchased)			£
BUY ALL THREE GUIDES AND SAVE £5.00 ON YOUR FINAL PAYMENT		GRAND TOTAL	£

☐ Please supply free of charge the Johansens newsletter *Excellent Secrets*

To: **Johansens Limited, FREEPOST,** Bateman Street, Cambridge CB2 1BR

All payments must be made in pounds sterling

☐ I enclose a cheque/Eurocheque for £ _____ made payable to **Johansens Limited**

☐ Please charge my credit card account (*please tick*)

☐ Visa ☐ Access ☐ AmEx ☐ Diners

Card no _____

Expiry date _____

Signature _____

Name _____

Address _____

_____

Postcode _____ Telephone _____

Please allow 28 days for delivery of UK orders.

If you would like to send part or all of your order as a gift to a friend, please supply the delivery address on a separate sheet of paper and enclose it with your order form.

GUEST SURVEY REPORT

To: **Johansens Limited, FREEPOST** Bateman Street, Cambridge CB2 1BR

Name and address of hotel: _____

Name and address of guest: _____

Date(s) of visit: _____ Purpose of visit (*please tick*): Business ☐ Pleasure ☐ Both ☐

Please tick one box in each category below:	Faultless	Excellent	Good	Disappointing	Poor
Bedrooms					
Public rooms					
Restaurant/Cuisine					
Service					
Welcome/Friendliness					
Value for money					

Additional comments: _____

Establishment(s) you would like to see in a Johansens guide:

Name: _____

Address or location: _____

Tel no (if known) _____

☐ Please send me free of charge the *Excellent Secrets* newsletter

Your own Johansens 'inspection' gives reliability to our guides

Please return your Guest Survey Report form